PSYCHOLOGICAL STATISTICS

An Introduction

THE DORSEY SERIES IN PSYCHOLOGY

EDITORIAL COMMITTEE

HOWARD F. HUNT
Columbia University

DONALD W. TAYLOR
Yale University

FLEISHMAN   *Studies in Personnel and Industrial Psychology*

FISKE & MADDI   *Functions of Varied Experience*

BARNETTE   *Readings in Psychological Tests and Measurements*

BENNIS, SCHEIN, BERLEW, & STEELE   *Interpersonal Dynamics: Essays and Readings on Human Interaction*

RATNER & DENNY   *Comparative Psychology: Research in Animal Behavior*

COURTS   *Psychological Statistics: An Introduction*

PSYCHOLOGICAL STATISTICS

AN INTRODUCTION

FREDERICK A. COURTS
Professor of Psychology
Reed College

1966
THE DORSEY PRESS
HOMEWOOD, ILLINOIS

Preface

This textbook has been written for use in introductory statistics courses for students of psychology. Several principles have guided my choice of topics, the order of presentation, and the manner of treatment. Although they are not logically independent nor separately attainable, there are three important objectives of the introductory course: (1) To provide a foundation for more advanced courses in statistics. (2) To develop a limited number of basic concepts and techniques, without which the student can obtain no more than a superficial acquaintance with many areas of modern psychology. (3) To contribute to the student's general intellectual development through creating a generalized attitude toward problems of inductive inference.

Computational facility and a wide knowledge of techniques, although useful and necessary for some advanced students, are not proper objectives of the introductory course. In fact, these results are even undesirable outcomes if achieved at the expense of failure to recognize the tentative nature of inductive inference and the risk of error incurred in making decisions in the face of incomplete or fallible information. The main business of statistics is the problem of refining and evaluating hypothetical interpretations of experience. It is inseparable from scientific method. For this reason, statistics should not be presented to the undergraduate as a descriptive methodology or as an encyclopedia of techniques for solving type problems. More important is the attitude of scientific inquiry, characterized by careful scrutiny of assumptions, testing hypotheses against the facts of experience, and comparative evaluation of rival interpretations according to a calculus of probability of error. The student who succeeds in generalizing this attitude to all areas of intellectual inquiry will have gone far toward attaining the self-critical objectivity which is one of the major goals of liberal education.

In this textbook no mathematical ability is assumed beyond the basic skills of arithmetic and the simple algebraic manipulations required for solving linear equations. Nevertheless, considerable attention is given throughout the book to algebraic manipulations and simple derivations. These are intended to be neither elegant nor refined; their purpose is pedagogical in that they are intended to clarify concepts and, if possible, to develop in the nonmathematical students an acceptance of mathematical formulation.

Notation presents a serious problem to the beginning student because of the variety of practices which have become traditional in different areas of applied statistics. I have attempted to introduce some semblance of systematic usuage of symbols without departing so far from tradition that the student will have difficulty in reading current literature in psychology. Greek letters have been used only for population values, although in some instances population values have been denoted by Roman letters.

The organization of the material is intended to make this book adaptable to the requirements of a variety of introductory courses in statistics. Exercises and problems have been placed at the ends of sections so that it will be easier for the instructor to omit or postpone parts of chapters which are not essential to the main line of development. A number of such sections have been included only because they describe statistical techniques which the student may encounter in reading the experimental literature of psychology. Although no attempt has been made to treat inferential and descriptive statistics separately, the first seven chapters are primarily concerned with description. If the instructor desires to proceed more rapidly to the basic ideas of statistical inference, he can postpone chapters 6 and 7 until after chapter 12 by omitting short sections of chapters 9, 10, and 11. Chapters 13, 14, and 15 can be omitted from a short introductory course without detracting from the presentation of the basic ideas of statistical inference.

It would be impossible to trace and properly acknowledge all of the sources of the ideas contained in an introductory statistics textbook. The contents are not original, and the author deserves no credit for their discovery or development. The order of presentation, the choice of illustrative material, and the selection of certain concepts for special emphasis can all be largely attributed to the reactions of my students, who over many years have unwittingly, and in some cases unwillingly, served as experimental subjects in my classes. Special credit is due one of my teachers, Quinn McNemar, in whose courses I first realized that statistics is much more than the mechanical application of cookbook formulas. I am indebted to Professor John A. Dudman of the Reed College Department of Mathematics for a critical reading of the entire manuscript. This, however, does not relieve me of full responsibility for any errors or ambiguities in the text. Finally, I am indebted to Grace Courts for continued encouragement and expert assistance in preparing successive versions of the manuscript as it evolved into its present form.

I am indebted to the Literary Executor of the late Sir Ronald A. Fisher, F.R.S., Cambridge; Dr. Frank Yates, F.R.S., Rothamsted, and Messrs. Oliver & Boyd Ltd., Edinburgh, for permission to reprint Tables III, IV, and VII from their book *Statistical Tables for Biological, Agricultural and Medical Research*. Professor E. S. Pearson has generously given permission to reprint the material of Table *H* from *Biometrika*. Specific acknowledgments of these and of the generosity of other authors and publishers appear in the Appendix.

Frederick A. Courts

April, 1966

Table of Contents

CHAPTER I

Introduction

It is a common notion that the term *statistics* refers to collections of numbers, as in a financial statement, an enrollment report of a city school system, or a tabulation of election returns. This popular impression is correct as far as it goes, but it is only part of the total picture. More interesting and significant than the collection of numbers is the fact that statistics is a fundamental tool of scientific inquiry—a method of discovery and proof—useful in any field of scientific study. It is a tool which enables the scientist to formulate general statements about the world in which he lives and to decide whether or not these statements are in agreement with the available evidence. Although essential to scientific inquiry, statistics is not a substitute for the attitude of objectivity necessary for critical thought, nor can it replace intelligent insight and understanding. But the quality of these can be greatly improved through the judicious use of statistical methods.

The purpose of statistical methods is to reduce collections of observations to convenient numerical descriptions and to aid in the process of formulating general inferences about the larger, unknown, universe of possible data which has not been observed. These methods are customarily classified as (1) *statistical description,* the characterization of groups of data in simplified terms, and (2) *statistical inference,* the inductive formulation of general propositions concerning the universe from which the data have been drawn. This traditional separation of statistical methods into two classes has little meaning to the user of statistics. Problems of inference cannot be solved without adequate description of data; and simple description alone, without meaningful interpretation, is of little significance to anyone.

Most of the methods of statistics have been developed to deal with problems usually encountered in one field of study, such as economics, agriculture, genetics, psychology, or education. Almost invariably, however, methods developed in one field have found

1

important applications elsewhere because the general theory of statistics is inseparable from general scientific method. Since certain methods are used more often in psychology than in other fields of study, we shall direct our attention primarily to those. Nevertheless, we must not lose sight of the general theory of statistics which underlies all of the procedures devised for special purposes.

Thorough understanding of statistical theory would require greater knowledge of mathematics than is possessed by most undergraduate students of psychology. It is possible, however, for the student to develop skill in the use of statistical methods and in the interpretation of data within a statistical frame of reference even though his mathematical background does not go beyond arithmetic and algebra. The student who has trouble with the operations of arithmetic and simple algebra, or the one who cannot face up to a formula without flinching, should systematically review these topics during the first few weeks of this course.*

The statistical frame of reference is an attitude, a way of approaching problems, of making decisions and drawing conclusions, which does not require a knowledge of advanced mathematics. It is characterized by a lack of absolute certainty concerning the truth or falsity of the proposition under study. From this point of view, all beliefs pertaining to observed events are in the nature of tentative hypotheses. These tentative beliefs are held more or less firmly according to a scale of confidence which approaches, but never quite reaches, complete acceptance or final rejection. The statistician never asks, "Is this statement true?" or "Is it false?" He inquires, "How likely is it that further observations will not agree with this hypothesis?" There is no magical point at which he can distinguish between false and true conclusions. He can only say that some conclusions are more likely to be true than are others, realizing that the evidence is subject to error and is incomplete.

The essential nature of statistics is to be found in the problems with which it deals. Usually these are problems involving making a decision in the face of uncertainty. The research worker in psychology or education must decide whether or not the results of his experiment support a certain theory of learning. A director of admissions must decide what is to be the lowest college aptitude

---

* An excellent review of elementary mathematical skills is to be found in H. M. Walker, *Mathematics Essential for Elementary Statistics* (New York: Henry Holt and Co., 1935; rev. ed., 1951).

test score which will qualify an applicant for admission to the university. We must decide whether or not to depend on the judgments of classroom teachers to detect early symptoms of later serious emotional disturbance in children. An employment manager must choose between test A and test B in screening applicants for a certain job.

Action based on decisions such as these is more likely to produce the desired result if the decision has been made according to facts rather than according to the dictates of prejudice or intuition. But the "facts" are never entirely dependable or complete, and the most careful decisions are subject to error. Nevertheless, decisions must be made, even though the outcome is uncertain. Although we are seldom, if ever, certain that a decision is correct, we can use statistics to estimate the risk of being wrong. Furthermore, statistics enables us to specify the amount of error as well as the risk.

It is not enough, however, merely to know the probability of error associated with each available choice. We must also consider the *consequences* of various courses of action. When ordering a meal in a restaurant we might be quite willing to accept the risk of one chance in four that our steak will turn out to be tough. The greatest loss which might result from our erroneous decision to order steak would be only a slight decrease in our enjoyment of the meal. A risk of the same magnitude might well cause us to reject a certain course of action if the consequence of error would be the loss of $1,000. But even though $1,000 constituted our entire life's savings, we might decide to take that risk if a correct choice would result in a gain of $5,000, an amount adequate to purchase something we desired greatly.

These simple examples illustrate the fact that statistical analysis does not automatically lead to "good" decisions. Statistics merely serves to create the possibility of intelligent decision by simplifying and emphasizing the significant orderly characteristics of a mass of data and by estimating the risk of error associated with the choice of various interpretations. *Decision theory,* an important branch of modern statistical theory, is concerned with evaluating the *utility* of various courses of action so that decisions can be made on the basis of their consequences. We can do no more than mention the problem of utility or value here, because our purpose is to develop an understanding of the more common statistical methods used in psychology, their applications, and their limitations. Without such understanding, the student will find it difficult, if not impossible, to comprehend many of the most important psychological concepts. A more thorough knowledge of statistics is necessary for anyone who intends to pursue advanced study or to carry on meaningful research.

SUGGESTED READINGS

1. Chernoff, H., and Moses, L. E. *Elementary Decision Theory*, chap. i. New York: John Wiley & Sons, Inc., 1959.
2. Cornell, F. G. *The Essentials of Educational Statistics*, chap. i. New York: John Wiley & Sons, Inc., 1956.
3. Diamond, S. *Information and Error*, chap. i. New York: Basic Books, Inc., 1959.
4. ———. *The World of Probability*, chap. i. New York: Basic Books, Inc., 1964.
5. Walker, H. M. "Statistical Understandings Every Teacher Needs," *NEA Journal*, Vol. 43 (January, 1954), pp. 21–22.

CHAPTER II

The Raw Data

Statistics deals with numerical data, but numbers have different meanings depending on how they are used. It is important to distinguish these meanings carefully, because different kinds of numerical data require different methods of statistical treatment.

MEASUREMENT

Any series of numbers assigned to observations of objects or events according to certain rules is called a *scale*. There are four different kinds of scales, each having its own properties and limitations. The meaning of a scale of measurement is determined by the rules used in assigning certain numbers to certain observations.*

1. Nominal Scales

Numbers which are used as names or labels constitute a nominal scale. Common examples are the assignment of distinctive numbers to the members of a basketball team or to the various items described in a mail-order catalog. These numbers have no mathematical properties. They indicate nothing about the things they represent except that each thing is different. The only reason for using numbers instead of names, or nonsense words, is to avoid a complicated and confusing set of labels.

2. Ordinal Scales

In this type of scale numbers signify the rank order in which observed persons, objects, or events can be arranged according to some attribute. For example, numbers are often used to indicate a pupil's rank in class, the serial order in which an automobile was

---

* S. S. Stevens, "Mathematics, Measurement, and Psychophysics," in *Handbook of Experimental Psychology* (New York: John Wiley & Sons, Inc., 1951), pp. 1–49

manufactured, or the hardness of a rock in relation to a standard set of rocks of different types. The objects referred to by an ordinal scale differ from one another, but they are also *related* to one another in a manner corresponding to the serial order of their numbers. Typical relationships of this sort are: more preferred, better adjusted, less desirable, more beautiful, etc. Although ranks can indicate the presence of more or less of the variable under observation, they do not imply anything about *how much* more or less of the variable is possessed by one person, object, or event in relation to others. An ordinal relationship can be conveniently designated by the symbols $>$ and $<$, which mean respectively "greater than" and "less than." The order of several letters of the alphabet can be denoted as $A > D > P > X$ or $X < P < D < A$. Here $>$ means "precedes," and $<$ means "follows."

3. Interval Scales

Interval scales indicate the *degree of separation* between any two items in an ordered series. The difference between any two objects which are assigned successive whole numbers is the same throughout the entire scale. A common example is the measurement of temperature on either the centigrade or the Fahrenheit scale. Although these thermometers have different zero points and their units are not the same, they are both interval scales because the units of measurement remain the same throughout the entire range. Although interval scales have equal distances between adjacent numerals, measurements on such a scale do not indicate *absolute* magnitudes. The reason for this is that their origin, or zero point, is arbitrary.

Because they have no meaningful zero, interval scales do not permit the comparison of one measurement with another in terms of ratios or percent of difference. For example, suppose that pupil A receives a score of 50 on a spelling test and that pupil B scores 60 on the same test. It is not correct to say that B has 20 percent more spelling ability than A. If the zero point of this scale were changed by adding fifteen very easy words to the test—words which could be spelled correctly by both pupils—A's score would be 65, and B's would be 75. Changing the arbitrary zero point in this way also changes the ratio between the two scores so that B's score is no longer 20 percent higher than A's.

4. Ratio Scales

If a scale of equal intervals has the additional property of a *true zero,* it is called a ratio scale. Ratios between measurements, or the percent of difference between them, will remain the same even though the units of the scale are changed. Since zero distance, unlike "zero" spelling ability, is a true zero, we can correctly state that 15 feet is 50 percent longer than 10 feet. Changing the units of measurement to inches, we find that 180 inches is 50 percent longer than 120 inches.

Ratio scales represent the most refined type of measurement. They are common in the physical sciences but occur rarely in other fields of study. However, ratio scales are found in any situation where measurement takes the form of counting the number of separate objects or events of a given class, since these can be considered equal and the zero point is a meaningful true zero.

DISCRETE AND CONTINUOUS VARIABLES

If it is impossible for fractional values of a measurement to occur, such as three-fifths of an automobile accident or one-third of an aggressive act, the variable to which the numerical measurements refer is said to be *discrete.* Discrete variables change in a stepwise fashion, jumping from point to point with no possibility of intervening steps. However, many measurements describe variables which might conceivably be of any magnitude within their range of possible variation. These are known as *continuous* variables. The number of possible numerical values which might be assigned to a continuous variable approaches infinity, because any fractional part of a unit of measurement might occur. Measurements of intelligence, time, reading comprehension, and auditory threshold, for example, refer to variables which are thought to vary in a continuous manner rather than by discrete steps. Nevertheless, even in measurements such as these the *numerical data* vary by discrete steps of a size dictated by the discriminative ability of the measuring instrument, the permissible range of error, and the range of discriminative measurement in which we are interested. Measurement of linear distance, by way of illustration, refers to a continuous variable. Yet such measurements may increase or decrease by miles, feet, or millimeters, depending on whether we are observing the length of a highway, the height of a building, or the width of a moving picture film.

Numerical measurements can increase or decrease by steps equal to the unit of measurement regardless of whether the underlying variable is continuous or discrete. Thus, the distinction between discrete and continuous data depends on our conception of what is being measured rather than on the method of measurement or the numerical scale.

Refined statistical work sometimes requires special procedures for discrete data. In most cases, however, the distinction between continuous and discrete data is not important. For this reason we shall apply to data of both types the more common statistical methods developed on the assumption of continuous data, except in a few instances where this would result in appreciable error.

It should be noted that data which fall into ordered numerical categories may be either continuous or discrete. Nominal scales, on the other hand, apply only to discrete phenomena because there can be no ordered gradations between their categories.

EXACT AND APPROXIMATE MEASUREMENTS

Measurements of a discrete variable can be precise because it is possible to count such things as automobiles, football players, telephones, and classrooms without error. As a matter of convenience, however, we often choose to measure discrete phenomena according to a scale of numbers which are only approximations of the underlying variable. For example, we usually state the populations of cities in thousands, towns in hundreds, and hamlets in units of one.

Measurements of continuous variables are by their very nature always approximate because they are designated by a discrete series of numbers on the measuring scale. We say that the distance between two towns is twenty miles, and it may actually be precisely twenty miles. But more often than not it is a bit less or a bit more than twenty miles. As a general rule what we really mean is that the *exact distance* is somewhere between nineteen and a half miles and twenty and a half miles. Here again, we have chosen the units of our scale of measurement as a matter of convenience. But, unlike discrete variables, which offer the possibility of precise measurement, continuous variables, such as distance, cannot be measured with complete precision even with the most refined methods.

THE INTERVAL OF APPROXIMATION

It is convenient in statistical work to regard any numerical value on a scale of measurement as the mid-point of an interval of approximation which extends in either direction halfway to the adjacent numerical values of the scale. Thus, in stating that a pupil's test score was 92, we imply that a more precise measurement of the underlying variable (his actual performance) would fall somewhere between 91.5 and 92.5. If we use X to denote the pupil's score, a mathematical statement of the value of X is $91.5 \leqq X \leqq 92.5$. This expression is read as "the number X is not less than 91.5 or greater than 92.5." † It will be convenient for us to consider all measurements in this way, regardless of whether the variable is really discrete or continuous. In a few instances, where this would lead to error, exceptions to the general rule will be necessary.

Some data are obtained under conditions of measurement which require a different interpretation. Ages, for example, are usually designated by numbers corresponding to the last birthday. Here the number refers to the *lower limit* of an interval of approximation which extends upward for one unit on the scale of years. The statement that a person is eighteen years old may thus mean that he has passed his eighteenth birthday but has not yet reached the nineteenth. The age X in this case would be represented as an inequality by $18 \leqq X < 19$.

There are other exceptions to the rule, but they are less common. For example, a timekeeper's report of the hours worked by various employees who receive full pay for fractional hours worked might consist of numbers whose interval of approximation extends downward for one unit. Thus, 42 hours of work would actually mean $41 < X \leqq 42$.

---

† The expression $A < B$ is called an *inequality*. It means "A is less than B" or "B is greater than A." Similarly, $B > A$ has exactly the same meaning. The expression $A > B$ means "A is greater than B" or "B is less than A." By combining the inequality sign with the more familiar sign of equality, we can specify that A is equal to or greater than B by writing either $A \geq B$ or $B \leq A$. The fact that A lies somewhere within the interval defined by the limits B and C is expressed by $B \leq A \leq C$.

SIGNIFICANT DIGITS

The precision of a measurement depends on the number of digits which convey information. For example, a length may be reported as 6.5 millimeters, .65 centimeters, or .0065 meters; and in each case the measurement has two-digit accuracy, and the interval of approximation is the same. The expenditures of a school district may be reported as $3,560,000, a rounded figure which has three-digit accuracy. It has the same number of significant digits, and the same precision, as the report of $356 thousand, or $3.56 million. The position of the decimal point is entirely unrelated to the number of significant digits unless the decimal follows a zero or is followed by one or more zeros. The number 3.0 is a member of the sequence 2.8, 2.9, 3.0, 3.1, etc. The number 30 belongs to the sequence 20, 30, 40, etc. However, if we write 30., with a decimal point following the zero, it is understood that this number is a member of the series 29, 30, 31. It is misleading to tack on extra zeros to the right of the decimal point. The interval of approximation denoted by 25.1 is from 25.05 to 25.15, while the interval defined by 25.10 extends from 25.095 to 25.105. A zero placed at the right of a decimal fraction is a statement of the precision of measurement, and it should never be used unless such a statement of precision is justified. When a number ending with zeros has no decimal point, it is convenient to place a dot or a bar above the last significant zero to specify the precision of measurement. The following examples serve to illustrate these principles.

Number	Interval	Number of Significant Digits
27	$26.5 < X < 27.5$	2
27.0	$26.95 < X < 27.05$	3
0.27	$0.265 < X < 0.275$	2
0.27000	$0.269995 < X < 0.270005$	5
2700	$2650 < X < 2750$	2
2700.	$2699.5 < X < 2700.5$	4
27$\bar{0}$0	$2695 < X < 2705$	3
270$\dot{0}$	$2699.5 < X < 2700.5$	4

ROUNDING NUMBERS IN COMPUTATION

If measurements are exact, computations may be carried to as many places as it seems worth while reporting. Computations based on approximate numbers are themselves approximate, and it is meaningless to report such a computation as an average to several non-significant digits. It is generally advisable to carry a computation through to the end without drastic rounding, and then to round off the final result to a figure which is meaningful in relation to the accuracy of the original data.

SUGGESTED READINGS

1. Cornell, F. G. *The Essentials of Educational Statistics,* chap. ii. New York: John Wiley & Sons, 1956.
2. Walker, H. M. *Mathematics Essential for Elementary Statistics,* chap. v. New York: Henry Holt and Company, 1951 (Rev. ed.).

EXERCISE

1. Which type of measuring scale is implied by each of the following?
   a) Reaction time to auditory stimulus.
   b) A test of achievement in arithmetic.
   c) The percent of correct answers to a selected list of multiple choice vocabulary items.
   d) A teacher's ratings of the pupils in a sixth grade class with respect to effectiveness of participation in discussion.
   e) The average daily attendance in the various schools of a county.

2. Give several examples of (*a*) discrete and (*b*) continuous data.

3. Distinguish between number of decimals and number of significant digits.

4. Is it correct to say that physical measurements are precise whereas measurements in psychology are always approximate? Give examples.

5. For each of the following write the limits of the interval of approximation and indicate the number of significant digits.
   a) 500
   b) 36.183
   c) 0.0008
   d) 2550.
   e) 2550
   f) 25000

6. Suppose the following numbers are to be added: 25.3, 6.247, 15, 24. What are the limits of the interval of approximation of the sum of these numbers?

Suggestion: Write the upper limit of the interval for each number and add these values. Do the same for the lower limits.

7. What assumption must be made if pupils' ages to the nearest month are said to constitute a ratio scale of measurement?

8. Describe methods which could be used to measure the heights of a group of children by (a) an ordinal, (b) an interval, (c) a ratio scale.

CHAPTER III

Frequency Distributions

The limitations of human intelligence are such that a scientist is seldom able to perceive meaningful relationships in the raw data of an experiment. Statistical description organizes and simplifies masses of quantitative data so that they become intelligible. Appropriate statistical treatment accentuates uniformities and regularities of the data while obscuring individual instances of irregularity and inconsistency. Thus, group characteristics and general relationships can be abstracted from observations of many separate individual instances.

When confronted with a mass of raw measurements the investigator must first of all group or classify his data into meaningful and convenient categories. Classification of raw data, whether discrete or continuous, whether ordered or unordered, requires a decision as to the number of classes to be used. It is awkward to work with a large number of narrowly defined categories; but if the categories are too broad and too few, much valuable information is lost.

THE CLASS INTERVAL

Statistical treatment is usually facilitated by transforming raw measurements into units even coarser than those of the original measuring scale. These need not be conventional units such as ounces, pounds, hundredweight, or tons. They may be of any size selected to provide maximum convenience without too great a loss in accuracy. Weights of people might be classified in units of one ounce, ten ounces, one pound, three pounds, or ten pounds, depending upon the necessity for fine discrimination and the number of such weight categories which could be conveniently handled. Such arbitrary units are called *class intervals*. Class intervals are simply an extension of the grouping which is a necessary part of the measurement of a continuous variable. Although they do not involve an interval of approximation, discrete data also can be

13

treated statistically with greater efficiency if they are grouped into class intervals.

The data in Table 1 are scores made by 90 college students on a personality inventory. The scores, arranged in the table according to the alphabetical sequence of the students' surnames, range from 6 to 93 and thus represent 88 intervals of approximation, each of which has a range of one score unit.

TABLE 1

Scores on a Personality Inventory

71	23	43	23	49	86	35	33	43
49	66	42	63	76	23	53	30	30
30	19	12	18	34	19	66	56	60
57	50	55	40	36	22	23	59	78
38	65	37	43	47	54	27	25	55
74	40	36	35	22	14	47	56	10
25	71	19	51	76	30	30	46	29
24	76	15	6	81	46	28	17	40
25	15	47	69	35	48	42	57	78
70	30	93	26	55	9	39	25	63

The confusing picture presented by such a table of data can be simplified by tabulating the scores into a *frequency distribution* as in Table 2. Here, the 88 score intervals have been listed in order of size, and a tally mark has been placed opposite the proper number for each student's score. This arrangement of the data is called a frequency distribution because it shows how many times, or how frequently, each of the different score intervals appeared within the group of raw data.

Although Table 2 is a better representation of the group characteristics of the data than is Table 1, it is inconvenient and confusing because it contains so many categories of classification. Further simplification may be achieved by grouping the scores into categories coarser than those implied in the original measurement, as in Table 3 and Table 4.

The larger the class intervals used, the less accurate is the designation of individual scores. For example, 93, the highest score tabulated in Table 2, conveys the information that the student who obtained that score is located somewhere between 92.5 and 93.5 on the scale. In Table 3 the situation is quite different. This distribution informs us that the highest score might be any one of the five score values included within the highest class interval: 90, 91, 92, 93, or 94. The range of possible score values included within a class

TABLE 2

FREQUENCY DISTRIBUTION IN INTERVALS OF ONE SCORE UNIT (FROM DATA OF TABLE 1)

Score	Tallies	Frequency	Score	Tallies	Frequency
93	I	1	49	II	2
92			48	I	1
91			47	III	3
90			46	II	2
89			45		
88			44		
87			43	III	3
86	I	1	42	II	2
85			41		
84			40	III	3
83			39	I	1
82			38	I	1
81	I	1	37	I	1
80			36	II	2
79			35	III	3
78	II	2	34	I	1
77			33	I	1
76	III	3	32		
75			31		
74	I	1	30	NHII	6
73			29	I	1
72			28	I	1
71	II	2	27	I	1
70	I	1	26	I	1
69	I	1	25	IIII	4
68			24	I	1
67			23	IIII	4
66	II	2	22	II	2
65	I	1	21		
64			20		
63	II	2	19	III	3
62			18	I	1
61			17	I	1
60	I	1	16		
59	I	1	15	II	2
58			14	I	1
57	II	2	13		
56	II	2	12	I	1
55	III	3	11		
54	I	1	10	I	1
53	I	1	9	I	1
52			8		
51	I	1	7		
50	I	1	6	I	1

interval, here 90 to 94, is called the *score limits* of the interval. The combined range of approximation of these scores, here 89.5 to 94.5, is specified by the *real limits* or *boundaries* of the interval. The particular numerical value used to describe any obtained score

TABLE 3

FREQUENCY DISTRIBUTION IN INTERVALS OF
FIVE UNITS (FROM DATA OF TABLE 1)

Class Interval	Tallies	Frequency
90–94		1
85–89		1
80–84		1
75–79		5
70–74		4
65–69		4
60–64		3
55–59		8
50–54		4
45–49		8
40–44		8
35–39		8
30–34		8
25–29		8
20–24		7
15–19		7
10–14		3
5– 9		2

TABLE 4

FREQUENCY DISTRIBUTION IN IN-
TERVALS OF TEN UNITS (FROM DATA
OF TABLE 1)

Class Interval	Frequency
90–99	1
80–89	2
70–79	9
60–69	7
50–59	12
40–49	16
30–39	16
20–29	15
10–19	10
0– 9	2

falling within a given class interval is, as in the case of raw
measurements, the mid-point of the range of approximation. The
mid-point of the interval 90–94 is 92. Thus, on the basis of information conveyed by Table 3, we would state the value of the
highest score as 92. In a similar manner, each score in the
distribution is denoted by the numerical value of the mid-point of
its class interval. (See Figure 1.)

FIGURE 1

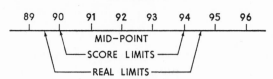

The frequency distribution in Table 4, where the class interval is ten score units, provides even less information concerning individual scores. Here the highest score is described by the value 94.5, which is the mid-point of the class interval whose score limits are 90 to 99. This score is specified as $89.5 < X < 99.5$.

Table 5 illustrates the same data tabulated into class intervals of 25 score units. Because the intervals are so large, relatively little

TABLE 5

FREQUENCY DISTRIBUTION IN INTERVALS OF 25 UNITS
(FROM DATA OF TABLE 1)

Score	Tallies	Frequency
75–99..............	ℍℍ ꜰ	8
50–74..............	ℍℍ ℍℍ ℍℍ ℍℍ ꜰ	23
25–49..............	ℍℍ ℍℍ ℍℍ ℍℍ ℍℍ ℍℍ ℍℍ ℍℍ	40
0–24..............	ℍℍ ℍℍ ℍℍ ℍℍ	19

information about individual scores is retained in this tabulation, and even the group characteristics are obscured.

The Number of Class Intervals

There is no hard and fast rule for the number of class intervals to be used in tabulating a frequency distribution. The preceding examples show that as the number of intervals decreases (and their size increases), the distribution portrays less accurately the individual measurements. On the other hand, as the number of intervals increases, the group characteristics of the data become less clear. As the number of intervals decreases, group characteristics are accentuated up to a certain point, but beyond this point both individual scores and group characteristics are less clearly represented. In general, data can be presented conveniently, with sufficient accuracy, and with clear delineation of group characteristics if the frequency distribution contains from twelve to twenty class intervals. Within this range the number of intervals to be used depends on the number of cases in the group of data. With a small number of observations the group pattern appears most vividly when only a few wide intervals are used. With large groups of data a larger number of narrower intervals is appropriate.

PROCEDURE FOR TABULATING A FREQUENCY DISTRIBUTION

1. Find the difference between the lowest and the highest scores to be tabulated. This is the *range*. The range in Table 1 is found to be from 6 to 93, or 87 score units. Actually the entire range is from the lowest real limit to the highest. In Table 1 this is from 5.5 to 93.5, or 88 units. However, for most purposes, the difference between the lowest and the highest score values provides an adequate measure of the range.

2. By trial and error find a convenient number which, when divided into the range, results in a quotient from 12 to 20. This number is the *size of class interval*. The range in Table 1 is 87. By rough approximation we evaluate several possible class intervals.

Size of Interval		Approximate Number of Intervals
4	(87 ÷ 4)	22
5	(87 ÷ 5)	18
6		15
7		13
8		11
9		10
10		9

If we use 4 as the class interval there will be more than 20 intervals. The rule of thumb that we should use 12 to 20 intervals limits our choice to intervals of 5, 6, or 7 units. These three values are not equally acceptable in terms of convenience. We finally decide to use intervals of 5 after considering the relative convenience of the three schemes of classification.

Size of Interval		
5	6	7
95–99	90–95	91–97
90–94	84–89	84–90
85–89	78–83	77–83
80–84	72–77	70–76
75–79	66–71	63–69
.	.	.
.	.	.
.	.	.
5– 9	6–11	0– 6

Since our number language is a decimal system, it is natural for us to find tabulation easiest when we use intervals of 10, 20, 30, or other multiples of 10. But many distributions cannot be appropriately represented by these intervals. In practice, most data can be conveniently grouped into intervals of 1, 2, 3, 4, 5, 10, or multiples of 10. These intervals are preferred except in very unusual situations.

3. Find the largest multiple of the interval which is less than the highest score to be tabulated. This number is the lower score limit of the highest class interval. In our illustrative problem (Tables 1 and 3) this limit is 90, since the highest score is 93.

The practice of using multiples of the class interval for the lower score limits is a convenient rule of thumb. When intervals are 5, 10, 20, and so on, this procedure greatly simplifies tabulation and thus makes errors less likely.

4. List in order the intervals to be used, designating them by their *score limits*. It is customary to place the highest or largest scores at the top of the tabulation sheet. Of course, it is not incorrect to list the real limits of class intervals; but this makes tabulation needlessly difficult and consequently increases the likelihood of error.

5. Place in the appropriate interval a tally mark corresponding to each raw measurement.

6. Count the tallies in each interval and record their number to the right. This column is labeled f (for frequency). The sum of the f's should be equal to the total number of cases in the distribution.

7. Place a brief descriptive title above the table.

EXERCISES

1. For each of the following ranges of measurement state (1) the size of class interval you would use, (2) the score limits of the highest interval, (3) the exact limits of this interval, and (4) its mid-point.
   a) 27 to 69   d) −15 to 26
   b) 40 to 56   e) 14503 to 22107
   c) 0.150 to 0.341   f) 28 to 131

2. Tabulate data A (below), using what you consider an appropriate size of class interval.

DATA A : SCORES MADE BY A GROUP OF COLLEGE STUDENTS
ON THE OTIS SA TEST

60	61	52	55	47	62	54	58	42	30	47	36	67
42	36	43	57	47	49	51	40	45	65	31	53	40
73	53	47	56	44	60	44	31	51	44	43	38	47
50	51	67	39	49	43	55	43	46	50	44	57	44
53	33	38	52	45	52	40	37	40	45	58	45	40
34	55	47	44	40	32	45	60	37	45	52	63	46
49	45	46	38	37	34	45	57	54	71	45	38	

3. Assuming that each of the following is a measurement of a continuous variable, write the inequality which expresses the interval of approximation.

a) 4900   d) 39.0   g) 16   j) 25.030
b) −71   e) .0018   h) 50.5   k) .68
c) 1.002   f) 70300   i) 6.01   l) 3.75

4. Write the score limits of each of the following class intervals.

a) $39.5 < X < 44.5$ d) $99.5 < X < 109.5$
b) $.095 < X < .0125$ e) $9.95 < X < 10.95$
c) $145 < X < 155$ f) $17.5 < X < 18.5$

5. What size of class interval would you use for the following?

a) Heights of adult males in the U.S.
b) Ages of sixth graders in a large city school system
c) IQ's of the adult population
d) IQ's of college students

6. Which of the following would you consider to be discrete variables?

a) Speaking vocabulary of five-year-old children
b) Reaction time
c) Size of family in the U.S.
d) Scores on a spelling test
e) Spelling ability

GRAPHIC REPRESENTATION

One of the most effective ways of describing a frequency distribution is by means of a graph. Graphs are used in a variety of situations to show how variations in one quantity are related to changes in another. Distances along the base line of a graph represent values of one quantity, while the varying height of the curve above the base line shows how the other quantity varies with changes in the first.

Each point on a graph is located by two numerical values—the distance along the base line, which is called the *abscissa,* and the height above the base line, which is called the *ordinate* of the point.

In Figure 2 the distance *OA* is the abscissa of the point *P.* The distance *OB* is the ordinate. The abscissa and the ordinate are known as the *coordinates* of a point.

FIGURE 2

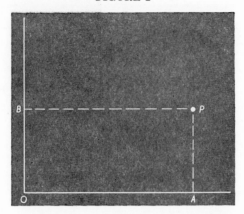

The following typical examples illustrate tabular and graphic presentation of several sets of data.

TABLE 6

VOLUME OF A GAS UNDER
VARIOUS PRESSURES

P (*Pounds per Square Inch*)	*V* *Cubic Inches*
20	525
25	420
30	350
35	300
40	262
45	233
50	210
55	191

FIGURE 3

VOLUME OF A GAS UNDER
VARIOUS PRESSURES

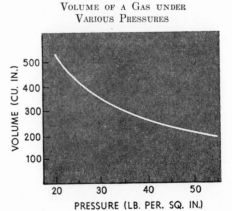

Note in Figure 4 that average Alpha scores are plotted above mid-points of the class intervals. The mid-point of the interval "under twenty" is taken as nineteen on the assumption that few, if any, officers would have been under eighteen years of age.

TABLE 7

AVERAGE ARMY ALPHA SCORES OF
OFFICERS IN WORLD WAR I.*

Age	Average Score
under 20	150
20–24	146
25–30	143
31–40	133
41–50	125
51–60	120

* Data from R. M. Yerkes (ed.), "Psychological examining in the U.S. Army," *Memoirs of the Nat. Acad. of Sci.*, Vol. 15 (1921).

FIGURE 4

AVERAGE ARMY ALPHA SCORES OF
OFFICERS IN WORLD WAR I AS A
FUNCTION OF AGE

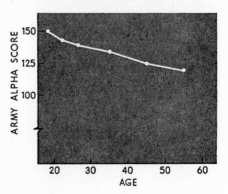

TABLE 8

NUMBER OF DOCTORATES IN PSYCHOLOGY
CONFERRED BY AMERICAN UNIVERSITIES
1899–1949*

Years	Number of Degrees	Average Number per Year
1899–1901	38	12.7
1902–04	36	12.0
1905–07	40	13.3
1908–10	67	22.3
1911–13	74	24.7
1914–16	63	21.0
1917–19	71	23.7
1920–22	93	31.0
1923–25	145	48.3
1926–28	198	66.0
1929–31	313	104.3
1932–34	309	103.0
1935–37	332	110.7
1938–40	343	114.3
1941–43	335	111.7
1944–46	189	63.0
1947–49	404	134.7

* Data from R. S. Harper, "Tables of American Doctorates in Psychology," *Amer. J. Psychol.*, No. 62 (1949), pp. 579–87.

The horizontal base line of a graph is customarily designated by the letter X, the vertical scale by Y. The X-variable is called the *independent variable,* since the particular values of X which appear in a graph (or table) are chosen by the investigator. Corresponding values of Y are regarded as dependent upon the values of X which the investigator has selected. Thus, Y is known as the *dependent variable*. Whenever Y varies systematically with changes in X, Y is said to be a *function* of X. The mathematical expression, $Y = f(X)$, is often used to mean that some sort of functional relationship exists between Y and X. Formulas, such as $Y = X^2$, or $Y = A + BX$, specify the nature of the relationship of Y to X.

FIGURE 5

AVERAGE NUMBER OF DOCTORATES IN PSYCHOLOGY FOR THREE-YEAR PERIODS, 1899–1949

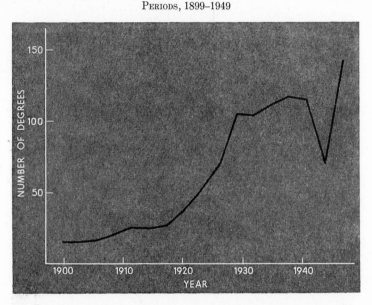

Graphs are also used to describe in detail the nature of a functional relationship between two variables.

Four different kinds of graphs are commonly used to describe frequency distributions. These are (1) the *frequency polygon*, (2) the *cumulative frequency* curve, (3) the *histogram*, and (4) the *bar diagram*. Relative frequencies, or percentages, are often represented by a pie chart in which the sizes of the sectors represent the proportions of cases falling into each category of classification. Graphs which represent frequencies by volume are not recommended for ordinary use, since they are not easily interpreted.

The Frequency Polygon

A frequency polygon is the many-sided figure formed by straight lines connecting the points representing frequencies in successive class intervals of a frequency distribution. The value of X, or the abscissa, for a given point is the mid-point of the class interval. The ordinate, or Y-value, is the frequency within the interval. Figure 6 is a frequency polygon constructed to represent the frequency distribution shown in Table 9.

TABLE 9

FREQUENCY DISTRIBUTION OF SCORES
ON A PERSONALITY INVENTORY
(FROM DATA OF TABLE 1)

Score	f
91–97	1
84–90	1
77–83	3
70–76	7
63–69	6
56–62	6
49–55	9
42–48	11
35–41	11
28–34	10
21–27	13
14–20	8
7–13	3
0– 6	1

Procedure for Constructing a Frequency Polygon. 1. Divide the available space on the graph paper into convenient units for X and Y. The X-axis requires two more units than the number of intervals in the frequency tabulation. The size of units on the Y-axis should

FIGURE 6

DISTRIBUTION OF SCORES ON A PERSONALITY INVENTORY (FROM TABLE 9)

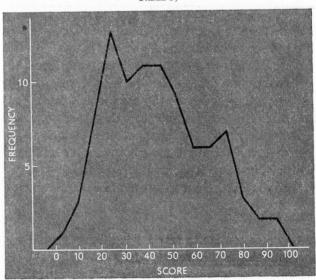

be such that the highest point to be plotted is from 60 to 75 percent of the total distance to be used on the X-axis. This is a useful rule designed to produce an attractive and easily understood graph. The zero point must be shown on the frequency scale, though it need not appear on the X-axis. Where Y does not represent frequency, its zero point may be omitted if that fact is suitably indicated by a break in the Y-axis, as in Figure 4, page 22.

2. Locate on the base line the mid-point of each class interval, including one interval with a frequency of zero at each end of the distribution.

3. Place a dot over the mid-point of each interval with an ordinate corresponding to the frequency in that interval.

4. Connect the dots above adjacent mid-points by drawing straight lines between them with a ruler. The graph should drop to the base-line for intervals having a frequency of zero.

5. Place numbers along the axes at convenient points to indicate the magnitude of X and Y. It is not necessary to designate the numerical value of each interval, although it is sometimes convenient to number the mid-points of the intervals where they fall on integral values.

6. Label each axis so as to state clearly what it represents.

7. Place a clear and concise title *below* the graph.

Comparing Frequency Polygons.   It is often of interest to compare two groups of scores. This can be done simply and conveniently by plotting the frequency polygons on a single sheet of graph paper so that one is superimposed upon the other. When the distributions have the same number of cases, frequencies can be plotted and directly compared. If the groups differ in size, each frequency must be converted into a percentage of the total number of cases in its group.

The Cumulative Frequency Curve

A frequency distribution may be represented by a graph which shows the total frequency for all class intervals below various points on the X-scale. Such a graph is called a *cumulative frequency curve* or an *ogive*. This type of curve is often plotted in cumulative percentages. The cumulative frequencies shown in Table 10 were obtained by adding to the frequency within each class interval the frequencies in all of the intervals below that one.

Note that the abscissas of the plotted points in Figure 7 are

TABLE 10

DISTRIBUTION OF PERSONALITY INVENTORY SCORES
(FROM DATA OF TABLE 1)

Score	f		cumulative f	cumulative percent
91–97	1		90	100.0
84–90	1		89	98.9
77–83	3		88	97.8
70–76	7		85	94.4
63–69	6		78	86.7
56–62	6		72	80.0
49–55	9		66	73.3
42–48	11		57	63.3
35–41	11...11 + 10 + 13 + 8 + 3 + 1		46	51.1
28–34	10..... 10 + 13 + 8 + 3 + 1		35	38.9
21–27	13......... 13 + 8 + 3 + 1		25	27.8
14–20	8.............. 8 + 3 + 1		12	13.3
7–13	3.................. 3 + 1		4	4.4
0– 6	1..................... 1		1	1.1

upper real limits of class intervals. This correctly represents the fact that the ordinate values are the numbers of cases below various points on the continuous X-axis. All of the scores within a class interval are known to lie below the upper real limit of that interval even though their exact positions within the interval are unknown.

FIGURE 7

CUMULATIVE DISTRIBUTION CURVE (FROM TABLE 10)

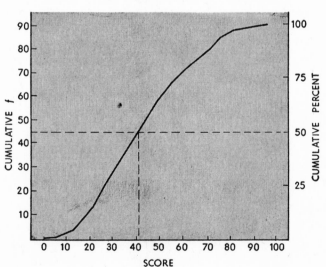

Frequency distributions for samples with different N's can be readily compared if they are plotted on the same graph paper as cumulative percentage distributions. This method is often used in comparing classes, age groups, etc.

The Histogram

A frequency distribution may be represented by a graph composed of rectangles where the width of a rectangle corresponds to the size of class interval on the X-scale and the height represents frequency within the interval. This type of graph, illustrated in Figure 8, is called a *histogram*. The frequency polygon would not ordinarily be superimposed on the histogram. In Figure 8, however, this is done to enable you to compare the two types of graph.

The rectangles of a histogram may be thought of as being made up of a number of smaller rectangles, each of which represents one of the individual scores in a distribution. Figure 8 illustrates how three small rectangles are combined into a larger one to represent the frequency in the class interval 7–13. If the class intervals are all equal in width the total *area* of a histogram thus corresponds to the number of scores in the distribution. The proportion of the total area which lies above a class interval represents the proportion of the total number of cases falling within that interval.

FIGURE 8

Histogram, with Superimposed Frequency Polygon

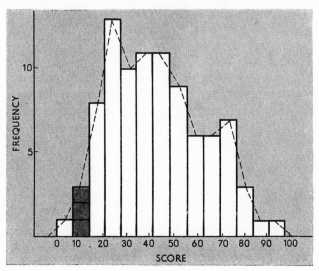

The Bar Diagram

The frequency polygon, the cumulative frequency curve, and the histogram all imply that the data represented by them are descriptive of a continuous variable, since these graphs continue with no

FIGURE 9

MOTOR VEHICLE ACCIDENTS DURING 1956 AT THE TEN MOST
DANGEROUS INTERSECTIONS IN PORTLAND, OREGON

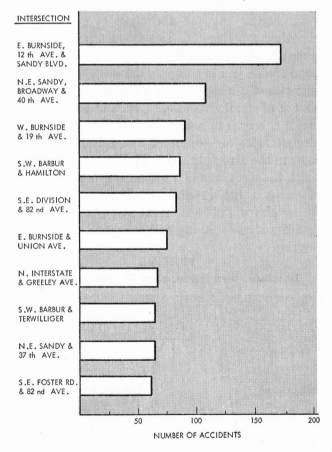

gaps above the entire range of the X-axis. An accurate representation of frequency distribution in a discrete series is provided by the *bar diagram*.

Above each category of classification designated on the base line of the figure, a bar is erected to represent the frequency within that category. In this type of figure the height of the bar represents frequency. A bar diagram resembles a histogram except that the bars are separated to suggest the discrete nature of the categories. The bars are often extended horizontally, as in Figure 9, to provide a more convenient space for designating the categories.

The Form of a Frequency Distribution

A variety of terms are used to describe the shape of a frequency polygon or histogram.

A distribution is said to be *bilaterally symmetrical*, regardless of its particular shape, if the curve can be folded at the center along a vertical line so that the two halves of the figure coincide.

FIGURE 10

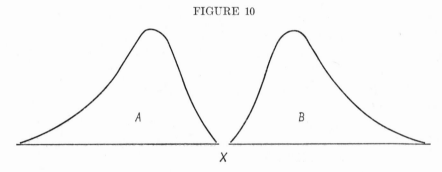

Skewness refers to the degree to which scores are asymmetrically distributed around the center of the distribution. Skewness is designated as positive or negative depending on whether the elongated tail of the distribution extends in the direction of high or low scores on X. In Figure 10, distribution A is negatively skewed. Distribution B illustrates positive skewness. (The X-variable is customarily plotted with low scores to the left.)

If each class interval has approximately the same frequency, a distribution is described as *rectangular*.

A *bell-shaped* distribution is one which resembles the silhouette of a bell with a single broad hump in the middle which tails off gradually on either side. One particular type of bell-shaped curve is known as the *normal distribution*. This curve can be precisely defined only by the mathematical equation used in plotting it. The mathematical model of the normal distribution, of great importance for statistics, will be treated in some detail in Chapter VIII.

If, in comparison with the normal distribution, a curve is tall and slender with a rather sharp inflection on each side, it is said to be

FIGURE 11

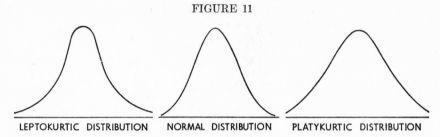

| LEPTOKURTIC DISTRIBUTION | NORMAL DISTRIBUTION | PLATYKURTIC DISTRIBUTION |

leptokurtic. If it is flatter and less sharply inflected than the normal distribution, it is called a *platykurtic* curve.

SUGGESTED READINGS

1. Arkin, H., and Colton, R. *Graphs: How to Make and Use Them.* 2d. ed. New York: Harper and Brothers, 1938.
2. Jenkinson, B. L. *Manual of Tabular Presentation.* Washington, D.C.: U.S. Government Printing Office, 1939.
3. Mudgett, B. D. *Statistical Tables and Graphs.* Boston: Houghton Mifflin Company, 1930.
4. Walker, H. M., and Durost, W. N. *Statistical Tables: Their Structure and Use.* New York: Bureau of Publications, Teachers College, Columbia University, 1936.

EXERCISES

1. Construct a frequency polygon showing the distribution of age for the entire class. *Make sure that frequencies are plotted above the midpoints of class intervals.*

2. Plot cumulative percentage curves on the same graph to compare men and women with respect to height. Does this seem like a useful technique for comparing groups?

3. *a)* Plot a histogram to show the total distribution of weight.
   b) Construct two histograms, one for men and one for women, to illustrate sex differences in weight. Note that frequencies cannot be directly compared since the men and women differ in total number.
   c) Construct polygons to show sex differences in weight.
   d) Which type of figure, the polygon or histogram, best illustrates group differences?
   e) How was the outline of the histogram in item *a* distorted by the fact that the class is made up of two sub-groups which differ in weight?

DATA *B:* STUDENTS ENROLLED IN A COURSE IN INDIVIDUAL DIFFERENCES

Student	Sex	Age to Last Birthday	Height in Inches	Weight in Pounds	Raw Score on Intelligence Test
E.T.	F	20	65	130	178
J.S.	M	24	69	200	173
W.H.	M	25	72	165	174
B.B.	M	20	72	193	189
B.M.	F	19	67	128	175
A.W.	F	19	65	115	173
J.W.	M	28	73	164	180
J.G.	F	21	63	125	176
S.P.	F	20	61	105	180
T.M.	M	22	71	145	172
F.M.	M	20	67	160	188
B.G.	M	24	69	148	184
L.C.	F	20	68	143	175
H.T.	F	22	63	122	185
I.T.	M	20	72	180	177
H.T.	M	26	72	170	173
W.M.	M	23	70	170	183
F.A.	F	21	67	134	182
E.I.	F	20	69	135	177
F.F.	F	20	63	110	177
H.B.	M	20	71	150	179
D.H.	M	23	71	155	189
N.H.	F	20	62	106	189
D.C.	M	22	70	180	188
C.L.	F	20	67	132	174
D.P.	M	27	68	137	178
N.M.	F	19	63	124	212
L.S.	M	20	68	153	187
A.H.	F	20	60	110	211
J.S.	M	22	72	155	190
H.K.	M	24	71	180	170
L.R.	M	21	72	151	163
N.M.	M	25	72	165	158
R.S.	M	20	73	183	200
E.Z.	F	21	65	115	196
W.C.	M	24	70	165	165
L.N.	F	19	65	124	190
P.H.	M	21	66	130	152
D.C.	M	20	72	170	151
J.C.	M	19	71	155	155
J.T.	F	20	68	138	192
J.B.	M	25	74	165	193
F.R.	M	22	72	168	169
J.M.	M	21	76	183	203
E.W.	F	20	65	111	198
S.P.	F	20	65	122	200
H.Q.	F	26	61	110	114
G.H.	M	25	71	165	214
D.S.	M	24	73	158	196
M.J.	F	21	69	150	196
W.K.	M	20	68	160	166
J.S.	M	28	68	178	164
W.J.	M	29	72	202	159
H.T.	M	20	71	170	161
J.R.	F	20	66	130	168
J.C.	M	27	72	206	193
R.D.	M	23	72	156	196
D.B.	F	19	67	120	169
J.P.	M	31	72	155	205
B.B.	F	20	66	116	196
K.W.	F	20	67	127	194

4. Represent the following data by means of a graph.

NUMBER OF DEGREES AWARDED IN EACH DIVISION OF A
LIBERAL ARTS COLLEGE BY TEN-YEAR INTERVALS

Division	1915–24	1925–34	1935–44	1945–54
History and Social Science......................	118	117	253	234
Letters and Arts...............................	130	121	157	125
Mathematics and Natural Science.................	87	152	271	374
Philosophy, Psychology and Education............	63	30	76	106

Does your graph clearly illustrate any generalized statement about the data?

5. Construct a graph to represent the following data.

OCCUPATIONAL OBJECTIVES OF A GROUP OF
COLLEGE STUDENTS

	Men	Women
Teaching...................	41	26
Scientific Research..........	76	14
Law.......................	16	0
Engineering................	25	1
Medicine..................	38	6
Psychology................	6	10
Social Work...............	0	12
Government Service.........	10	2
Art, Drama, Music..........	4	9
Journalism................	7	3
Business..................	6	0
Unclassified...............	8	10

Does your graph show the *relative frequency* of each objective for men and women?

6. How would you represent the following data by a graph?

Score	Frequency
100 and above...............	15
90–99......................	10
80–89......................	23
70–79......................	30
60–69......................	47
50–59......................	24
below 50...................	32

CHAPTER IV

Measures of Central Tendency

It is often useful to describe a set of data by an average value which is typical of all of the separate measurements. Averages are *measures of central tendency* or of *location,* since they are designed to describe the middle, or typical, value of the distribution. A number of different kinds of averages have been devised, but only three are commonly used in education and psychology. These are: (1) The *mode.* This is the particular score or measurement which occurs most frequently in a group of data. (2) The *median.* This is the value on the scale of measurement which divides the number of cases in the group into two equal parts. (3) The *arithmetic mean.* This is the sum of all of the scores in a group divided by the number of such scores. It is popularly called "the average."

THE MODE

For most purposes the mode, denoted by Mo, can be found by inspection. If a frequency distribution is tabulated according to raw measurements, the Mo is simply the X-value having the greatest frequency. If the data are grouped into class intervals, the Mo is taken as the mid-point of the interval having the greatest frequency. In advanced work, the Mo found in this way is called the "crude mode" to distinguish it from the value obtained through more precise calculation. The crude mode, however, is sufficiently accurate for most psychological applications.

THE MEDIAN

If a group of measurements is arranged in order of size, the median, denoted by Mdn, is the middlemost value when there are an odd number of measurements. It is the point midway between the two middle values if there are an even number of scores.

Example:

25	30	43	45
20	30	30	45
16	28	29	44
5	20	28	26
5			20
Mdn = 16	Mdn = 29	Mdn = 29.5	Mdn = 44

When a distribution contains duplications of scores, ordering is impossible, and it often happens that the median does not fall exactly upon a score value or midway between two scores. Nevertheless, it is still possible to divide the total frequency into two equal parts.

Example:

24
20
18
18
15

The median is, by definition, the point above and below which 50 percent of the scores are located. A distribution of this sort presents no difficulty if we recall that the numerical symbol assigned to a given measurement refers to an interval of approximation on a continuous scale, and not to a point. Thus, the two scores of 18 are measurements which fall *somewhere* between the points 17.5 and 18.5. If we assume that these two scores are evenly distributed within the interval of approximation, one of them can be considered to be higher on the scale of measurement than the other. This higher score, since it is the middlemost score of the distribution, is the median. The assumed position of the scores and the range occupied by each can be represented by a diagram (Figure 12). In Figure 12 the middlemost score occupies a range whose mid-point is 18.25. This value is the Mdn.

The same result can be achieved by simple arithmetic interpola-

FIGURE 12

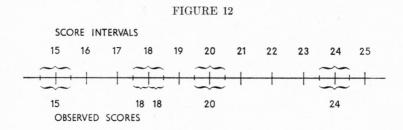

SCORE INTERVALS

tion: (*a*) $N = 5$, the number of scores. (*b*) $N/2 = 2.5$, the number of scores which, by definition, must lie below the median. (*c*) There is one score below 17.5, and three fall below 18.5. The median must, therefore, be a value between these two real limits of score intervals. $17.5 < \text{Mdn} < 18.5$. (*d*) The median, then, is the point within the interval 17.5 to 18.5 which is above 1.5 of the two scores contained in that interval. Assuming the scores to be evenly distributed within the interval, we locate the median at 1.5/2 of the distance above the lower real limit of the interval. (*e*) The score value of the median is thus 1.5/2 score units above the lower limit because the interval of approximation is equal to one score unit. (*f*) $\text{Mdn} = 17 + (1.5/2) = 18.25$.

Finding the Median of Grouped Data

Exactly the same procedure is followed in finding the median of any frequency distribution.

Example (from data of Table 10):

Class Interval	f	cum. f
91–97	1	90
84–90	1	89
77–83	3	88
70–76	7	85
63–69	6	78
56–62	6	72
49–55	9	66
42–48	11	57
35–41	11	46
28–34	10	35
21–27	13	25
14–20	8	12
7–13	3	4
0– 6	1	1

(*a*) N = 90. (*b*) N/2 = 45. (*c*) Therefore, 34.5 < Mdn < 41.5. (*d*) There are thirty-five scores below 34.5. But there must be forty-five below the median. If we assume the eleven scores to be evenly distributed within the interval, the median is 10/11 of an interval above 34.5. (*e*) The median is 10/11 · (7) score units above 34.5. (*f*) Mdn = 34.5 + (10/11) (7) = 40.9.

There is no algebraic formula for the median. The computation can be summarized as follows.

Let LL = lower real limit of interval containing Mdn.
F_c = cumulative frequency up to that interval.
f_i = frequency within that interval.
i = number of score units within that interval.

$$\text{Mdn} = LL + \frac{N/2 - F_c}{f_i} \cdot i \qquad (1)$$

The histogram of Figure 13 illustrates graphically this method of finding the median. The area of each bar of the histogram corresponds to the number of cases in the class interval represented by that bar. An ordinate erected at the median must divide the area of the histogram into two equal parts, each containing $N/2$ units. In the present example this ordinate must be to the right of exactly

FIGURE 13

USE OF ARITHMETIC INTERPOLATION TO LOCATE MEDIAN

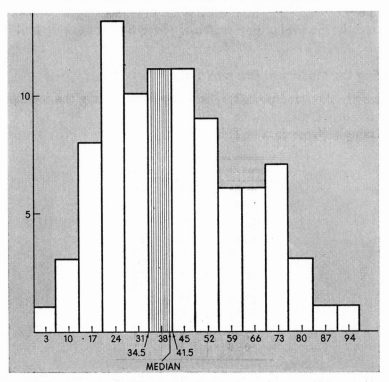

$10/11$ of the area within the class interval 34.5 to 41.5. This is $10/11 \times (7)$ score units to the right of 34.5 on the X-scale. Figure 13 represents graphically the assumption that the scores are evenly distributed within the interval which contains the median.

It is possible to estimate the median from a cumulative distribution curve. Graphically, the median is the abscissa of a point on the X-scale such that an ordinate erected at that point has a height of 50 on the cumulative percentage scale (or a height of $N/2$ on the cumulative frequency scale). This point is easily found by placing a ruler horizontally at 50 percent, or $N/2$, on the Y-scale and dropping an ordinate to the X-scale from the point where the ruler intersects the curve. (See Figure 7, p. 26.)

EXERCISES

1. Using Data B (p. 31), construct a cumulative distribution curve for the intelligence test scores. Find the approximate median from this graph.

2. Compute the median intelligence test score from Data B by arithmetic interpolation (a) using raw scores, and (b) using an appropriate class interval.

3. Plot two cumulative distribution curves for weight: one for men and one for women. What is the difference between the median weights for men and women?

THE MEAN

The most useful measure of central tendency is the *arithmetic mean*, commonly referred to simply as the mean, and denoted either by M or by $\bar{X}$. M, unlike Mo and Mdn, is equally representative of all of the scores within the distribution. Moreover, its mathematical properties make it a much more versatile statistic than either of these other measures of central tendency.

Definition

The mean is the sum of the scores in a distribution divided by the number of cases. It can be defined clearly and concisely by means of a formula.

Let X stand for any score in the distribution.
N = the number of cases.
Σ means "the sum of."

$$\bar{X} = \frac{\Sigma X}{N} \tag{2}$$

In statistical work Σ should never be called "sigma," since that practice invites confusion with σ (lower-case sigma), which is ordinarily called "sigma," and which has a meaning entirely different from Σ. Σ is simply read as "the sum of."

A second definition of the mean is implied by the following statement.

$$\Sigma(X - \bar{X}) = 0$$

That is, the sum of the differences between the individual scores and their mean is equal to zero. Another way of stating this fact is

$$\Sigma x = 0$$
$$\text{where} \quad x = (X - \bar{X})$$

Note that x is positive when X is larger than $\bar{X}$ and negative when X is smaller. Scores expressed in terms of x are known as *deviation scores*.

Example:

X		x
37	......37 $- M$	$+1$
32	......32 $- M$	-4
50		$+14$
28		-8
32		-4
44		$+8$
29		-7
$\Sigma X = 252$		$\Sigma x = 0$

$$\bar{X} = \frac{\Sigma X}{N} = \frac{252}{7} = 36$$

The fact that the sum of the deviations of the scores from the mean of the distribution is equal to zero ($\Sigma x = 0$) can be proved by simple algebra.

Proof:

1. $\Sigma x = \Sigma(X - \bar{X})$
2. $\quad = \Sigma X - \Sigma \bar{X}$
3. $\quad = \Sigma X - N\bar{X}$
4. $\Sigma x = \Sigma X - N\left(\dfrac{\Sigma X}{N}\right) = 0$

Let us illustrate the four steps in the proof by performing the indicated operations on the seven scores in the preceding example:

1. $\Sigma x = (37 - 36) + (32 - 36) + (50 - 36) + (28 - 36)$
$+ (32 - 36) + (44 - 36) + (29 - 36)$
$= \quad (+1) \quad + \quad (-4) \quad + \quad (+14) \quad + \quad (-8)$
$+ \quad (-4) \quad + \quad (+8) \quad + \quad (-7)$

2. Since the sum of a set of numbers is independent of the order in which they are added together, the scores can be rearranged thus:

$\Sigma X - \Sigma \bar{X} = (37 + 32 + 50 + 28 + 32 + 44 + 29)$
$- (36 + 36 + 36 + 36 + 36 + 36 + 36)$

3. Instead of subtracting $\bar{X}$ seven separate times in the summation, we can obtain the same result by subtracting at one time seven $\bar{X}$'s, or $N\bar{X}$.

$\Sigma X - N\bar{X} = 37 + 32 + 50 + 28 + 32 + 44 + 29 - (7 \times 36)$

When a formula calls for the sum of N constant values, it is always possible to substitute in this way multiplication of the constant value by N. However, when the summation refers to a variable, such as ΣX, multiplication by N cannot be substituted because the variable assumes different values.

4. $\Sigma X - N\left(\dfrac{\Sigma X}{N}\right) = 37 + 32 + 50 + 28 + 32 + 44 + 29$
$- \left[7\left(\dfrac{252}{7}\right)\right] = 252 - 252 = 0$

The Use of Summation

The preceding proof of $\Sigma x = 0$ illustrates several important points concerning the use of Σ. In much statistical work it is necessary to specify precisely the limits over which the operation of summation is to be performed. If we designate each item in a set of data by a subscript, as X_1, X_2, X_3, etc., the last item would be denoted by X_N. To make a statement about certain items we specify their subscripts. To make a statement about any item in general, we write X_i, where i is a variable subscript which can take any integral value from one to N.

In this more complete notation the sum of all items of data in a table is written as

$$\sum_{i=1}^{N} X_i = X_1 + X_2 + X_3 + X_4 + \ldots + X_N$$

This expression is read as "the summation of X_i, i going from one to N." In the following chapters the limits of summation will generally be omitted where it is clear from the context that "i goes from one to N."

Several examples of summations encountered in elementary statistics are given below.

$$\Sigma Y^2 = Y^2_1 + Y^2_2 + Y^2_3 + \ldots + Y^2_N$$
$$\Sigma XY = X_1 Y_1 + X_2 Y_2 + X_3 Y_3 + \ldots + X_N Y_N$$
$$\Sigma X \cdot \Sigma Y = (X_1 + X_2 + X_3 + \ldots + X_N)(Y_1 + Y_2 + Y_3 + \ldots + Y_N)$$

There are four basic theorems which should be remembered in the use of summations. Two of these were involved in our proof of $\Sigma x = 0$. Since summation signs will be used in our derivations of many statistical formulas, you should memorize these theorems and practice using them until you feel sure that you know how to handle such manipulations.

Theorem I: The summation of the sum of two or more variables is equal to the sum of their separate summations.

$$\sum_{i=1}^{N} (X_i + Y_i + Z_i) = \sum_{i=1}^{N} X_i + \sum_{i=1}^{N} Y_i + \sum_{i=1}^{N} Z_i$$

This is easily demonstrated to be the case by writing the two sides of the equation without summation signs and showing that they are identical.

$$(X_1 + Y_1 + Z_1) + (X_2 + Y_2 + Z_2) + \ldots + (X_N + Y_N + Z_N)$$
$$= (X_1 + X_2 + \ldots + X_N) + (Y_1 + Y_2 + Y_3 + \ldots + Y_N)$$
$$+ (Z_1 + Z_2 + \ldots + Z_N)$$

Both sides contain the same items, and, when the parentheses are removed, they differ only in the order of the items. Since the order in which items are added does not affect the result, the two sides of the equation are the same.

Theorem II: The summation of the difference between two variables or terms is equal to the difference between their separate summations.

$$\sum_{i=1}^{N} (X_i - Y_i) = \sum_{i=1}^{N} X_i - \sum_{i=1}^{N} Y_i$$

The proof of this, which is similar to the proof of Theorem I, is left as an exercise for the student.

Theorem III: The summation of a constant times a variable is equal to the constant times the summation of the variable.

$$\sum_{i=1}^{N} CX_i = C \sum_{i=1}^{N} X_i$$

Proof:

$$CX_1 + CX_2 + CX_3 + \ldots + CX_N = C(X_1 + X_2 + X_3 + \ldots + X_N)$$

Theorem IV: The summation of a constant C, from one to N, equals the product of C and N.

$$\sum_{1}^{N} C = CN$$

Since C is constant, it has no subscript i.

This theorem follows from the fact that when we multiply a number C by another number N, we are actually adding N of these numbers C together.

EXERCISES

1. Show in the proof of $\Sigma x = 0$ which summation theorems were used.

2. Prove Theorem II.

3. Express each of the following by means of a summation sign.

1. $f_1 X_1 + f_2 X_2 + f_3 X_3 + f_4 X_4 + f_5 X_5$
2. $Z_6 + Z_7 + Z_8 + Z_9 + Z_{10} + Z_{11}$
3. $X_1 + X_2 + X_3 + X_4 + \ldots + X_N + NC$
4. $(X_1 - Y_1) + (X_2 - Y_2) + (X_3 - Y_3) + (X_4 - Y_4)$
5. $ax_1 + ax_2 + ax_3 + ax_4 + ax_5 + ax_6$

4. Write out in full the following.

1. $\displaystyle\sum_{i=6}^{10} x_i y_i$

2. $\displaystyle C \sum_{i=1}^{5} X_i$

3. $\displaystyle\sum_{j=1}^{8} (W_j - 2)$

Short Cuts in Computing the Mean

If a constant amount is subtracted from every score in a distribution, the mean of these transformed scores is equal to the mean of the original scores minus the constant.

Proof:

$$M_{(x-c)} = \frac{\Sigma(X - C)}{N}$$

$$= \frac{\Sigma X - \Sigma C}{N} \text{ (Theorem II)}$$

$$= \frac{\Sigma X}{N} - \frac{\Sigma C}{N}$$

$$= \bar{X} - \frac{NC}{N} \text{ (Theorem III)}$$

$$= \bar{X} - C$$

Subscripts, such as $(x - c)$ in $M_{(x-c)}$ have no numerical significance. They serve to denote the particular set of scores to which a statistic applies.

It then follows that:

$$\bar{X} = M_{(x-c)} + C$$

This fact makes it possible to simplify computation of the mean, since we can carry through the necessary addition and division with relatively small numbers.

Example:

X	where $C = 28$ $(X - C)$, or d	where $C = 34$ $(X - C)$, or d
37	9	+3
32	4	−2
50	22	+16
28	0	−6
32	4	−2
44	16	+10
29	1	−5
$\Sigma X = 252$	$\Sigma(X - C) = 56$	$\Sigma(X - C) = +14$
$\bar{X} = 36$	$M_{(x-c)} = 8$	$M_{(x-c)} = +2$
	$\bar{X} = 8 + 28 = 36$	$\bar{X} = 2 + 34 = 36$

$(X - C)$ is represented by d (for deviation or difference) because it is the difference between X and C. Thus, C is a point of reference on the scale of measurement. It is the *origin* of the numbers represented by d. Letting C stand for any abitrary origin, we can represent the mean obtained from d-scores as

$$\bar{X} = C + \frac{\Sigma d}{N}$$

C can be set at any numerical value without affecting the result. If it is near the middle of the distribution, the mean can be computed from relatively small numbers. Note that d, like x, must be designated as $+$ or $-$, since it represents direction as well as amount of deviation.

The relationship among X, x, and d is represented by the following diagram. All three types of score signify distances on the scale of measurement. They are expressed in the same units of measurement, but they are distances from different points of reference.

FIGURE 14

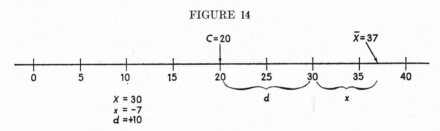

Further saving in time and effort can be achieved when calculating the mean of a tabulated frequency distribution by first adding together the scores in each class interval and then summing the totals for the various intervals to find the sum of all of the scores. Since all of the scores in a class interval are represented numerically by the mid-point of the interval, the sum of the scores within an interval can be obtained by multiplying the mid-point of the interval by its frequency. (Which summation theorem describes this procedure?)

Example:

Class Interval	f	X (Mid-point)	fX
90–94	1	92	92
85–89	5	87 . . . 87 + 87 + 87 + 87 + 87 =	435
80–84	8	82	656
75–79	12	77	924
70–74	9	72	648
65–69	2	67	134
	N = 37		ΣfX = 2889

$$\bar{X} = \frac{\Sigma fX}{N} = \frac{2889}{37} = 78.1$$

Another property of the mean, which leads to further simplification of calculation, is the fact that multiplication of each X by a constant produces a set of values whose mean is equal to the product of that constant and the mean of X.

Proof:

$$M_{(cx)} = \frac{\Sigma CX}{N}$$

$$= \frac{C\Sigma X}{N}$$

$$= C\bar{X}$$

Since C is a factor common to all of the terms it can be placed before the summation sign (Theorem III).

It follows, then, that $\bar{X} = \dfrac{M_{(cx)}}{C}$.

Example:

X	where $C = 3$ CX	where $C = \frac{1}{5}$ CX
37	111	7.4
32	96	6.4
50	150	10.0
28	84	5.6
32	96	6.4
44	132	8.8
29	87	5.8
$\Sigma X = 252$	$\Sigma CX = 756$	$\Sigma CX = 50.4$
$\bar{X} = 36$	$M_{cx} = 108$	$M_{cx} = 7.2$

$$\bar{X} = \frac{108}{3} = 36 \qquad \bar{X} = \frac{7.2}{\frac{1}{5}} = 36$$

We have seen that it is possible to calculate the mean of a distribution through the use of an arbitrary origin by adding to the point of origin the mean of the d's. Now if each d is multiplied by a constant, we can carry through the calculation of the mean of the d's with these new values and then divide by the constant to obtain the correct mean of the d's. If we choose as a constant multiplier the value $1/i$, where i is the size of the class interval, the calculation of the mean is greatly simplified. The d's are now expressed in a unit of measurement equal in size to the class interval. To indicate the new unit of measurement we will denote the deviations by d_i. The transformation of d to d_i is exactly analogous to converting a set of linear measurements of distance from feet to yards by dividing the measurements in feet by three (or multiplying them by one-third). If the mean number of yards is known, we can convert this value back into feet by multiplying it by three (or dividing it by one-third).

The values of the scores in a frequency distribution may thus be expressed in several different ways, depending upon the origin and the units of measurement.

Score	Units of Measurement	Point of Origin
X...............	raw score units	zero on raw score scale
x...............	raw score units	$\bar{X}$
d...............	raw score units	arbitrary origin
d_i............	class interval units	arbitrary origin

The following example illustrates the calculation of the mean in terms of X, d, and d_i.

Example:

Class Interval	f	(a) X	fX	(b) d	fd	(c) d_i	fd_i
90–94.........	1	92	92	+15	+15	+3	+3
85–89.........	5	87	435	+10	+50	+2	+10
80–84.........	8	82	656	+5	+40	+1	+8
75–79.........	12	77	924	0	0	0	0
70–74.........	9	72	648	−5	−45	−1	−9
65–69.........	2	67	134	−10	−20	−2	−4

$$N = 37 \qquad \Sigma X = 2889 \qquad \Sigma fd = 40 \qquad \Sigma fd_i = 8$$

(a) $\quad \bar{X} = \dfrac{2889}{37} = 78.1$

(b) $\quad \bar{X} = 77 + \dfrac{40}{37} = 77 + 1.1 = 78.1$

(c) $\quad \bar{X} = 77 + \dfrac{8}{37} (5) = 77 + \dfrac{40}{37} = 78.1$

The three short cuts—(1) expressing scores as d's with reference to a convenient origin, (2) multiplying the mid-point of the class interval by f to obtain the sub-total for the interval, and (3) converting the unit of measurement from score units to class interval units—can be combined to provide the easiest method for finding the mean of a tabulated distribution. This is known as the *short method*. The procedure, illustrated in (c) of the preceding example, is summarized by the following formula.

$$\bar{X} = C + \frac{\Sigma fd_i}{N} i \tag{3}$$

Formula (3) is the one commonly used in calculating the mean of a distribution. Table 11 illustrates its application to the data of Table 10. Two complete calculations are shown for illustration. The result is the same regardless of the value chosen for C. When it is taken near the center of the distribution, the computation involves small numbers. When the mid-point of the lowest class interval is selected for an arbitrary origin, there are no negative values of d_i, which is an advantage in some types of machine calculation.

TABLE 11

SHORT METHOD OF COMPUTING $\bar{X}$

Score	f	d_i	fd_i	d_i	fd_i
91–97	1	+7	+7	13	13
84–90	1	+6	+6	12	12
77–83	3	+5	+15	11	33
70–76	7	+4	+28	10	70
63–69	6	+3	+18	9	54
56–62	6	+2	+12	8	48
49–55	9	+1	+9	7	63
42–48	11	0	0	6	66
35–41	11	−1	−11	5	55
28–34	10	−2	−20	4	40
21–27	13	−3	−39	3	39
14–20	8	−4	−32	2	16
7–13	3	−5	−15	1	3
0– 6	1	−6	−6	0	0

$$N = 90 \qquad\qquad\qquad \Sigma fd_i = 512$$

$$
\begin{aligned}
&+\ 95 \\
&-123 \\
\hline
\Sigma fd_i = &-\ 28
\end{aligned}
$$

$$\bar{X} = 45 + \frac{-28}{90}\,(7) = 42.8 \qquad\qquad \bar{X} = 3 + \frac{512}{90}\,(7) = 42.8$$

Mid-points of class intervals can be used as d_i's, but the calculation involves larger numbers. This method is often used with calculating machines and computers. (What value would you use for the arbitrary origin in formula (3) if mid-points are used as d_i's?)

COMPARISON OF MEAN, MEDIAN, AND MODE

Measures of central tendency are used to describe frequency distributions in terms of a typical value. In most instances the mean provides a value which is typical of the group. Unless there is reason to doubt its adequacy as a typical statistic for a given distribution of scores it should be used in preference to the median or the mode.

Advantages of the Mean

In comparison with the median the mean has several characteristics which make it more useful.

1. The mean, since it is defined by arithmetic operations, can be manipulated arithmetically and algebraically.

A simple example of algebraic manipulation of the mean occurs in the procedure used for finding the mean of a distribution made up of several smaller groups whose means are already known.

Example:

Group I X_1	Group II X_2	Groups I and II X
43	48	43
55	56	55
49	49	49
50	54	50
53	55	53
$\Sigma X_1 = 250$	43	48
$N_1 = 5$	59	56
$\bar{X}_1 = 50$	$\Sigma X_2 = 364$	49
	$N_2 = 7$	54
	$\bar{X}_2 = 52$	55
		43
		59
		$\Sigma X = 614$
		$N = 12$
		$\bar{X} = 51.7$

It is incorrect to average the means of the two sub-groups, since they are based on different numbers of cases. The mean of the two sub-group means is 51, whereas the mean computed from the combined groups is 51.7. The correct mean of the combined groups can be found from the means of the sub-groups by the following.

$$M_t = \frac{N_1 M_1 + N_2 M_2 + \ldots + N_k M_k}{N_1 + N_2 + \ldots + N_k}, \text{ where } k = \text{number of groups} \quad (4)$$

Applying (4) to the present example, we find the mean of the combined groups to be

$$M_t = \frac{5(50) + 7(52)}{5 + 7} = \frac{614}{12} = 51.7$$

Medians of sub-groups cannot be combined to give the median of the combined groups. To find the median of combined groups it is necessary to tabulate the combined distribution and obtain its median.

2. Another advantage of the mean is that in most applications it is more *reliable* than the median. That is, if a number of samples of scores are obtained, the means of those samples are more nearly the same value than are the medians. In other words, the *sampling error* of the mean is usually smaller than that of the median. Sampling errors will be considered in a later chapter.

3. The mean equally represents every score in the distribution. It thus reflects the actual numerical values of those scores. The median, on the other hand, does not depend upon the magnitude of individual scores beyond the mere fact that they are included within the upper or the lower half of the distribution. In the following examples the medians are the same for all of the four distributions although the individual scores are different. The means differ, since they reflect the magnitude of every score within the group.

Examples:

(a)	(b)	(c)	(d)
10	15	10	40
9	9	9	9
8	8	8	8
7	4	7	7
6	4	1	6
Mdn = 8	Mdn = 8	Mdn = 8	Mdn = 8
$\bar{X} = 8$	$\bar{X} = 8$	$\bar{X} = 7$	$\bar{X} = 14$

When to Use the Median

In some situations the median should be used in preference to the mean. In (*d*) above, for instance, the mean is higher than all but one score in the distribution. It thus gives a distorted representation of the central tendency of that distribution. The median, however, remains at the center of the distribution despite the presence of an extremely atypical score. Because it is insensitive to extreme deviations the median is an appropriate measure of central tendency for skewed distributions.

Sometimes it is impossible to compute the mean of a distribution without making unwarranted assumptions concerning the data. A common example of this is the truncated or "cut tail" distribution, where the limits of one, or both, of the end intervals are unknown. In order to compute the mean a definite score value must be assigned to these intervals. The median, on the other hand, can be calculated without knowledge of the score values of extreme intervals.

Example:

$$
\begin{array}{cc}
Score & f \\
\text{over } 39 \ldots . & 8 \\
35\text{--}39 \ldots . & 5 \\
30\text{--}34 \ldots . & 10 \\
25\text{--}29 \ldots . & 9 \\
20\text{--}24 \ldots . & 3 \\
15\text{--}19 \ldots . & 1 \\
\end{array}
$$

$$\text{Mdn} = 29.5 + \frac{5}{10}\,(5) = 32$$

When measurements are known to be on an ordinal scale, the median is a more appropriate measure of central tendency than is the mean because the median does not imply that the intervals of the scale of measurement are equal.

When to Use the Mode

Although the mode is usually less reliable than either the mean or the median, it is the appropriate measure of central tendency in certain situations. More often than not, when dealing with the distribution of frequencies into discrete categories, the mean or median of the distribution take values which cannot occur on the X-scale. In such cases neither of these measures realistically describes the central tendency of the group. The crude mode, however, which is the value of the X-category having the greatest frequency, does give a meaningful typical value for distributions of discrete variables. For example, the modal number of classrooms in the elementary school buildings of a state would be more meaningful and useful in most contexts than either the mean or the median number.

SUGGESTED READINGS

1. Freund, J. E. *Modern Elementary Statistics,* chap. i. 2d. ed. New York: Prentice-Hall, 1960.
2. Walker, H. M. *Mathematics Essential for Elementary Statistics,* chap. vii. Rev. ed. New York: Henry Holt and Co., 1951.

EXERCISES

1. Find the median of each of the following.
    a) 10, 23, 14, 17, 20, 16, 14, 15, 19, 12, 15, 16
    b) 85, 90, 78, 83, 64, 83
    c) 32, 34, 26, 32, 33, 30, 32, 33, 29, 33
    d)

X	f
90–99	1
80–89	4
70–79	12
60–69	23
50–59	18
40–49	13
30–39	9
20–29	6
10–19	3
0– 9	2

2. Compute the mean for the distribution in *d*, above. Compare the M and Mdn as representations of the central tendency of this distribution. Is the distribution positively or negatively skewed?

3. Compute the mean of the raw scores of Table 1 (p. 14), using formula (2). By means of the short method, formula (3), find the mean of Table 3 and Table 4 (p. 16). Why would you expect these three computations of the mean to give slightly different results?

4. If you were the business manager of a labor union which would you be likely to publicize as the "average" annual salary of all employees of a large corporation: median, mean, or mode? Explain. If the chairman of the board of directors reported a figure higher than yours, what might be the explanation?

5. Discuss the relative merits of the mean, median, and mode as a measure of central tendency for a sample of data obtained by an ordinal measuring scale which is strongly suspected to have unequal and unknown units of measurement.

6. Four means were found to be: 14, 17, 20, and 21. These were computed from samples in which the N's were 5, 12, 10, and 8, respectively. Compute the mean of the combined sample of thirty-five observations. For comparison, compute an unweighted mean of the four means.

7. Suppose you have made twenty measurements of a certain individual's reaction time to a visual stimulus and that nineteen of these readings are within a range of 0.15 seconds, but the longest reaction time is 0.5 seconds longer than the shortest. What measure of central tendency would you use to describe this sample?

8. If $\bar{X} = $ Mdn, what can you say about the frequency polygon of a distribution?

9. In which of the following distributions would you expect the mean and median to be approximately equal? In which would they be noticeably different?
   a) Weights of fourth-grade boys
   b) Salaries of city school superintendents in the U.S.
   c) Ages of college freshmen
   d) Number of cigarettes smoked per week by seniors in a large public high school

10. Can you derive a formula for $\bar{X}$ from the following definition? The mean of a distribution is the point on the X-scale around which the algebraic sum of deviations is zero. (Start with $\Sigma(X - \bar{X}) = 0$.)

11. If you have had an introduction to differential calculus, or if you remember from high school algebra how to solve a quadratic equation by "completing the square," you can derive the formula for $\bar{X}$ from the following definition. The mean of a distribution is the point on the X-scale around which the sum of squared deviations is minimum. [Start with $y = \Sigma(X - \bar{X})^2$.]

12. Suppose that a frequency polygon (or histogram) has been carefully plotted on a sheet of metal and that the figure has been carefully cut out with tin snips so that we have only the portion between the X-axis and the graph. What measure of central tendency would correspond to: (a) the point on the X-axis at which the metal would balance on a knife edge placed at a right angle to the X-axis; (b) the point on the X-axis at which one must make a cut at a right angle to the X-axis in order to obtain two pieces of metal having the same weight?

CHAPTER V

Measures of Dispersion

A measure of the central tendency of a group of data does not in itself provide an adequate characterization of the group. Distributions may have the same mean, median, or mode and yet differ greatly from one another in other respects.

Dispersion, or *variability,* refers to the extent of differences among the individual scores in a group. Distribution *A*, for example, has greater dispersion than *B*, although they are quite similar in central tendency.

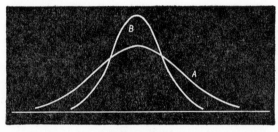

FIGURE 15

Most distributions of psychological and educational measurements can be adequately described by (1) *N*, the number of observations, (2) a measure of central tendency, and (3) a measure of dispersion. Statistics descriptive of dispersion are of two general types: (1) measures of position, which are based on the distance on the *X*-scale between points defined by frequency, and (2) measures of deviation, which are derived from the amounts by which the individual scores of a distribution deviate from some measure of central tendency.

MEASURES BASED ON POSITION

The Total Range

This is simply the distance between the highest and the lowest score of a distribution, or the distance on *X* within which the total frequency lies. Since the range is determined by only two scores, regardless of how many there are in the distribution, it is an extremely unreliable statistic. The range is seldom used as a measure of dispersion where precise description is desired. Even in stating the extreme limits of variation expected of a phenomenon the range is inferior to other measures of dispersion.

The Interquartile Range

The *quartiles* of a frequency distribution, designated as Q_1, Q_2, and Q_3, are the points on the X-scale which are above 25, 50, and 75 percent of the cases. The median, then, is the same as Q_2. The method of computing quartiles is the same as that used in finding the median. To obtain the median we find the point below which there are $N/2$ scores. To find Q_1 we locate the point below which there are $N/4$ scores. Similarly, Q_3 is the point below which there are $3N/4$ scores.

Example:

Score	f	cum. f
91–97	1	90
84–90	1	89
77–83	3	88
70–76	7	85
63–69	6	78
56–62	6	72
49–55	9	66
42–48	11	57
35–41	11	46
28–34	10	35
21–27	13	25
14–20	8	12
7–13	3	4
0– 6	1	1

$$\text{Mdn} = LL + \frac{N/2 - F_c}{f_i}. \quad (i)$$

$$\text{Mdn} = 34.5 + \frac{45 - 35}{11}(7) = 40.9$$

$$Q_1 = 20.5 + \frac{22.5 - 12}{13}(7) = 26.2$$

$$Q_3 = 55.5 + \frac{67.5 - 66}{6}(7) = 57.2$$

The *interquartile range* is defined simply as the distance $(Q_3 - Q_1)$. In the example this is $57.2 - 26.2$, or 31.

As in the case of the median, it is possible to approximate Q_1 and Q_3 from the cumulative distribution curve.

The Semi-interquartile Range

A more commonly used statistic is the *semi-interquartile range,* which is defined as

$$Q = \frac{Q_3 - Q_1}{2} \qquad (5)$$

Note that Q without a numerical subscript denotes a range or *distance* on the X-scale, whereas Q_1, Q_2, and Q_3 designate *points* on the scale.

The interquartile range and Q do not make use of all of the available information of a frequency distribution. They, like the median, are based on the frequency of scores above or below a certain point rather than on the numerical values of the scores. However, when the median is appropriate to describe the central tendency of a distribution, dispersion should be described by a statistic which, like the median, is based on position of scores.

In view of the fact that the median is often used to describe the central tendency of skewed distributions, it is important to note

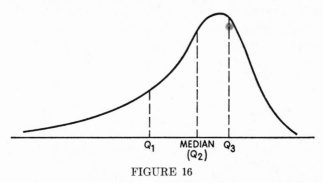

FIGURE 16

The total area under the curve corresponds to N. An ordinate erected at the median divides the area into two equal parts. Similarly, ordinates erected at Q_1, Q_2, and Q_3 divide the area into four equal parts.

that neither Q nor the interquartile range is capable of conveying information concerning skewness. For this reason it is much better when describing a skewed distribution to present Mdn, Q_1 and Q_3. The difference $(Q_3 - Q_1)$ describes dispersion. Comparison of $(Q_3 - \text{Mdn})$ with $(\text{Mdn} - Q_1)$ provides information concerning skewness. (See Figure 16.)

Percentile Points

The quartiles of a distribution are the points below which one, two, or three quarters of the individual scores are located. *Deciles* are points below which one-tenth, two-tenths, etc. of the total number of cases are found. For example, the seventh decile is the point below which there are seven-tenths, or .70, of the total N. Quintiles divide the total frequency into five equal parts. *Percentiles* (or more accurately, *centiles*) are points which divide N into

100 equal parts. The median of a distribution is thus the same as Q_2, the fifth decile, or the fiftieth centile. Any point on the X-scale defined by frequency can be located by the same method that is used in finding the median, or it can be approximated from a graph of cumulative percent.

Since the area under a frequency curve represents N, the spacing on the X-scale of points which divide the area into symmetrically equal portions on each side of the median provides a description of the dispersion and shape of a frequency distribution.

Any percentile point of a distribution can be estimated from a cumulative percentage curve such as Figure 7 (p. 26). To do this, draw a horizontal line at the desired percent and drop an ordinate to the base line from the point where the horizontal line intersects the graph of the cumulative distribution. This ordinate will intersect the base line at the value of the desired percentile point.

Percentile Ranks

If we wish to know what percent of a distribution is below a certain score, we erect a perpendicular at the desired score, extending it upward until it intersects the graph. A horizontal line drawn from this point will intersect the Y-axis at the value of the required percent. Thus, if we know that a certain person in the group made a raw score of 60 on the Personality Inventory, we can readily ascertain from Figure 7 that his score was higher than about 77 percent of the group. His *percentile rank* on the test is then said to be 77. Percentile ranks are useful in expressing the relative scores of individuals on a scale which cannot be considered to possess equal intervals. In expressing scores as percentile ranks it is always necessary to specify the group to which the percentile rank refers.

Percentile ranks are easily computed by expressing the cumulative frequency below the *mid-points* of various score intervals as percentages of N.

EXERCISES

1. Which of the following statements suggest that the distribution is symmetrical?
   a) Q_1 and Q_3 are equidistant from Mdn.
   b) Exactly 34 percent of the scores are below P_{34} (the thirty-fourth centile).
   c) $Q_1 = \frac{1}{2}$ Mdn

   d) $(P_{15} - P_3) = (P_{97} - P_{85})$

   e) Ordinates erected at Q_1, Mdn, and Q_3 divide the area into four equal parts.

   f) $M = \text{Mdn}$

2. Which of the following distributions is (1) bell-shaped, (2) rectangular (approximately the same frequency for every score), (3) U-shaped, and (4) positively skewed?

   a) $P_{90} = 70,\quad P_{80} = 60,\quad P_{70} = 55,\quad P_{60} = 54,\quad P_{40} = 46,\quad P_{20} = 40,$
      $P_{10} = 30$

   b) $Q_1 = 35$, Mdn $= 45$, $Q = 14$

   c) Range $= 50$, $Q_1 = 130$, $Q_3 = 165$

   d) $P_{10} = 25$, $P_{30} = 35$, $P_{70} = 55$, $P_{90} = 65$, Mdn $= 45$

3. Compute Q_1, P_{36}, the seventh decile, and Q for data A (p. 20).

4. Construct a cumulative distribution curve for data A (p. 20), and find from it Q_1, Mdn, and Q_3.

5. From Table 2 (p. 15) compute the percentile ranks of the following scores: 30, 44, 45, 54. Be sure to use cumulative frequency below the *mid-point* of the score. How do you explain the relative values of the percentile ranks corresponding to the scores 44 and 45?

6. Explain clearly the difference between a percentile point and a percentile rank.

7. If a pupil made a score of 85 percent correct on a spelling achievement test and 90 percent correct on a test of arithmetic achievement, what can you say concerning his relative achievement in these two subjects? Suppose that in relation to a large group of pupils in his grade, his percentile ranks on the tests were 94 for spelling and 87 for arithmetic. How would you change your statement concerning his relative achievement in these subjects?

8. From Figure 7 (p. 26) estimate the following.

   a) Q_1, Q_2, and Q

   b) P_{80}, P_{15}, P_{25}

   c) The percentile rank of the raw scores 25, 70, and 50

MEASURES BASED ON DEVIATIONS

We have seen that the mean is the most generally useful measure of central tendency because it depends on the numerical value of every score in the distribution and also because it possesses characteristics which permit it to be subjected to mathematical manipulation. For the same reasons the most generally useful measures of dispersion are those which measure deviations from the mean.

The Mean Deviation

A simple measure of dispersion can easily be obtained from the *absolute* values of deviations from the mean of the distribution. It is the mean of these deviations taken without regard to positive and negative signs. Absolute arithmetic values must be used because the sum of positive and negative values is always zero.

$$\text{Mean Deviation, M.D.} = \frac{\Sigma|x|}{N}, \quad \text{where } |x| \text{ is the } absolute \quad (6)$$
$$\text{value of } (X - \bar{X})$$

M.D. is often used when N is small and precise measurement of dispersion is not necessary, but the utility of this statistic is limited by the fact that it is computed from absolute deviations. In discarding the signs of the deviations we destroy their algebraic properties, which makes it difficult to subject the M.D. to further mathematical manipulation.

The Variance

This useful statistic is defined as the mean of the squared deviations from $\bar{X}$. The variance, sometimes called the *mean square deviation,* will be denoted by S^2.*

$$S^2 = \frac{\Sigma(X - \bar{X})^2}{N} = \frac{\Sigma x^2}{N} \quad (7)$$

Squaring the deviations, a legitimate algebraic operation, does away with negative values without impairing the algebraic properties of the resulting statistic. Thus, since S^2 can easily be subjected to further mathematical treatment, it is a very useful statistic. Nevertheless, it suffers from one important limitation as a descriptive measure—its value cannot be directly interpreted with reference to the X-scale because it is the mean of *squared* deviations.

---

* Sometimes you will find S^2 denoted by σ^2; and S, by σ. Since this older notation is rapidly becoming obsolete, we shall follow the rule of reserving lower-case Greek letters for population values and denoting sample statistics by the commonly used English symbols. This is a convention generally observed in mathematical treatments of statistics.

The Standard Deviation

S^2 can be transformed from squared units of deviation to X-units by extracting its square root. The resulting value is known as the standard deviation and is designated by S. S is defined as the square root of the mean of the squared deviations from the mean of the distribution, or the *root mean square deviation*. Formula (8) is a symbolic statement of this definition.

$$S = \sqrt{\frac{\Sigma x^2}{N}} \tag{8}$$

Several points concerning the standard deviation must be clearly understood:

1. S is not a measure of magnitude of the scores in a distribution; it measures only *the extent to which the scores differ from one another.*
2. S is a *distance or range* on the X-scale, rather than a point.
3. Since the numerical value of S depends on the *units of measurement,* as well as upon the amount of variation among the scores, standard deviations based on different kinds of measures cannot be compared. It is not possible to discover whether a group of people differ more from each other in intelligence than they do in reading comprehension through a comparison of standard deviations. A score unit on one test cannot be considered equal to a different score unit on another test.

Tchebycheff's Theorem

An important characteristic of the standard deviation is that in any frequency distribution at least $\frac{3}{4}$ of the measurements lie within the interval extending from $\bar{X} - 2S$ to $\bar{X} + 2S$. At least $\frac{8}{9}$ of the measurements in any distribution lie within the interval $\bar{X} - 3S$ to $\bar{X} + 3S$. In general, the proportion of the N measurements in any frequency distribution which lie within the interval $\bar{X} \pm hS$ is at least $1 - 1/h^2$. This is known as Tchebycheff's theorem, inequality, or criterion.

Let us consider first the question of what proportion of the measurements in a distribution lie within the range of $\bar{X} \pm 2S$ According to Tchebycheff's theorem this interval will include at least $\frac{3}{4} N$.

Proof:

Suppose that N measurements of X are distributed in any

fashion, but so that $\bar{X}$ and S can be computed. Set A, containing $N - r$ elements, includes all measurements which do not deviate beyond $2S$ from $\bar{X}$. Set B, with r elements, contains those measurements which differ from $\bar{X}$ by more than $2S$. The two sets are defined mathematically by

$$A = \{X | \bar{X} - 2S \leq X \leq \bar{X} + 2S\}$$
$$B = \{X | X < \bar{X} - 2S \text{ or } X > \bar{X} + 2S\}$$

Let us now recall the definition of S^2.

$$S^2 = \frac{\sum_{i=1}^{N} (X_i - \bar{X})^2}{N} \tag{7}$$

Using subscripts $1, 2, 3, \ldots r$ for set B and subscripts $r + 1, r + 2, r + 3, \ldots N$ for set A, S^2 can be written in a form which separates the squared deviations contained in A and B.

$$S^2 = \underbrace{\frac{\sum_{i=1}^{r} (X_i - \bar{X})^2}{N}}_{(B)} + \underbrace{\frac{\sum_{i=r+1}^{N} (X_i - \bar{X})^2}{N}}_{(A)}$$

If B is an empty set—that is, if there are no measurements outside of the interval $\bar{X} \pm 2S$—the theorem is obviously correct because at least ¾ of the measurements are contained in set A.

Suppose, on the other hand, that $r \geq 1$ and that there is an unknown number of measurements in set B. How large can that number be? The largest number will lie outside of the interval when the interval is as small as it can possibly be. This will occur when S^2 assumes its minimum value. For measurements in set A, $(X - \bar{X})$ can be as small as zero. For measurements in set B, $(X - \bar{X})$ must be, by definition, greater than $2S$. Substituting these minimum deviations, we find the minimum value of S^2.

$$S^2 \geq \frac{\sum_{i=1}^{r} (2S)^2}{N} + \frac{\sum_{i=r+1}^{N} (0)^2}{N}$$
$$S^2 \geq \frac{4rS^2}{N}$$

Dividing the inequality through by $4S^2$, we obtain

$$\frac{1}{4} \geq \frac{r}{N}$$

Thus, the fraction of the measurements lying outside the interval $\bar{X} \pm 2S$ is not greater than $\frac{1}{4}$. Therefore, at least $\frac{3}{4}$ of the measurements must lie within the interval $\bar{X} \pm 2S$.

We can generalize this proof by replacing $2S$ by hS. This leads to the inequality

$$\frac{1}{h^2} \geq \frac{r}{N}$$

Thus we can prove that the proportion of measurement in any distribution which lie within the interval $\bar{X} \pm hS$ is at least $1 - 1/h^2$.

The beginning student of statistics often asks, "Why must I work with squared deviations when the mean deviation is so much simpler and easier to compute?" The answer to this question is suggested by Tchebycheff's theorem. If we were to attempt to derive the theorem using M.D. instead of S, we would very soon discover that setting the sum of unsquared deviations in set B equal to zero would tell us nothing about the number of measurements falling in set A and set B, and we would not be able to make a statement regarding the proportion of measurements which must be contained within an interval of $\bar{X} \pm h$ (M.D.). For this reason M.D. is much less useful than S^2 or S.

By simply reporting $\bar{X}$, S, and N, you can describe any frequency distribution to anyone who speaks the language of statistics well enough to know what is meant by these three symbols and who understands Tchebycheff's inequality.

EXERCISES

1. Make the required substitutions and generalize the proof of Tchebycheff's theorem to intervals of $\bar{X} \pm hs$.

2. What is the value of h required to justify the assertion that the interval $\bar{X} \pm hs$ includes at least 95 percent of the measurements? 99 percent?

3. Tchebycheff's theorem is useless when $h \leqq 1$. Why?

4. If for a group of 100 pupils the mean score on an arithmetic test is 62.4, and $S = 8.2$, what can you say about the number of pupils who scored above 85?

5. Can you make a statement concerning the probability that it will require 20 days for a person to recover from an illness if it is known that the mean time required for recovery is 12.1 days and the standard deviation is 2.9 days?

Evaluating Test Scores

Tchebycheff's theorem is useful for interpreting the mean and standard deviation of *any* frequency distribution, regardless of its form. When the form of a frequency distribution is known it is possible to make more precise statements about the proportion of measurements which lie within a specified interval. Many distributions of measurements of behavior resemble the mathematically defined *normal distribution*. For distributions of this type, which have a peak near the center and which gradually tail off symmetrically on either side of $\bar{X}$, the following relationship is found.

Scores	Approximate Percent of N between These Points
$\bar{X} - S$ to $\bar{X} + S$	68 percent
$\bar{X} - 2S$ to $\bar{X} + 2S$	95 percent
$\bar{X} - 3S$ to $\bar{X} + 3S$	99.7 percent

Thus, practically all of the scores in a bell-shaped frequency distribution fall within a range of 6 standard deviations. If, for example, it is known that $\bar{X} = 50$, $S = 10$, and $N = 100$, we can infer that few, if any scores in such a distribution are below 20 or above 80. We also know that about 68 of them are between 40 and 60, and about 95 between 30 and 70. This interpretation of the standard deviation does not apply to distributions which are markedly skewed, or which differ in other respects from the usual bell-shaped pattern.

The standard deviation makes it possible to evaluate the raw score of an individual in relation to the performance of a group. For example, suppose that a certain student earned a score of 88 on an achievement test. That fact, in itself, is relatively meaningless. However, if we know that for his class $\bar{X} = 78$ and $S = 9$, we can infer that this student is among the highest 16 percent of his class.

(This statement assumes that the class is large and that the scores form a bell-shaped distribution.) If you knew nothing about the form of the distribution, what could you say about the quality of his score from your knowledge of Tchebycheff's inequality?

Raw measurements are in most instances of little use in evaluating the performance of an individual. The numerical value of a raw score depends on (1) the origin or reference point of the measurement, and (2) the size of the units.

To illustrate this, let us imagine measuring people's heights by a set of operations similar to those of most tests in psychology and education. Our "test" of height will consist of 100 sticks of various unknown lengths. To "test" a person's height we will stand the sticks on end and count the number which do not reach from the floor to the top of our subject's head. The sticks are the "items" of the test. If the subject is longer than a certain item, he passes it. If

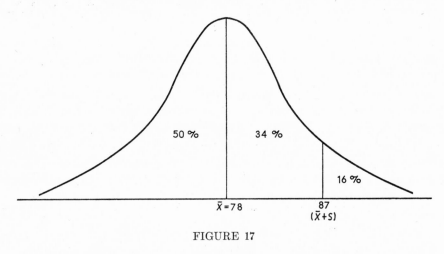

FIGURE 17

shorter, he fails. His "height" is the number of items passed. If his score is low on the scale of possible scores (zero to 100), we can assert either that he is very short, or that the items are very long. The magnitude of his raw score depends entirely on how many and how "difficult" are the "items" contained in the test.

Suppose now that several hundred subjects are "measured" by the same set of sticks and that the scores form a frequency distribution with $\bar{X} = 57$. This distribution provides a point of reference, permitting us to state that an individual's height is above or below the mean of the group, but how far he is above or below remains unknown. If only the mean is known, it might even be misleading to state that the subject who scores 70 is thirteen points above the mean. Not only are the units of this measurement unknown, but they may vary greatly in size. Our measurement of height by this method constitutes an ordinal scale. Even though the units of measurement are unknown, and presumed to be unequal, the relative heights of various individuals can be assigned scores if we can designate their positions in a distribution of heights for a specified group of people. As we have seen, this can be done by means of percentile ranks, even though the original measurements are not on a scale of equal units of height.

If it were known that the sticks differed from one another by equal amounts of length and that no two sticks were of the same length, even though we had no standard unit and the actual lengths of the sticks were unknown, the assignment of different numbers to different heights by counting the number of sticks would produce an interval scale of measurement. With an interval scale, the question of *how much* taller or shorter a person is in relation to $\bar{X}$ can be given a meaningful answer, even though the size of the interval of measurement is unknown, if we know S and the form of the distribution. For example, if the distribution of heights is roughly bell-shaped, and $S = 3$, a person with a height score of 70 is a giant among a group of people whose heights have $\bar{X} = 57$. If $S = 6$, we know that this person is taller than about 98 percent of the group, and if $S = 13$, he is taller than about 84 percent. The standard deviation of a bell-shaped distribution of measurements on an interval scale enables us to specify where the score of an individual stands within a group.

Although it is seldom possible to demonstrate that psychological test scores are on a scale of exactly equal intervals, careful attention to the relative difficulty of the items makes it possible to construct tests which give reasonable approximations of interval scales. For this reason it is generally assumed that scores obtained from carefully constructed tests can be treated as measurements on an interval scale.

Standard Scores. A raw test score acquires meaning if it can be expressed as being a specified number of standard deviations above or below the mean of a certain distribution. A *standard score,* denoted by z, is the numerical expression of a score on a scale of standard deviation units with the origin at the mean of the distribution.

It denotes how far and in which direction a person's raw score differs from the mean of a distribution.

$$z = \frac{(X - \bar{X})}{S} = \frac{x}{S} \qquad (9)$$

Since z-scores depend on the mean and standard deviation of a certain distribution, they have meaning only in reference to that group.

If the raw scores of any frequency distribution, no matter what the scale of measurement, are transformed into z-scores, the resulting distribution is a *standard* distribution in which $M = 0$ and $S = 1.00$.

Proof:

$$M_z = \frac{\sum \frac{x}{S}}{N} = \frac{\frac{\Sigma x}{S}}{N}$$

Since $\Sigma x = 0$, $M_z = 0$, and it follows that

$$\left(\frac{x}{S} - M_z\right) = \frac{x}{S}$$

Thus, the deviation of a z-score from the mean of the distribution is the same as the score itself. Taking advantage of that fact, we can express the variance of a distribution of z-scores as

$$S^2_z = \frac{\Sigma z^2}{N}$$

The numerical value of this variance turns out to be 1.00 for any distribution.

$$S^2_z = \frac{\left(\frac{\Sigma x^2}{S^2}\right)}{N}$$

$$S^2_z = \frac{\left[\frac{\frac{\Sigma x^2}{\left(\frac{\Sigma x^2}{N}\right)}}{}\right]}{N} = 1.00$$

Since $S^2_z = 1.00$, $S_z = 1.00$.

Thus, the standard deviation is more than a measure of dispersion. It is a *standard unit of measurement*. If any set of test scores is converted to standard scores, the resulting distribution of converted scores will have $M_z = 0$ and $S_z = 1.00$. Because every distribution of standard scores has the same mean and standard deviation, an individual's scores on several tests can be directly compared with each other. For instance, knowing the distributions of achievement scores in arithmetic and in spelling for the fifth-grade pupils in a school system, a teacher can ascertain whether a certain pupil is better in arithmetic than he is in spelling by comparing his standard scores. It would even be possible in this way to give a meaningful answer to the question as to whether a pupil is as tall as he is intelligent! Of course, such comparisons can be made only where the standard scores for the various tests have been computed from distributions of raw scores earned by the same group, or very similar groups, of pupils.

A disadvantage of z-scores is the fact that most people are unfamiliar with test scores which range from −3.00 to +3.00, and which assign a value of 0.00 to the average pupil. For this reason z-scores are often transformed to a more familiar numerical scale by assigning arbitrary values to their mean and standard deviation. Two commonly used schemes are shown in the table below.

Raw Score X	Standard Score z	Transformed Standard Scores	
		$\bar{X} = 50$ $S = 10$	$\bar{X} = 500$ $S = 100$
50	+1.00	60	600
32	−1.25	37.5	375
42	0.00	50	500
62	+2.50	75	750

From original distribution of raw scores:

$$\bar{X} = 42$$
$$S = 8.0$$

EXERCISES

1. For a distribution of raw scores, $M = 87.3$, and $S = 9.5$. Express each of the following as a z-score and indicate approximately how good a score it is in relation to the group: 97, 120, 106, 78, 82. (Remember that z-scores below the mean have a negative sign.)

2. If a student made a score of 51 on an intelligence test and a score of

82 on a test of reading comprehension, would you recommend that he be given training in remedial reading? The group of students of which he is a member gave the following results.

	Intelligence Test	Reading Test
Mean	47	108
S	8.0	12.1

3. If you were the teacher of two classes in eleventh-grade algebra and you had the following information, which class would you expect to be easier to teach? Explain.

	Intelligence Test Scores	
	Class A	Class B
Mean	36	37
S	3.8	6.1

4. Try to prove that for any distribution $M_z = 0$ and $S_z = 1.00$.

5. Given: $\bar{X} = 49$, and $S = 4.3$. Convert the following raw scores to a standard scale where $M_z = 50$ and $S_z = 10$: 35, 47, 58, 50, 62, 54.

6. Describe each score in Problem 5 as "average" or "very high" or "fairly good," etc. In each case, explain your reasons.

7. Compute M.D. and S for the following group of scores: 10, 17, 8, 11, 14, 9, 15, 19, 9, 10.

Advantages of Standard Deviation and Variance

The standard deviation of the theoretical normal curve, a particular type of bell-shaped distribution to be described in a later chapter, permits exact specification of the area under the curve between any two points on the X-axis. This standard deviation is denoted by σ since it refers to a theoretical distribution rather than to the distribution of a particular sample. Since area represents frequency, it is possible to state the exact frequency to be found within any range of scores in a normal distribution. Unfortunately, the distributions of scores obtained in practice differ more or less from the mathematical ideal. In most cases, however, the discrepancy is not great, because psychological and educational tests are commonly designed to produce approximately normal distributions of scores.

If an investigator is content to limit himself to the mere factual description of a particular set of data, making no attempt to generalize about the universe represented by these data, he will find the standard deviation less useful than certain other descriptive statistics. A frequency tabulation in raw units of measurement would describe the variation in a sample more precisely than would a standard deviation. But precise description of data is not in itself a goal of scientific inquiry. Science deals with general principles, and precise description of individual events is often sacrificed in order to achieve more effective generalizations. Precise description is desirable and necessary, but only to the extent that it facilitates meaningful interpretation of data. The major purpose of scientific work is to formulate dependable generalizations about the world of experience, and statistical methods which serve this purpose are better scientific tools than those which merely describe. The variance and the standard deviation have properties which make them especially useful as tools of inductive inference. For this reason, they are commonly used in preference to other measures of dispersion.

Calculation of S

The definition formula of the standard deviation (8) is not convenient for computation because the deviations of scores from the mean usually turn out to be decimals. If enough digits are retained in rounding these approximate deviations to avoid the possibility of serious error in the final result, the computation of a standard deviation can become quite laborious.

In order to develop a simpler method of computation, let us first find an expression of S in terms of raw scores. We shall begin with S^2 to avoid having to write a square root symbol at each step.

$$S^2 = \frac{\Sigma x^2}{N}$$
$$= \frac{\Sigma(X - \bar{X})^2}{N}$$

Carrying out the indicated operation of squaring $(X - \bar{X})$, we find

$$S^2 = \frac{\Sigma(X^2 - 2X\bar{X} + \bar{X}^2)}{N}$$

Through summing the separate terms and dividing by the common denominator, N, this becomes

$$S^2 = \frac{\Sigma X^2}{N} - 2\bar{X}\frac{\Sigma X}{N} + \frac{\Sigma\bar{X}^2}{N} \qquad \text{(Theorem I, p. 40)}$$

But

$$\frac{\Sigma X}{N} = \bar{X}, \quad \text{and} \quad \Sigma \bar{X}^2 = N\bar{X}^2$$

because $\bar{X}^2$ is a constant (Theorem III, p. 40). Substituting these terms, we have

$$S^2 = \frac{\Sigma X^2}{N} - 2\bar{X}^2 + \bar{X}^2$$

$$= \frac{\Sigma X^2}{N} - \bar{X}^2$$

$$= \frac{\Sigma X^2}{N} - \left(\frac{\Sigma X}{N}\right)^2$$

$$S = \sqrt{\frac{\Sigma X^2}{N} - \left(\frac{\Sigma X}{N}\right)^2} \qquad (10)$$

This formula can be expressed in a slightly different form for use with calculating machines.

$$S = \frac{1}{N}\sqrt{N\Sigma X^2 - (\Sigma X)^2} \qquad (11)$$

Since large numbers enter into the calculation of S by either (10) or (11), these formulas are most useful for machine calculation or for small groups of data.

Example, three methods for computing S:

(a)

X	x	x^2
39	+ 2.1	4.41
32	− 4.9	24.01
50	+13.1	171.61
27	− 9.9	98.01
35	− 1.9	3.61
47	+10.1	102.01
37	+ 0.1	0.01
28	− 8.9	79.21
$\Sigma X = 295$		$\Sigma x^2 = 482.88$

$$X = \frac{295}{8} = 36.9$$

$$S = \sqrt{\frac{\Sigma x^2}{N}} = \sqrt{\frac{482.88}{8}} = 7.8 \qquad (8)$$

(b)

X	X^2
39	1521
32	1024
50	2500
27	729
35	1225
47	2209
37	1369
28	784

$\Sigma X = 295 \quad \Sigma X^2 = 11361$

$$S = \sqrt{\frac{\Sigma X^2}{N} - \left(\frac{\Sigma X}{N}\right)^2} \tag{10}$$

$$= \sqrt{\frac{11361}{8} - \left(\frac{295}{8}\right)^2}$$

$$= \sqrt{60.35} = 7.8$$

(c)

$$S = \frac{1}{N}\sqrt{N\Sigma X^2 - (\Sigma X)^2} \tag{11}$$

$$= \frac{1}{8}\sqrt{8(11361) - (295)^2}$$

$$= \frac{1}{8}\sqrt{3863} = 7.8$$

The standard deviation is more easily computed if the scores are expressed as d's, or deviations from an arbitrary origin, C. The S of a distribution of d is the same as the S of the corresponding distribution of X.

Proof:

A single deviation from C is

$$d = (X - C)$$

The mean of a distribution of d is

$$M_d = \frac{\Sigma d}{N}$$

$$= \frac{\Sigma(X - C)}{N}$$

$$= \bar{X} - C$$

The standard deviation of a distribution of d is

$$S_d = \sqrt{\frac{\Sigma(d - M_d)^2}{N}}$$

But

$$(d - M_d) = (X - C) - (\bar{X} - C)$$
$$= (X - \bar{X})$$

Since the deviation of a d from the mean of the distribution of d is the same as the deviation of the corresponding X from the mean of the distribution of X, it follows that

$$S_d = S_x$$

The standard deviation of a group of scores is the same no matter what value of X is taken as the arbitrary origin. This appears reasonable if we remember that S is not a point on the X-scale, but a distance. It reflects the amount by which the scores differ from each other.

Thus, (10) and (11) can be written in terms of deviations from an arbitrary origin merely by substituting d for X.

$$S = \sqrt{\frac{\Sigma d^2}{N} - \left(\frac{\Sigma d}{N}\right)^2} \tag{10a}$$

$$S = \frac{1}{N} \sqrt{N\Sigma d^2 - (\Sigma d)^2} \tag{11a}$$

Example:

	where $C = 36$			where $C = 45$	
X	d	d^2		d	d^2
39	+ 3	9		− 6	36
32	− 4	16		−13	169
50	+14	196		+ 5	25
27	− 9	81		−18	324
35	− 1	1		−10	100
47	+11	121		+ 2	4
37	+ 1	1		− 8	64
28	− 8	64		+17	289
	7	489		−65	1011

$$S = \sqrt{\frac{489}{8} - \left(\frac{7}{8}\right)^2} \qquad S = \sqrt{\frac{1011}{8} - \left(\frac{-65}{8}\right)^2}$$

$$= \sqrt{60.36} = 7.8 \qquad = \sqrt{60.36} = 7.8$$

The Standard Deviation of Grouped Data

If the scores are tabulated into class intervals the computation of S can be further simplified by obtaining fd^2 for each class interval and adding these sub-totals to find the total $\Sigma f d^2$. To indicate this operation formulas (10) and (11) can be written in terms of fd and fd^2.

$$S = \sqrt{\frac{\Sigma f d^2}{N} - \left(\frac{\Sigma f d}{N}\right)^2}$$ (10b)

$$S = \frac{1}{N} \sqrt{N \Sigma f d^2 - (\Sigma f d)^2}$$ (11b)

In the following example, note the fd^2 can easily be obtained by multiplying fd by d. *Do not square the values in the fd column.* The square of fd, for which we have no use, would be represented as $f^2 d^2$, or $(fd)^2$.

Example (from data of Table 1):

Score	f	d	fd	fd^2
91–97	1	42	42	1764
84–90	1	35	35	1225
77–83	3	28	84	2352
70–76	7	21	147	3087
63–69	6	14	84	1176
56–62	6	7	42	294
49–55	9	0	0	0
42–48	11	− 7	− 77	539
35–41	11	−14	−154	2156
28–34	10	−21	−210	4410
21–27	13	−28	−364	10192
14–20	8	−35	−280	9800
7–13	3	−42	−126	5292
0– 6	1	−49	− 49	2401

$$N = 90 \qquad\qquad \Sigma f d = -826 \quad \Sigma f d^2 = 44688$$

$$S = \sqrt{\frac{44688}{90} - \left(\frac{-826}{90}\right)^2} = 20.3$$

The standard deviation is a distance or range on the X-scale. Therefore, if the raw scores of a distribution are transformed to a new unit of measurement, the standard deviation of the transformed scores will also be in this new unit. For example, if measurements are expressed in feet and we convert them to yards, the transformed measurements will be one-third as large as the original measurements and the standard deviation of the converted measurements will be in yards. But the S in yards can be converted back to S in feet by multiplying it by three. To transform a measurement to a different unit we multiply it by a factor.

The standard deviation of a set of scores, where each score has been multiplied by a constant, is equal to the product of that constant and the standard deviation of the original scores.

$$S_{(cx)} = CS_x$$

Proof:

Where each X is multiplied by C

$$M_{cx} = \frac{\Sigma(CX)}{N} = \frac{C\Sigma X}{N} = C\bar{X}$$

A deviation of a converted score from the mean of the distribution is

$$CX - M_{cx} = C(X - \bar{X})$$
$$= Cx$$

Thus, the standard deviation of the converted scores is

$$S_{(cx)} = \sqrt{\frac{\Sigma(Cx)^2}{N}}$$
$$= \sqrt{C^2\left(\frac{\Sigma x^2}{N}\right)}$$
$$S_{(cx)} = C\sqrt{\frac{\Sigma x^2}{N}} = CS_x$$

It follows, then, that

$$S_x = \frac{S_{(cx)}}{C}$$

If the d's in the preceding example were multiplied by the constant $1/i$ and thus transformed into class interval units (d_i), the S of the d_i's should turn out to be 2.9. In the example, S_x was found to be 20.3 *score units,* which is 2.9 class interval units where $i = 7$.

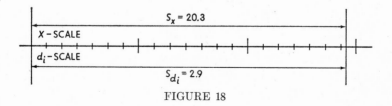

FIGURE 18

Much work can be saved by carrying through the entire computation in d_i units. This method, which is ordinarily used with tabulated data, can be summarized in two ways:

$$S = i\sqrt{\frac{\Sigma fd^2_i}{N} - \left(\frac{\Sigma fd_i}{N}\right)^2} \tag{10c}$$

$$S = \frac{i}{N}\sqrt{N\Sigma fd^2_i - (\Sigma fd_i)^2} \tag{11c}$$

Compare the computation in the following example with the example given on page 71 and note how much less work is required when d_i units are used.

Example:

Score	f	d_i	fd_i	fd^2_i
91–97	1	+7	+ 7	49
84–90	1	+6	+ 6	36
77–83	3	+5	+15	75
70–76	7	+4	+28	112
63–69	6	+3	+18	54
56–62	6	+2	+12	24
49–55	9	+1	+ 9	9
42–48	11	0	0	0
35–41	11	−1	−11	11
28–34	10	−2	−20	40
21–27	13	−3	−39	117
14–20	8	−4	−32	128
7–13	3	−5	−15	75
0– 6	1	−6	− 6	36

$$N = 90 \qquad\qquad \Sigma fd_i = -28 \quad \Sigma fd^2_i = 766$$

$$S = 7\sqrt{\frac{766}{90} - \left(\frac{-28}{90}\right)^2} \tag{10c}$$

$$= 7(2.9) = 20.3$$

Note that the values of fd^2_i can be obtained easily by multiplying for each class interval $d_i \cdot fd_i$.

GROUPING ERRORS

Tabulation of frequencies into class intervals serves the dual function of accentuating the group characteristics of a set of data and, at the same time, simplifying the computation of statistics which describe these characteristics. But these advantages are gained only through a sacrifice in accuracy. Scores lose their individuality when they are grouped into a class interval. *Grouping errors* in the final outcome of a computation result from the fact that mid-points do not accurately represent the scores within the intervals.

Grouping errors are of two kinds—random and systematic. *Random errors* are those which follow no apparent pattern with respect to magnitude or direction. They are said to be "chance" errors because they are unpredictable. Random errors of grouping cause a statistic computed from a frequency tabulation to be sometimes smaller and sometimes larger than if it were computed from raw scores. Because such errors are random, they tend more and more to cancel each other as the number of scores in the distribution increases. Thus, they can be ignored where N is large. *Systematic errors,* on the other hand, are consistent errors. They tend to occur in the same direction and in a predictable manner. Systematic errors may cause a statistic computed from grouped data to be generally smaller, or larger, than it would be if computed from raw scores.

In working with tabulated data we assume the mid-point of the class interval to be representative of the scores within the interval. Actually, because of random errors the mid-point is in most instances too high or too low to represent accurately the scores within the interval. But, if enough intervals are used, these positive

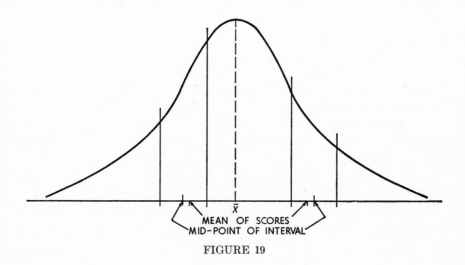

MEAN OF SCORES
MID-POINT OF INTERVAL

FIGURE 19

and negative errors can be expected to balance each other. However, this assumption is incorrect because there is a *systematic* error involved in representing scores by the mid-points of class intervals. Scores are usually distributed within the class interval with decreasing frequency as the distance from the mode increases. Thus, in a bell-shaped distribution the mid-point of any class interval is farther from the mean of the distribution than is the mean of the scores within the interval. (An exception is the special case of a class interval which lies exactly in the center of the distribution.)

Imagine, for example, an interval above the mean containing three raw score units and having a frequency of twenty-four. Suppose that the mid-point is four units above the mean and that the scores are actually distributed as follows.

	Actual Deviations			*Deviations of Mid-point*			
x	f	fx	fx^2	x_i	f	fx_i	fx^2_i
$+5$	6	30	150				
$+4$	8	32	128	$+4$	24	$+96$	384
$+3$	10	30	90				
	$\Sigma x = 92$		$\Sigma x^2 = 368$				

The sum of the x's within the interval is 92, whereas, if the mid-point is taken to represent the interval, $fx_i = 96$. Furthermore, the sum of the separate x^2 values is 368, but fx^2_i for the mid-point is 384. The use of class intervals makes $\Sigma|x|$ and Σx^2 larger than they would be if computed from raw scores.

This error, although systematic, has no effect on the mean of a symmetrical distribution because the positive error above the mean is balanced by the negative error below.

In computing S, however, the situation is quite different, because squaring removes the negative signs of the deviations, and the errors do not balance. Thus, Σx^2 is larger when computed from grouped data than it is when computed from raw scores. The magnitude of the error systematically increases with increases in the size of class interval. However, if twelve or more class intervals are used, the error becomes negligible. For this reason a frequency distribution should contain at least twelve class intervals.

Sometimes the nature of the raw scores makes it impossible to use twelve or more intervals. In such cases the computed standard deviation should be corrected for the grouping error by

$$S_c = \sqrt{S^2 - \frac{i^2}{12}}, \quad \text{where } i \text{ is the number of score units in a class interval} \tag{12}$$

This formula includes a factor known as Sheppard's correction for grouping. It is based on W. H. Sheppard's demonstration that in a normal distribution σ^2 is too large by $\frac{1}{12}$ when σ^2 and the $\frac{1}{12}$ are in units of i^2.

SUGGESTED READINGS

1. Guilford, J. P. *Fundamental Statistics in Psychology and Education*, chap. xii. 2d ed. New York: McGraw-Hill Book Company, 1950.
2. Monroe, W. S. (ed.). *Encyclopedia of Educational Research*, pp. 795–802. New York: Rev. ed. The Macmillan Company, 1950.
3. Thorndike, R. L., and Hagen, E. *Measurement and Evaluation in Psychology and Education*, chap. vii. New York: John Wiley & Sons, 1955.
4. Walker, H. M. *Elementary Statistical Methods*, pp. 59–74. New York: Henry Holt and Company, 1943.

EXERCISES

1. Compute S for data A, (p. 20) (a) by the raw score method, formula (10) or (11), and (b) from a tabulated distribution using formula (10c) or (11c). Do these methods give exactly the same results? Explain why they might be expected to differ.

2. Show by algebraic manipulation that

   a) $\Sigma x = 0$

   b) $\Sigma x^2 = \Sigma X^2 - \dfrac{(\Sigma X)^2}{N}$

   c) $S_{(x+c)} = S_x$

   (If you cannot perform the above demonstrations you should go back and study this chapter more carefully.)

3. In the example on page 73 count the number of cases within the range $X \pm S$. Is this approximately $\frac{2}{3}$ of the total N?

4. Compute S from Table 3 (p. 16) and for the same data as tabulated in Table 5 (p. 17). Explain the difference in results. Apply formula

(12) to the standard deviation obtained from Table 5. Does this reduce the difference between the two?

5. Would you say that W. H., the third student listed in data B (p. 31), is as intelligent as he is tall? Present evidence to support your answer.

6. Compute $\Sigma(X - \bar{X})^2$ from the following set of scores: 24, 30, 19, 18, 21, 12, 27, 23, 20, 21.

7. Observe that

$$\Sigma x^2 = \Sigma d^2 - \frac{(\Sigma d)^2}{N}$$

This statement can be easily derived from formula (11a) by using the relationship $\Sigma x^2 = NS^2$. Using the scores in the preceding problem, perform three separate computations of

$$\Sigma d^2 - \frac{(\Sigma d)^2}{N}, \quad \text{where the origin is taken as 10, 20, and 30}$$

Each computation should give the same result.

COMPUTATIONAL AIDS

1. Arkin, H., and Colton, R. *Tables for Statisticians*. New York: Barnes and Noble, Inc., 1950.

2. *Barlow's Tables of Squares, Cubes, Square Roots, Cube Roots and Reciprocals of Integer Numbers up to 12,500.* 4th ed. New York: Chemical Publishing Co., 1944.

3. Pease, K. *Machine Computation of Elementary Statistics*. New York: Chartwell House, 1949.

4. Walker, H. M. *Mathematics Essential for Elementary Statistics,* chaps. ii, iii, iv, xv. Rev. ed. New York: Henry Holt and Co., 1951.

CHAPTER VI

Linear Relationships

We have considered the statistical methods commonly used to describe the general features of frequency distributions. But our needs extend far beyond the description of frequency distributions. We must also be able to describe *functional relationships* between different kinds of measurements. Methods designed to discover, describe, and analyze functional relationships between variables are known as correlation techniques.

When one quantity Y varies in some regular fashion with changes in another quantity X, the two are said to be correlated. If knowledge of the magnitude of X enables us to know exactly the magnitude of Y, the correlation is said to be perfect. If knowledge of X does not tell us the exact magnitude of Y but enables us to estimate Y more accurately than we could if the magnitude of X were unknown, we speak of varying degrees of correlation, depending on how accurately Y can be estimated. Empirical data secured by observing or measuring events or objects seldom produce perfect correlations between variables. Mathematical functions, however, are examples of perfect correlation. For instance, if $Y = X^2$, the value of Y is specified exactly by this equation for any value of X. A mathematical function of this sort contains no error or approximation because it is an abstract model, created as an ideal, and not derived from approximate measurements. The functional relationships of empirical science are quite different from the purely abstract models of theoretical science and mathematics. They are statistical in nature, since they describe the general trend or average tendency characteristic of a large number of observations.

The function $S = 16t^2$ is an *exact* mathematical relationship. It permits no exceptions, and the correlation of S with t is perfect. If, however, this equation is used to represent the distance (S feet) through which an object will have fallen towards the ground when t seconds have elapsed following its release in space, it is no longer exact. It has become a statement of average tendency, according to which few, if any, objects have ever actually fallen. Even if we introduce qualifications to account for the influence of factors such as air resistance, the formula still remains only an approximation of the central tendency of a large number of actual observations.

Let us consider another example. The area of a square depends on the length of its side. This fact can be represented symbolically by

$$A = f(x), \quad \text{where } A \text{ represents units of area,}$$
$$\text{and } x \text{ represents units of length}$$

This is merely a statement of the fact that area is a function of length without specifying a particular type of functional relationship. A more precise formulation of the relationship is given by

$$A = x^2$$

This specifies the exact nature of the function. It is a mathematical ideal. It would hold true for a perfect square, if such a hypothetical figure could be observed by means of an errorless measuring instrument.

The relationship $A = x^2$ is not derived from actual measurements of "square" objects. In fact, if we set out to test this equation against concrete data, we would be unlikely to find any *perfectly* square plane surfaces upon which to perform the test. Furthermore, even if such surfaces could be found, we would not be able to measure them without error. But areas computed from approximate measurements of approximately square objects would agree fairly well with this equation. Even though the equation is a pure mathematical ideal, it can be used to describe a set of empirical observations. It is a general description of the pairs of observed measurements in the same way that an average is a general description of a frequency distribution. When used in this way it is an *empirical relationship*.

The functional relationships with which statistics is primarily concerned are empirical relationships which provide generalized descriptions of observed data. Such descriptive functions are not blindly discovered as the inevitable result of accumulating huge masses of data; rather, they originate in the minds of mathematicians and are part of the rational structure of mathematics. They are mathematical models which empirical science borrows and uses in its attempt to find meaningful organization in the data of experience.

In describing the empirical relationship between two variables the statistician must perform three operations.

1. He must select from the great variety of rational relationships known to mathematics a general type of function which roughly resembles the observed data.

2. After selecting the general type of function to be used, he must next find the best particular function of this type for describing this particular set of data.

3. The third step in the descriptive process is a statement of the extent to which the actual observations differ from the mathematical model used to describe them.

Let us now apply these steps to an hypothetical set of paired observations. Suppose we have two scores for each of twelve people —a score on test X and a score on test Y.

Subject	X-Score	Y-Score
A	54	32
B	68	48
C	49	22
D	70	47
E	50	30
F	56	29
G	47	20
H	62	40
I	55	37
J	60	37
K	59	31
L	66	35

Inspection of the table above suggests that there is some sort of relationship between X and Y. Since it is difficult to interpret such a table of raw data, even when it is no larger than this one, let us tabulate the pairs of scores. This tabulation will differ from the frequency distribution of scores on one scale of measurement because here we have *two* scores for each person. Our tabulation must show how often each particular combination of X-score and Y-score appears in the raw data. Figure 20 illustrates how this can be accomplished. This type of tabulation is called a *scatter diagram* or *scattergram*. Here each subject is represented by a plotted point located with reference to his score on X and Y. The coordinates of each point are the two scores.

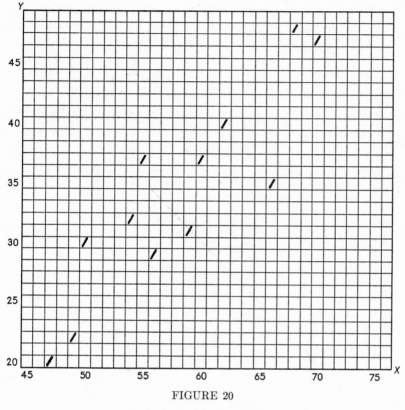

FIGURE 20

Scatter Diagram

The scatter diagram shows clearly that Y increases as X increases. The simplest mathematical function which could reasonably be used to describe the group characteristics of these plotted points is a straight line. Thus, the relationship between X and Y in our illustrative problem is identified as a *linear* function.

Having identified the general mathematical model which adequately describes the data, we must now find the particular linear function which provides the best description.

The generalized equation of a straight line is

$$Y = BX + A,$$ where A and B are numerical (13)
constants which define a par-
ticular straight line

Figure 21 illustrates five of the innumerable straight lines which could be drawn to represent particular relationships between the two sets of hypothetical scores. Each of these lines is uniquely defined by the numerical values of A and B, and by the sign of B. B represents the *slope* of the line. It is the number of units that Y changes as X increases one unit. If B is positive, Y increases as X increases. If B is negative, Y decreases as X increases, and the relationship between X and Y is said to be *inverse*. B, the slope of the line, thus specifies *how rapidly* and in *which direction* Y changes as the value of X increases.

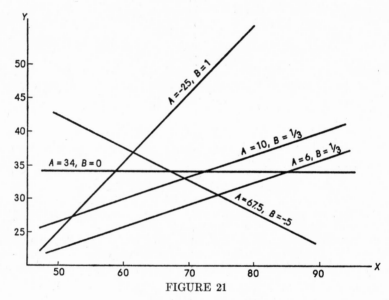

FIGURE 21

FIVE LINEAR RELATIONSHIPS BETWEEN X AND Y

Two of the lines in Figure 21 have the same value for B (⅓), but these lines are not the same. The difference between them results from different values for A. A is known as the *Y-intercept*. It specifies the value of Y when $X = 0$. The value of A is the point of reference on the Y-scale to which the change in Y produced by a change in X is added. For example, the equations of these two lines are

$$(A) \quad Y = \tfrac{1}{3}X + 10$$
$$(B) \quad Y = \tfrac{1}{3}X + 6$$

As X changes from 0 to 60, both of these lines change ⅓ (60), or 20 units on the Y-scale. In (A), when $X = 60$, $Y = 20 + 10$, or 30. In

(B), however, $Y = 20 + 6$, or 26 when X is 60. Thus, A specifies the height of the line with reference to the scale of Y.

EXERCISES

1. Plot on the same graph:

a) $Y = .5X + 3$
b) $Y = 1.2X + 3$
c) $Y = -.5X + 3$
d) $Y = -.5X - 3$

2. Plot and find from the graph the equation of each of the following.

a) $(X = 10, Y = 15)$, $(X = 20, Y = 20)$
   (These two sets of coordinates define a particular straight line.)
b) $(X = 18, Y = 24)$, $(X = 27, Y = 21)$

3. Write the equation $Y = BX + A$ which fits the values in each of the following.

(a)		(b)		(c)	
X	Y	X	Y	X	Y
−7	21	10	7.8	5	5.5
0	28	11	8.2	6	5.2
5	33	12	8.6	7	4.9
10	38	15	9.8	8	4.6

4. Plot each of the following equations. First select what appears to be a representative series of numerical values for X. Then compute the corresponding values of Y and mark the points on your graph corresponding to these coordinates. In some cases the form of the function will be obvious at this point, but in others you will need to compute more coordinates from the equation in order to be sure.

a) $x^2 + y^2 = 25$ (Remember that x and y can both be negative.)
b) $Y = 2x^2 + x - 3$,   from $x = -5$ to $x = +4$
c) $Y = x^2 + 6$,   from $x = -5$ to $x = +5$

THE BEST FIT STRAIGHT LINE

An infinite variety of straight lines, each uniquely defined by particular values of A and B, might be drawn through the scatter diagram of Figure 20. Our problem is to find particular values of A and B to define the line most representative of the overall pattern of plotted points. The line must describe adequately the *central tendency* of the functional relationship between the observed scores on X and Y.

Now, the most generally descriptive measure of central tendency in a frequency distribution is the mean. The mean, it will be recalled, is that numerical value about which the deviations of the individual scores sum algebraically to zero. Similarly, the line which best describes the central tendency of a scatter diagram must be one around which the deviations of observed values sum algebraically to zero. Let us see what kind of a line meets this requirement.

The equation of this line can be expressed as

$$Y' = BX + A \tag{14}$$

For any observed value of X, there is an observed value Y and a theoretical value from the equation Y'. The deviation of an observed Y from the descriptive straight line is

$$(Y - Y')$$

The requirement we have specified for the descriptive line is that

$$\Sigma(Y - Y') = 0$$

Our problem is greatly simplified if we now transform the measurements of X and Y to deviations from their respective means.

$$x = (X - \bar{X})$$
$$y = (Y - \bar{Y})$$

In Figure 22 the pairs of scores from our illustrative problem have been plotted according to X and Y and according to deviation scores, x and y. The pattern of the plotted points is the same regardless of which type of score is used. Similarly, the equation of any straight line can be represented in raw scores or in deviations from the means, and the line will be exactly the same. The equation expressed in deviation scores would be

$$y' = bx + a \tag{14a}$$

Since Y' and X have been replaced by y' and x, A and B are replaced by a and b. Because B and b specify *rate of change*, they will be the same value for any line. A, however, represents a *point*

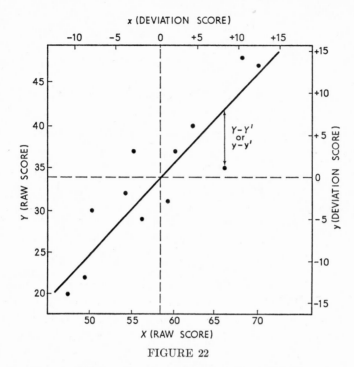

FIGURE 22

SCATTER DIAGRAM PLOTTED IN RAW AND DEVIATION SCORES

of reference on the scale of raw scores; therefore, it is not the same as *a*, which is a point of reference on the scale of deviation scores.

Inasmuch as raw scores and deviation scores differ only in their points of origin, the difference between two scores remains the same regardless of which scale is used to express them. Thus, the discrepancy of an observed Y from the theoretical Y' can be expressed as

$$(y - y') = (Y - Y')$$

For example, the straight line drawn in Figure 22 shows Y' to be 43 when X is 66. The observed value, Y, for this value of X is 35, and the discrepancy is -8. In corresponding deviation scores, $y' = 9$, $y = 1$, and the discrepancy $(y - y') = -8$.

The sum of the discrepancies between observed and theoretical values of Y can now be represented as

$$\Sigma(y - y')$$

But, since $y' = bx + a$,

$$\Sigma(y - y') = \Sigma[y - (bx + a)]$$
$$= \Sigma y - b\Sigma x - Na$$

And, because $\Sigma y = 0$ and $\Sigma x = 0$

$$\Sigma(y - y') = -Na$$

Since N must be a positive whole number, this means that if the sum of discrepancies is zero, $\Sigma(y - y') = 0$, a must be zero, and the line which fulfills this requirement can be represented by

$$y' = bx \tag{15}$$

Any line represented by equation (15) must pass through the point with coordinates $y' = 0$ and $x = 0$. These are the same as $Y' = \bar{Y}$ and $X = \bar{X}$. Thus, the line around which discrepancies sum algebraically to zero must pass through the intersection of $\bar{X}$ and $\bar{Y}$ in the scatter diagram.

This condition, however, does not in itself define the "best fit" line because there are an infinity of lines which can be drawn through this point. For all of these, $\Sigma(y - y') = 0$. Of course, only one of them is the "best" line, the line which most closely approximates observed values of Y.

If the discrepancies are squared, their magnitude can be easily evaluated, enabling us to find the "best" line for any set of paired X, Y values. The situation here is analogous to the measurement of dispersion in a frequency distribution through the use of squared deviations from the mean. The sum of squared deviations within a frequency distribution is smallest when deviations are taken from the mean. This is shown by the following.

$$S^2 = \frac{\Sigma x^2}{N}$$

$$\Sigma x^2 = NS^2$$

From formula (10a), we have

$$S^2 = \frac{\Sigma d^2}{N} - \left(\frac{\Sigma d}{N}\right)^2$$

$$NS^2 = \Sigma d^2 - \frac{(\Sigma d)^2}{N} = \Sigma x^2$$

In the special case where d's are taken from the mean

$$\frac{(\Sigma d)^2}{N} = 0, \quad \text{and } \Sigma d^2 = \Sigma x^2$$

If d's are taken from any other point of reference, Σd^2 is greater than Σx^2, and $\dfrac{(\Sigma d)^2}{N}$ must be subtracted to give the correct sum of squared deviations from the mean.

The mean can be viewed as "the best fit point" in a frequency distribution because the sum of squared deviations around that point is smaller than around any other point on the X-scale. The mean is also the *expected* value of X because if we attempt to predict the result of additional measurements, the error of prediction, measured by squared discrepancies between the prediction and the actual measurements, will be as small as possible if we always predict $\bar{X}$.

Similarly, the line which best describes the central tendency of a scatter diagram is the line which represents *expected* values of Y, designated by Y'. If we attempt to predict Y from our knowledge of X, the error in a number of predictions of this sort is measured by $\Sigma(Y - Y')^2$. Thus, the best fit line, which represents *expected* values of Y, is defined as that particular straight line about which the sum of squared discrepancies is a minimum. This definition of best fit is known as the *criterion of least squares.*

Let us now apply the criterion of least squares to the problem of discovering the line which best describes the pairs of scores plotted in Figure 22. We have already found that this line must pass through the intersection of means and can therefore be represented by

$$y' = bx$$

Our problem is to find a value of b such that the following function is as small as it can possibly be.

$$\Sigma(y - y')^2 = f(b)$$

By substituting bx for y', we can see how the sum of squared discrepancies varies with changing values of b.

$$
\begin{aligned}
\Sigma(y - y')^2 &= \Sigma(y - bx)^2 \\
&= \Sigma(y^2 - 2bxy + b^2x^2) \\
&= \Sigma y^2 - 2b\Sigma xy + b^2\Sigma x^2
\end{aligned}
$$

This can be arranged in a more conventional form as

$$\Sigma(y - y')^2 = (\Sigma x^2)b^2 - 2(\Sigma xy)b + (\Sigma y^2) \tag{16}$$

You may recognize this as a quadratic equation of the general form $Ab^2 - 2Bb + C$, where A, B, and C are constants, and b is variable. For any particular set of observed data the values of A, B, and C can be computed. Although short cut methods are commonly used for this, the following computation for our illustrative problem is carried through in terms of deviations from the means.

Subject	X-score	Y-score	x	x^2	y	y^2	xy
A	54	32	−4	16	−2	4	+8
B	68	48	+10	100	+14	196	+140
C	49	22	−9	81	−12	144	+108
D	70	47	+12	144	+13	169	+156
E	50	30	−8	64	−4	16	+32
F	56	29	−2	4	−5	25	+10
G	47	20	−11	121	−14	196	+154
H	62	40	+4	16	+6	36	+24
I	55	37	−3	9	+3	9	−9
J	60	37	+2	4	+3	9	+6
K	59	31	+1	1	−3	9	−3
L	66	35	+8	64	+1	1	+8

$\Sigma X = 696$ $\Sigma Y = 408$ $\Sigma x^2 = 624$ $\Sigma y^2 = 814$ $\Sigma xy = 634$

$$\bar{X} = \frac{696}{12} = 58, \qquad \bar{Y} = \frac{408}{12} = 34$$

Substituting the numerical values for Σx^2, Σy^2, and Σxy, we obtain the following expression.

$$\Sigma(y - y')^2 = 624b^2 - 1268b + 814$$

This gives us the sum of squared deviations from any straight line which passes through the intersection of $\bar{X}$ and $\bar{Y}$ in the scatter diagram of Figure 22. The magnitude of this sum for any specific line depends on the value of b.

Now, if we can by some means find the particular value of b which makes this sum smaller than it would be for any other value of b, we can specify exactly the best fit line for this set of data. In order to do this, let us first construct a graph to show how the sum of squared discrepancies is related to b.

The following values for the sum of squared discrepancies were computed by substituting various values of b in the preceding expression. When b is zero, the discrepancies are great. As b increases, they become smaller up to a certain point, beyond which they increase. The slope of the *best fit* line is the value of b for which the discrepancies are as small as they can possibly be.

b	$\Sigma(y - y')^2$
0.0	814.00
.2	585.36
.4	406.64
.6	277.84
.8	198.96
1.0	170.00
1.2	190.96
1.5	316.00
2.0	774.00

These paired values are shown graphically in Figure 23. The graph reaches its lowest point approximately where $b = 1.02$. Thus, the best fit line for the pairs of scores in our illustrative problem is defined by

$$y' = 1.02x$$

This equation, however, is only approximately correct because the graphical method used in finding the value of b is subject to error. In another section we will develop an exact method for finding the slope of the best fit line.

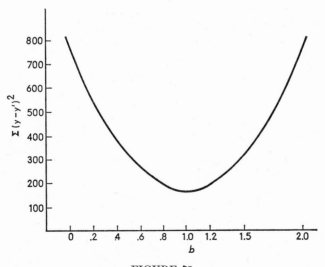

FIGURE 23

RELATIONSHIP OF SQUARED DISCREPANCIES TO SLOPE OF LINE

DISPERSION ABOUT THE BEST FIT LINE

The statement that $y' = 1.02x$ best describes the relationship between the two variables of our illustrative problem is not in itself a complete description of the data. This equation describes only the *central tendency* of the empirical relationship. Complete description requires that something be said about the dispersion of the observed data about this best fit line. The situation is similar to that found in describing the central tendency and dispersion of a frequency distribution. The best fit line in a scatter diagram and the mean in a frequency distribution are both measures of central tendency about which the sum of squared deviations is a minimum. Dispersion in a scatter diagram, as well as in a frequency distribution, is concerned with the magnitude of these deviations.

The measure of dispersion about the best fit line of a scatter diagram is a form of standard deviation known as the *standard error of estimate* and is designated by $S_{y \cdot x}$. The double subscript shows that we are dealing with discrepancies between observed values of Y and the values which can be estimated from X. Note especially the point of reference for the deviations measured by the standard error of estimate, formula (17). Compare this point of reference with the point of reference for the deviations measured by the standard deviation of the Y-distribution,

$$S_{y \cdot x} = \sqrt{\frac{\Sigma(y - y')^2}{N}} \qquad (17)$$

For comparison

$$S_y = \sqrt{\frac{\Sigma(Y - \bar{Y})^2}{N}}$$

The sum of squared deviations from the best fit line in our present problem can be found by substituting the appropriate numerical values in formula (16).

$$\Sigma(y - y')^2 = (\Sigma x^2)b^2 - (2)(\Sigma xy)b + (\Sigma y^2)$$
$$\Sigma x^2 = 624$$
$$\Sigma xy = 634$$
$$\Sigma y^2 = 814$$
$$b = 1.02 \quad \text{(estimated from the graph, Figure 23, p. 89)}$$
$$\Sigma(y - y')^2 = (624)(1.02)^2 - (2)(634)(1.02) + (814) = 169.85$$

The standard error of estimate is

$$S_{y \cdot x} = \sqrt{\frac{169.85}{12}} = 3.8$$

The empirical relationship plotted in the scatter diagram of Figure 20 (p. 81) can now be adequately described by the following.

$$y' = 1.02x$$
$$S_{y \cdot x} = 3.8$$
$$N = 12$$

These values specify (1) the particular linear function which best describes the data, (2) how well the function fits the observations, and (3) the number of observations upon which this description is based.

EXERCISES

1. Find graphically the slope of the straight line which best fits the following data. Construct a scatter diagram showing the observed data and the best fit line.

X	Y
17	5
14	2
20	4
16	3
27	6
10	2
12	1
15	4
16	2
23	5

2. Compute $S_{y \cdot x}$ for the above data, using formulas (16) and (17).
3. Prove that if $\Sigma(Y - Y') = 0$, the line $Y' = BX + A$ must pass through the point $(\bar{X}, \bar{Y})$. (If you cannot do this, you should review the demonstration on pp. 85–86).
4. Show that $\Sigma(X - A) = 0$ and that $\Sigma(X - A)^2$ is minimum when $A = \bar{X}$.

A PRECISE METHOD FOR FINDING *b*

A simpler and more accurate method for finding b can easily be derived. The derivation requires that we find an algebraic formula for b which fulfills the criterion of least squares. In other words, we must find an expression for b such that $\Sigma(y - y')^2$ is a minimum.

The sum of squared deviations from the best fit line (page 88) can be expressed as

$$\Sigma(y - y')^2 = Ab^2 - 2Bb + C, \text{ where } A = \Sigma x^2$$
$$B = \Sigma xy$$
$$C = \Sigma y^2$$

Multiplication of the first two terms of the expression by A/A produces

$$\Sigma(y - y')^2 = \frac{1}{A} (A^2b^2 - 2ABb) + C *$$

Now, let us add B^2/A and subtract B^2/A.

$$\Sigma(y - y')^2 = \frac{1}{A} (A^2b^2 - 2ABb) + C + \frac{B^2}{A} - \frac{B^2}{A} *$$

Rearranging the terms, we have within the parentheses a perfect squared binomial.

$$\Sigma(y - y')^2 = \frac{1}{A} (A^2b^2 - 2ABb + B^2) + C - \frac{B^2}{A}$$
$$= \frac{1}{A} (Ab - B)^2 + C - \frac{B^2}{A}$$

The parenthetical term $(Ab - B)^2$ is the only one which varies with changing values of b. Since this term is squared, it cannot assume a negative value; it must equal zero or a number greater than zero. Thus, the smallest possible value of $\Sigma(y - y')^2$ occurs when $(Ab - B)^2 = 0$.

We see then that the slope of the best fit line is the value of b when $(Ab - B)^2 = 0$. Let us set the expression equal to zero and solve for b.

$$(Ab - B)^2 = 0$$
$$(Ab - B) = 0$$
$$Ab = B$$
$$b = \frac{B}{A}$$

---

*These two operations are quite legitimate, since they do not change the value of the expression. They are performed in order to arrive at an expression of $\Sigma(y - y')^2$ which will allow us to specify the slope of the best fit line.

Substituting the expressions represented by A and B, we have

$$b = \frac{\Sigma xy}{\Sigma x^2} \quad \text{(slope of best fit line)*} \tag{18}$$

Formula (18) is seldom used for computation because it is expressed in deviations from $\bar{X}$ and $\bar{Y}$. A more convenient formula, which can be used with raw scores, can be obtained by substituting $(X - \bar{X})$ and $(Y - \bar{Y})$ for x and y in formula (18) and simplifying the resulting expression.

$$b = \frac{\Sigma XY - \dfrac{\Sigma X \Sigma Y}{N}}{\Sigma X^2 - \dfrac{(\Sigma X)^2}{N}} \tag{19}$$

Let us now apply this formula to the problem as a check on the graphical solution.

Subject	X	Y	X^2	XY
A	54	32	2916	1728
B	68	48	4624	3264
C	49	22	2401	1078
D	70	47	4900	3290
E	50	30	2500	1500
F	56	29	3136	1624
G	47	20	2209	940
H	62	40	3844	2480
I	55	37	3025	2035
J	60	37	3600	2220
K	59	31	3481	1829
L	66	35	4356	2310
Sums	696	408	40992	24298

$$b = \frac{24298 - \dfrac{(696)(408)}{12}}{40992 - \dfrac{(696)^2}{12}} = 1.016$$

---

* If you are familiar with differential calculus, you can get the same result by

$$f = \Sigma y^2 - 2b\Sigma xy + b^2 \Sigma x^2$$

$$\frac{df}{db} = -2\Sigma xy + 2b\Sigma x^2 = 0$$

$$b = \frac{\Sigma xy}{\Sigma x^2}$$

This result agrees with the graphical approximation, which was 1.02.

The value of b, together with $\bar{X}$ and $\bar{Y}$, completely defines the best fit line because b is the slope of a line which, by definition, must pass through the point, $x = 0$, $y = 0$.

If the best fit line is to be expressed in raw scores, we must use two values to specify its equation, A and B. We have seen that b and B must be the same, because raw scores and deviation scores are expressed in units of the same magnitude. Thus, the slope, or *rate of change,* is the same for both types of score. The point of origin, however, is different because the measurements are on different scales. In the raw score formula for the best fit line, A is the point of origin for changes in Y which accompany changes in X. A simple method for computing A can easily be derived.

$$y' = bx$$
$$Y' - \bar{Y} = B(X - \bar{X})$$
$$Y' = \bar{Y} + B(X - \bar{X})$$

Since $Y' = A$ when $X = 0$, we can substitute these equalities.

$$A = \bar{Y} - B\bar{X} \qquad (20)$$

Applying this formula to the example, we find

$$\bar{X} = \frac{696}{12} = 58$$
$$\bar{Y} = \frac{408}{12} = 34$$
$$B = b = 1.016$$
$$A = 34 - (1.016)(58) = -24.928$$

The equation of the best fit line can now be written in two forms.

$$y' = 1.016x \qquad \text{(deviation scores)}$$
$$Y' = 1.016X - 24.928 \quad \text{(raw scores)}$$

Time series, in which X represents a temporal sequence and Y represents measurements of a social or economic phenomenon, are often described by a best fit straight line. Such a description reflects the trend of growth over a period of time. Table 8 (p. 22), is an example of the type of data ordinarily described in this way. The coefficient of correlation, which is so extensively used in psychology and education, is directly related to the method of describing a functional relationship by means of the best fit straight line. A thorough mastery of this material will lead to better understanding of the coefficient of correlation.

SUGGESTED READING

1. Walker, H. M. *Mathematics Essential for Elementary Statistics*, chap. x. Rev. ed. New York: Henry Holt and Co., 1951.

EXERCISES

1. Compute for the data of Exercise 1 on page 91.
   a) the slope *b* of the best fit straight line using formula (19)
   b) the *Y*-intercept *A* by formula (20)

2. The following are the numbers of errors made by fifteen students on the first two examinations in a course in general psychology.

Student	First Test	Second Test
A	39	53
B	22	24
C	14	14
D	40	53
E	27	51
F	19	28
G	29	35
H	35	41
I	15	28
J	12	17
K	34	64
L	51	62
M	46	29
N	31	49
O	20	34

Plot this information in a scatter diagram and draw freehand a straight line $[Y' = f(X)]$ which appears to be a reasonably good fit. Compute the equation of the best fit line and draw this line on the graph. A good way to approximate the best fit line is to hold each end of a black thread, stretching it over the graph and moving it about until it appears to pass through the central tendency of the plotted points.

3. If you know only that a certain student was a member of the class presented in Exercise 2 but had no other information about him, what

would be your best guess concerning his error score on the second test? Explain. What score would you predict on the second test if you knew that he had made eighteen errors on the first one?

4. Find the equation of the best fit line showing the relationship between height (X) and weight (Y) for the male students in data B, p. 31.

5. Plot the relation of weight (Y) to height (X) separately for men and women in data B, p. 31. Is the mathematical model of a linear function adequate for describing both sets of data? If not, what might be the reasons?

CHAPTER VII

The Product Moment Coefficient of Correlation

One of the most useful statistical tools is the *product moment coefficient of correlation,* which is denoted by the letter r. A method of quantifying the degree of correlation between two variables was developed by Sir Francis Galton toward the latter part of the nineteenth century. Further refined by the great scientist Karl Pearson, the coefficient of correlation is often called the Pearson r.

The coefficient of correlation measures the degree to which empirical observations of X and Y conform to a straight line functional relationship. There are numerous interpretations of the meaning of r. The simplest of these is with reference to the slope of the best fit line. If X and Y are expressed in z-scores (x/S_x and y/S_y), r is the slope of the line which best fits the observed pairs of scores. Thus, the equation of the line can be written in three different ways, depending on the scale of measurement. Two of these equations do not include the term A because the Y-intercept is zero when X and Y are expressed as deviations from their respective means.

$$Y' = BX + A \quad \text{(raw scores)} \tag{14}$$
$$y' = bx \quad \text{(deviation scores)} \tag{15}$$
$$z'_y = rz_x \quad \text{(standard scores)} \tag{21}$$

The slope, then, is represented by B, b, or r, depending on the type of score. B and b are the same value because the units of raw scores and deviation scores are equal. The coefficient of correlation is not the same as b, because it is based on standard deviation units. Only in the special case where $S_x = S_y$ does r have the same value as b. This can be inferred from equations (15) and (21).

$$z'_y = rz_x$$
$$\frac{y'}{S_y} = r\left(\frac{x}{S_x}\right)$$

$$y' = r\left(\frac{S_y}{S_x}\right)x$$

$$y' = bx \qquad\qquad \text{from (15)}$$

$$b = r\left(\frac{S_y}{S_x}\right)$$

when $b = r$, $S_y = S_x$

We have thus far considered X to be the independent variable and have been concerned with Y as a function of X. If the situation were reversed—that is, if we wished to define the best fit line for the values of X which accompany certain values of Y—we could interchange X and Y in each of the equations and obtain another expression for b.

$$\frac{x'}{S_x} = r\left(\frac{y}{S_y}\right)$$

$$x' = r\left(\frac{S_x}{S_y}\right)y$$

and, since $x' = by$,

$$b = r\left(\frac{S_x}{S_y}\right)$$

It is convenient to distinguish these two b's by subscripts which indicate whether X or Y is taken as the independent variable.

$$b_{y \cdot x} = r\left(\frac{S_y}{S_x}\right) \quad \begin{array}{l}(Y \text{ is considered} \\ \text{dependent on } X.)\end{array} \qquad (22)$$

$$b_{x \cdot y} = r\left(\frac{S_x}{S_y}\right) \quad \begin{array}{l}(X \text{ is considered} \\ \text{dependent on } Y.)\end{array} \qquad (23)$$

These two quantities are known as *regression coefficients*. From their formulas it can be seen that $b_{y \cdot x} = b_{x \cdot y}$ only when $S_x = S_y$, or when $r = 0.00$.

When X is taken as the independent variable, we are interested in the best fit values of Y', and when Y is considered the independent variable, our interest is in X'. Consequently, there are two best fit lines for any scatter diagram, one showing how Y' changes with X, the other showing how X' changes with Y. In correlation analysis these lines are known as *regression lines*, and their equations are called *regression equations*. In deviation score form, these equations are

$$y' = r\left(\frac{S_y}{S_x}\right) x \qquad (24)$$

$$x' = r\left(\frac{S_x}{S_y}\right) y$$

Formula (24) can be transformed to a regression equation in raw score form.

$$y' = r\left(\frac{S_y}{S_x}\right) x$$

$$Y' - \bar{Y} = r\left(\frac{S_y}{S_x}\right)(X - \bar{X})$$

$$Y' = r\left(\frac{S_y}{S_x}\right) X + \left[\bar{Y} - r\left(\frac{S_y}{S_x}\right)\bar{X}\right] \qquad (26)$$

By analogy, the regression of X' on Y is

$$X' = r\left(\frac{S_x}{S_y}\right) Y + \left[\bar{X} - r\left(\frac{S_x}{S_y}\right)\bar{Y}\right] \qquad (27)$$

Formulas (26) and (27) show that the coefficient of correlation—r, together with $\bar{X}$, $\bar{Y}$, S_x, and S_y—defines the best fit regression line for Y' on X and for X' on Y. If these formulas are compared with the generalized formula for a straight line, $Y' = BX + A$, it is seen that

$$B_{y \cdot x} = r\left(\frac{S_y}{S_x}\right), \quad B_{x \cdot y} = r\left(\frac{S_x}{S_y}\right)$$

and $A_{y \cdot x} = \left[\bar{Y} - r\left(\frac{S_y}{S_x}\right)\bar{X}\right], \quad A_{x \cdot y} = \left[\bar{X} - r\left(\frac{S_x}{S_y}\right)\bar{Y}\right]$

EXERCISES

1. Write the regression equation for Y' on X in (1) raw score form and (2) deviation score form, where

$$r_{xy} = +.53$$
$$\bar{X} = 48$$
$$S_x = 6.2$$
$$\bar{Y} = 2.8$$
$$S_y = 1.1$$

2. Assume that X in the above problem represents intelligence test scores made by entering freshmen and Y' represents grade point averages for the first semester of the freshman year. What grade point average would you expect from students who made the following scores on the intelligence test?
   a) 54
   b) 36
   c) 48   (the mean intelligence test score)

3. If $r_{xy} = +.72$, what standard score on Y is most likely to be made by the students who have the following z-scores on X?
   a) $+1.00$
   b) -2.10
   c) 0.00

4. Suppose that for a certain table of data the correlation was computed to be $r = +.63$. If $b_{y \cdot x}$, computed by formula (19) turned out to be $+.441$, what could you say about S_x and S_y?

FORMULAS FOR THE COEFFICIENT OF CORRELATION

The slope of the best fit line in a scatter diagram was shown to be given by

$$b_{y \cdot x} = \frac{\Sigma xy}{\Sigma x^2}$$

This formula expresses the slope in *raw score units*. The coefficient of correlation was defined as the slope of the best fit regression line in *standard score units*. Let us then substitute standard scores for raw scores in the above formula and denote the resulting expression by the symbol r.

$$r_{y \cdot x} = \frac{\Sigma z_x z_y}{\Sigma z^2_x}$$

This expression can be simplified, since its denominator is equal to N.

$$\Sigma z^2_x = \Sigma \left(\frac{x}{S_x} \right)^2$$
$$= \frac{\Sigma x^2}{\frac{\Sigma x^2}{N}}$$
$$= N$$

The coefficient of correlation can now be written as

$$r_{y.x} = \frac{\Sigma z_x z_y}{N} \qquad (28)$$

Thus, the coefficient of correlation can be defined as the mean of products of paired standard scores on X and Y.

Regression coefficients, $b_{y.x}$ and $b_{x.y}$, must be distinguished by subscripts because they do not necessarily have the same numerical value. It can easily be shown, however, that $r_{y.x}$ is always equal to $r_{x.y}$. For that reason it is common practice to use the notation r_{xy} regardless of whether X or Y is taken as the independent variable.

The coefficient of correlation is often defined by a formula based on deviation scores and standard deviations. This formula is easily obtained by substitution in formula (28).

$$r_{xy} = \frac{\Sigma z_x z_y}{N}$$

$$= \frac{\Sigma \dfrac{x}{S_x} \dfrac{y}{S_y}}{N}$$

$$r_{xy} = \frac{\Sigma xy}{N S_x S_y} \qquad (29)$$

Formula (29) is seldom used for computation because of the inconvenience of working with deviation scores.

COMPUTATIONAL FORMULAS FOR r

Numerous schemes have been devised for computing r, all of which are algebraic transformations of the basic formula (28). The four formulas presented here are adequate for most of the data encountered in psychology.

$$r_{xy} = \frac{M_{xy} - \bar{X}\bar{Y}}{S_x S_y} \qquad (30)$$

This is useful for computing the correlation between two variables whose means and standard deviations are already known. The additional information required for computing r is obtained by multiplying each X-score by its paired Y-score and finding the mean of these products.

$$r_{xy} = \frac{N\Sigma XY - \Sigma X \Sigma Y}{\sqrt{N\Sigma X^2 - (\Sigma X)^2}\sqrt{N\Sigma Y^2 - (\Sigma Y)^2}} \qquad (31)$$

Formula (31) is used to compute r directly from raw scores. It requires, in addition to the columns of raw scores, a column of X^2 and of Y^2, which can be obtained from a table of squares, and a column of XY products. The sums of these columns are substituted in the formula. Means and standard deviations can easily be computed from these sums.

The procedure implied by formula (31) can be used when the scores are represented as deviations from arbitrary points of origin. Formula (32) describes this method of computation.

$$r_{xy} = \frac{N\Sigma d_x d_y - \Sigma d_x \Sigma d_y}{\sqrt{N\Sigma d^2{}_x - (\Sigma d_x)^2}\sqrt{N\Sigma d^2{}_y - (\Sigma d_y)^2}} \qquad (32)$$

Formulas (30), (31), and (32) can be used with data which have not been arranged in a scatter diagram. Nevertheless, such a diagram should be constructed for most correlation problems, even though it is not required for the actual computation of r, because r should be used only if the data can be adequately described by a straight line. In most cases the use of r is justified if the scatter diagram shows no systematic departure from linearity. We shall discuss in a later chapter a precise method for deciding whether a straight line adequately describes the observed data.

After the data have been tabulated, r can be computed directly from the scatter diagram. The entire process can be carried through with deviations in class interval units from any convenient point of origin. The size of interval and the point of origin do not need to be the same for X and Y. The number of intervals for X and for Y should be separately determined by the method used earlier in tabulating a frequency distribution.

Formula (33) expresses the procedure for computing r from the scatter diagram.

$$r_{xy} = \frac{N\Sigma fd_{i_x} d_{i_y} - \Sigma fd_{i_x} \Sigma fd_{i_y}}{\sqrt{N\Sigma fd^2{}_{i_x} - (\Sigma fd_{i_x})^2}\sqrt{N\Sigma fd^2{}_{i_y} - (\Sigma fd_{i_y})^2}} \qquad (33)$$

The approximation of r by this formula will agree closely with the results of formulas (31) and (32) if the usual precautions are observed in choosing class intervals for the scatter diagram.

PROCEDURE FOR COMPUTING *r*

As part of a program of test construction, sixty-eight students in a school of journalism were given a test of inductive reasoning and a test of deductive reasoning. Their scores, shown below, will be used to illustrate the computation of *r*.

Student	Inductive	Deductive	Student	Inductive	Deductive
N.A.Z.	54	48	C.M.	53	48
E.A.F.	54	48	W.E.W.	48	50
W.M.	32	38	R.C.F.	67	61
F.L.W.	65	74	D.M.	48	40
C.F.	45	43	D.W.	57	57
A.L.M.	54	45	B.E.	41	34
J.T.	48	45	V.L.	39	52
K.D.	48	40	M.T.	54	52
A.L.L.	57	45	R.E.D.	38	55
E.T.	60	44	E.M.L.	46	44
D.C.	48	40	J.E.T.	54	51
C.L.	54	38	J.H.C.	52	55
H.R.T.	51	50	P.L.	55	50
E.C.	32	32	I.S.	53	54
C.H.K.	60	48	G.C.	52	40
L.K.S.	57	50	C.W.H.	63	60
V.C.	52	44	H.W.S.	45	40
H.K.	53	50	J.W.C.	31	26
C.E.S.	58	55	G.K.	48	60
J.C.	34	46	M.S.	54	50
E.W.J.	48	50	R.M.B.	31	46
A.E.S.	48	37	C.W.I.	45	50
B.J.B.	48	50	D.S.	38	40
J.H.	45	40	C.B.	32	34
H.A.S.	48	38	H.J.H.	51	54
M.B.	32	36	B.Q.	43	40
B.H.	63	49	J.M.B.	54	40
H.P.	63	50	J.F.H.	53	43
H.B.	45	44	N.O.	60	60
H.H.	27	36	W.J.B.	63	56
J.O.	57	66	R.L.H.	54	56
F.B.	57	52	C.E.A.	42	43
M.C.G.	53	55	A.A.	43	38
C.T.N.	48	52	M.J.G.	52	55
W.M.	61	65	R.W.M.	54	48
C.G.	51	48	T.L.	66	58
R.L.M.	54	48	B.C.G.	54	43
A.M.	40	31	L.M.	63	60
J.L.G.	56	48	F.G.	43	45

Constructing the Scatter Diagram

The first step is to choose an appropriate size of class interval for *X* and for *Y* just as if we were setting out to tabulate two separate frequency distributions (see p. 18). These intervals are then laid off on a sheet of cross-sectional paper as in Figure 24, where intervals on the X-axis represent inductive reasoning and those on the Y-axis represent deductive.

The next step is to tabulate the *pairs* of scores. Each pair of scores is represented by a tally placed in the cell formed by the intersection of the X-interval and the Y-interval which contain those scores.

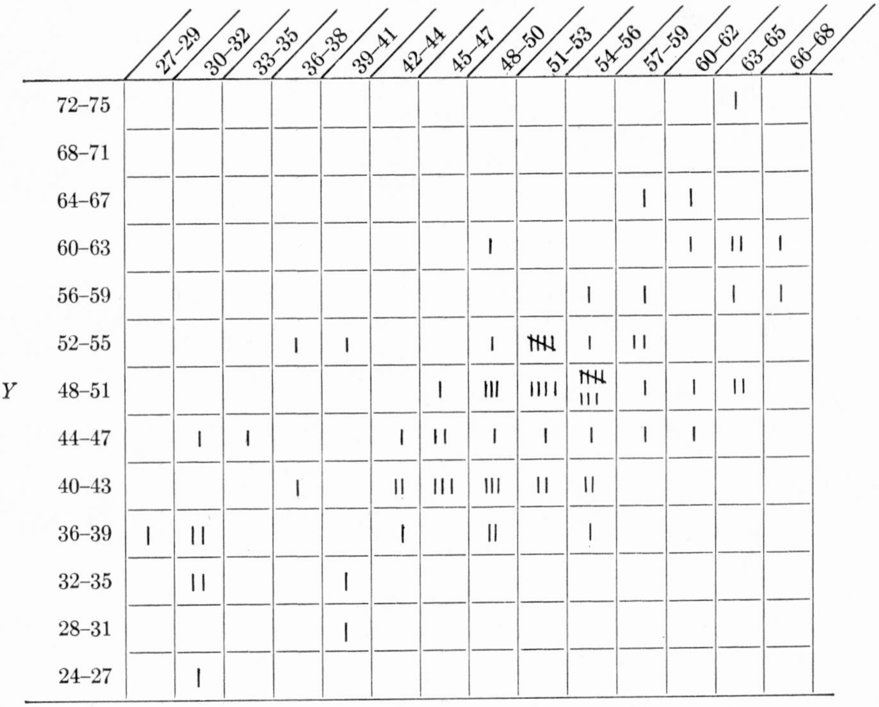

Y	27-29	30-32	33-35	36-38	39-41	42-44	45-47	48-50	51-53	54-56	57-59	60-62	63-65	66-68
72-75													I	
68-71														
64-67										I	I			
60-63							I				I	II	I	
56-59									I	I		I	I	
52-55			I	I			I	THL	I	II				
48-51						I	III	IIII	THL III	I	I	II		
44-47	I	I			I	II	I	I	I	I	I			
40-43				I		II	III	III	II	II				
36-39	I	II			I		II			I				
32-35		II			I									
28-31					I									
24-27		I												

FIGURE 24

SCATTER DIAGRAM FOR SCORES ON TWO TESTS OF REASONING

Computation

Figure 25 illustrates the computation of r from a scatter diagram. Here the data of Figure 24 have been grouped into larger intervals because of limited space. The frequencies in each row (horizontal array) are counted and their sum is entered in the f_y column at the right of the scatter diagram. This gives us the frequency distribution on Y. Similarly, by counting the tallies in each column (vertical array) the frequency distribution on X is obtained. The frequencies for the X-distribution are entered below the scatter diagram. A convenient class interval is chosen as the arbitrary origin for each distribution and Σfd_i and Σfd^2_i are computed for each by the method we used earlier in finding a standard deviation.

	27-35	36-44	45-53	54-62	63-71	f_y	d_{i_y}	fd_{i_y}	$fd^2_{i_y}$	$\overset{c}{\Sigma}fd_{i_z}$	$d_{i_y}\overset{c}{\Sigma}fd_{i_z}$
72-80					1	1	+4	4	16	2	+8
64-71				2		2	+3	6	18	2	+6
56-63			1	3	5	9	+2	18	36	13	+26
48-55		2	14	13	2	31	+1	31	31	15	+15
40-47	2	4	12	5		23	0	0	0	-3	0
32-39	5	2	2	1		10	-1	-10	10	-11	+11
24-31	1	1				2	-2	-4	8	-3	+6
f_x	8	9	29	24	8						
d_{i_x}	-2	-1	0	+1	+2						
fd_{i_x}	-16	-9	0	24	16						
$fd^2_{i_x}$	32	9	0	24	32						
$\overset{R}{\Sigma}fd_{i_y}$	-7	-2	+14	+24	+16						
$d_{i_x}\overset{R}{\Sigma}fd_{i_y}$	+14	+2	0	+24	+32						

$N = 78$ $\Sigma fd^2_y = 119$ $\Sigma fd_x = 15$ $\Sigma fd^2_x = 97$ $\Sigma fd_y = 45$ $\Sigma fd_x d_y = 72$

$$r = \frac{78(72) - (15)(45)}{\sqrt{78(97) - (15)^2}\ \sqrt{79(119) - (45)^2}} = +.671$$

FIGURE 25

COMPUTATION OF r*

* The number of class intervals has been reduced to simplify the illustration. A more accurate result would be obtained from the tabulation shown in Figure 24.

Our formula (32) calls for one new term, $\Sigma fd_{i_x}d_{i_y}$, the sum of cross-products of deviations on X and Y. Each cell in the scatter diagram is identified by its coordinates, d_{i_x} and d_{i_y}. Thus, each cell has its own cross-product. The sum of cross-products is the summation for all of the pairs of scores in the scatter diagram of the cross-products of the cells in which they are tabulated. This can be obtained by finding $fd_{i_x}d_{i_y}$ for each cell which contains a tally and then summing these values for the entire scatter diagram. Let us illustrate this procedure for several cells from the scatter diagram of Figure 25. Note especially the signs of the cross-products and their relation to the signs of the d_i's upon which they are based.

CELL		f	d_{i_x}	d_{i_y}	$fd_{i_x}d_{i_y}$
X-interval	Y-interval				
63–71	56–63	5	+2	+2	+20
45–53	56–63	1	0	+2	0
54–62	32–39	1	+1	−1	−1
27–35	32–39	5	−2	−1	+10

Much labor can be saved by taking advantage of the fact that all of the cells in a single horizontal array have the same d_{i_y} value. Thus, the cross-products in one array all have this value as a common factor. This permits us to add all of the fd_{i_x} values in a horizontal array $(\overset{c}{\Sigma}fd_{i_x})^*$ and then to multiply that sum by the d_{i_y} value for the array $(d_{i_y}\overset{c}{\Sigma}fd_{i_x})$. This gives the sum of cross-products for that array. For example, the sum of cross-products for the 56–63 horizontal array in Figure 25 could be obtained by working separately with each cell:

$$(1)(0)(+2) + (3)(+1)(+2) + (5)(+2)(+2) = +26$$

By using the common factor (the d_{i_y} for this array), the same result is obtained more easily:

$$(+2)[(0)(+2) + (3)(+1) + (5)(+2)] = +26$$

The two columns in bold-face type at the right of Figure 25 have been computed by this short cut procedure.

The computation should be checked at two points as the work

---

* Here we will use the symbol $\overset{c}{\Sigma}$ to indicate that the summation is across the columns of the scatter diagram. Similarly, $\overset{R}{\Sigma}$ will indicate summation within a vertical column of the values in the various rows of a table.

progresses. (1) After the marginal frequencies have been entered, check to see that $\Sigma_{f_x} = \Sigma_{f_y} = N$. (2) After computing entries in the $\overset{c}{\Sigma} fd_{i_x}$ column, compare the sum of these entries with Σfd_{i_x} obtained directly from the fd_{i_x} entries below the scatter diagram.

A further check can be made by carrying out the short cut calculation of the sum of cross-products on the vertical as well as the horizontal arrays.

These checks do not by any means insure a correct result. Errors often occur in tabulation and these can be discovered only by constructing another scatter diagram and comparing the two.

EXERCISES

1. Using formula (31), compute r between Columns 2 and 3 for the first twenty-five students in data C. Now apply formula (32) to the same data, taking a different point of origin for each variable, and compare the results.

2. Plot scatter diagrams and compute by means of formula (33) such correlations as your instructor might assign for data C. Ten separate combinations of variables are possible!

3. Starting with $b_{y \cdot x}$ and $b_{x \cdot y}$, and using formula (28), show that $r_{xy} = r_{yx}$.

4. Using standard deviation units, draw a separate graph for each pair of regression lines corresponding to the following values of r: 0.00, +0.25, 0.50, +0.75, and +1.00. What can you say concerning the relationship between the size of r and the angle formed by the two regression lines?

5. Compute r from the scatter diagram of Figure 24 and compare the result with the computation accompanying Figure 25 in the text. Now apply Sheppard's correction to the standard deviations obtained from Figure 25 and use the corrected standard deviations and formula (11c) to obtain a corrected denominator for formula (33). What can you conclude concerning the number of class intervals to be used in a scatter diagram?

6. Using Variables 1 and 2, compute from data C five separate coefficients of correlation, each obtained from a successive set of twenty paired scores. (Use formula (31) or (32) for this. If (32) is used, note that the arbitrary origins chosen for X and Y do not need to be the same for the five computations.) Explain why you would not expect to find the same value for r in each computation.

DATA *C*: SCORES MADE BY 115 COLLEGE FRESHMEN ON A BATTERY OF
ENTRANCE EXAMINATIONS

1. Quantitative score, ACE Psychological Examination for College Freshmen
2. Linguistic score, ACE Psychological Examination for College Freshmen
3. Reading comprehension test
4. Ohio State University Psychological Test
5. General Mathematics Test

Student	1	2	3	4	5
A.A.	50	90	102	137	47
F.A.	64	90	79	102	45
M.B.	35	69	90	115	44
R.B.	45	85	94	141	41
T.B.	46	72	64	100	28
V.B.	63	105	107	142	44
W.B.	62	108	123	131	41
A.C.	41	67	53	115	18
C.C.	47	69	66	116	21
E.C.	52	92	119	125	49
F.C.	62	80	67	122	43
I.C.	46	70	60	122	21
J.C.	61	83	72	127	54
L.C.	28	77	82	136	16
P.C.	41	82	77	133	24
S.C.	46	80	74	189	37
J.D.	48	68	42	85	22
K.D.	59	88	62	128	33
N.D.	36	83	56	116	27
R.D.	33	67	56	75	10
J.E.	53	61	62	197	18
A.F.	43	90	76	134	28
C.F.	33	64	68	144	27
M.F.	52	99	114	105	23
B.G.	64	93	105	138	48
C.G.	46	92	95	112	17
F.G.	42	73	51	90	27
G.G.	63	98	113	120	34
H.G.	45	93	89	131	16
L.G.	44	82	72	93	41
N.G.	44	63	61	122	19
O.G.	46	79	107	106	35
T.G.	66	80	70	118	49
B.H.	42	88	87	135	51
C.H.	57	84	90	113	34
D.H.	41	66	73	109	28
E.H.	50	89	87	124	33
E.H.	73	90	98	134	53
J.H.	65	117	138	136	49
K.H.	42	78	61	92	23
M.H.	48	90	72	128	31
O.H.	52	71	66	97	22
R.H.	50	87	85	110	43
S.H.	65	99	39	116	22
T.H.	46	84	103	132	24
F.I.	41	71	66	119	25
L.I.	49	89	90	124	43
A.J.	50	96	95	126	29
E.J.	61	75	59	111	49
K.J.	49	84	53	124	30
D.K.	50	94	69	115	36
E.K.	39	55	47	90	17

Student	1	2	3	4	5
J.K.	51	86	88	135	47
L.K.	57	76	76	117	33
W.K.	59	96	112	130	45
A.L.	58	88	108	126	31
B.L.	45	93	110	124	28
J.L.	33	75	69	106	21
J.L.	30	75	65	135	10
N.L.	60	65	33	87	44
O.L.	35	64	51	107	29
R.L.	43	74	35	84	32
T.L.	42	71	89	121	34
A.M.	42	91	106	121	25
C.M.	41	77	63	120	36
D.M.	50	86	94	139	25
F.M.	31	74	61	87	20
H.M.	50	98	114	128	39
H.M.	38	64	39	94	23
K.M.	49	94	108	132	49
L.M.	64	87	91	101	53
M.M.	53	75	62	110	46
P.M.	51	71	72	114	49
T.M.	35	82	74	87	18
W.M.	43	74	91	99	50
W.M.	50	67	75	104	44
J.N.	43	58	48	103	29
S.N.	50	67	66	126	30
D.O.	42	78	67	82	16
V.O.	52	57	44	103	39
W.O.	40	67	67	115	31
B.P.	41	91	104	107	14
E.P.	57	72	37	102	35
R.P.	33	85	84	123	19
A.R.	61	93	74	129	50
D.R.	49	81	76	136	37
G.R.	44	72	61	118	29
H.R.	36	75	89	112	7
L.R.	47	59	44	69	44
N.R.	55	64	38	88	11
R.R.	37	79	83	121	42
A.S.	51	86	92	105	34
B.S.	35	102	90	94	31
D.S.	45	64	44	86	11
D.S.	49	66	46	97	17
F.S.	41	93	121	137	22
G.S.	48	92	70	135	39
G.S.	43	59	59	86	24
H.S.	41	91	77	111	37
I.S.	48	89	90	130	32
J.S.	46	88	89	118	33
K.S.	62	88	64	135	51
L.S.	74	98	91	128	44
M.S.	56	70	49	122	45
P.S.	41	94	121	117	30
R.S.	50	92	74	147	41
R.S.	33	80	80	107	27
W.S.	44	77	49	95	17
G.T.	40	77	50	77	31
M.T.	43	83	82	116	41
T.T.	72	102	98	130	51
R.U.	38	73	40	107	31
C.W.	29	83	69	95	34
T.W.	47	74	47	96	27
C.Y.	35	80	58	101	35

INTERPRETATION OF r

The coefficient of correlation possesses many mathematical properties. Consequently, it may be interpreted in a variety of ways. Three of these interpretations are especially useful in psychology: (1) r defines the best fit straight line, (2) r measures the accuracy of prediction from this line, and (3) r^2 is the proportion of variance in Y which can be predicted from a knowledge of X.

Slope of the Regression Line

We have seen that the coefficient of correlation, together with S_x and S_y defines the slope of the best fit straight line for the relationship of Y to X or of X to Y. Of course, this interpretation of r, as well as any other, assumes that the relationship can be adequately described by a straight line. The slope of the line is given by r when measurements of X and Y are both expressed as z-scores. When X and Y are in raw score units, the regression of Y' on X is defined by $b_{y \cdot x}$ and that of X' on Y by $b_{x \cdot y}$.

Accuracy of Prediction

A second interpretation, and one which is extremely useful in evaluating the degree of relationship denoted by various numerical values of r, is based on the extent to which the observed pairs of scores deviate from the regression line. This is measured by the standard error of estimate (pp. 90–91)—which, it will be recalled, is the standard deviation of the observed scores about the regression line and is denoted by $S_{y \cdot x}$.

When $r = \pm 1.00$, $S_{yx} = 0$ because with perfect correlation every observed pair of scores falls exactly on the regression line and there are no discrepancies. When $r = 0$, $S_{y \cdot x} = S_y$ because the slope of the regression line is zero and deviations from it are identical with deviations from $\overline{Y}$. With intermediate values of r, $S_{y \cdot x}$ varies between zero and S_y, depending upon the magnitude of r.

The relationship of $S_{y \cdot x}$ to r can be demonstrated through algebraic manipulation of formula (17).

$$S_{y \cdot x} = \sqrt{\frac{\Sigma(y - y')^2}{N}} \tag{17}$$

$$S^2_{y \cdot x} = \frac{1}{N} \Sigma(y - y')^2$$

$$\text{but} \quad y' = r\left(\frac{S_y}{S_x}\right)x$$

Substituting this expression, we have

$$S^2_{y \cdot x} = \frac{1}{N} \Sigma (y - r \left(\frac{S_y}{S_x}\right) x)^2$$

$$= \frac{1}{N} \Sigma (y^2 - 2r \left(\frac{S_y}{S_x}\right) xy + r^2 \left(\frac{S^2_y}{S^2_x}\right) x^2)$$

$$= \frac{\Sigma y^2}{N} - 2r \left(\frac{S_y}{S_x}\right) \frac{\Sigma xy}{N} + r^2 \left(\frac{S^2_y}{S^2_x}\right) \frac{\Sigma x^2}{N}$$

But

$$r_{xy} = \frac{\Sigma xy}{N S_x S_y}, \quad \text{and} \quad \frac{\Sigma xy}{N} = r_{xy} S_x S_y$$

Moreover

$$\frac{\Sigma y^2}{N} = S^2_y, \quad \text{and} \quad \frac{\Sigma x^2}{N} = S^2_x$$

By substitution we now have

$$S^2_{y \cdot x} = S^2_y - 2r \left(\frac{S_y}{S_x}\right) r S_x S_y + r^2 \left(\frac{S^2_y}{S^2_x}\right) S^2_x$$

$$= S^2_y - 2r^2 S^2_y + r^2 S^2_y$$

$$= S^2_y - r^2 S^2_y$$

This expression can be factored to give

$$S^2_{y \cdot x} = S^2_y (1 - r^2)$$

This leads to a convenient formula for the standard error of estimate.

$$S_{y \cdot x} = S_y \sqrt{1 - r^2} \tag{34}$$

The radical term in formula (34) is known as the *coefficient of alienation*, which is denoted by k.

$$S_{y \cdot x} = k S_y, \quad \text{where} \tag{34a}$$
$$k = \sqrt{1 - r^2} \tag{35}$$

Whereas r is a measure of *correlation*, k measures *lack of correlation*.

By squaring both sides of (35) and transposing r^2 to the left, we find that

$$k^2 + r^2 = 1$$

The relationship between *correlation* and *alienation* can be clearly seen by considering the values which k must assume for different values of r. The following values for k and r are computed by substituting various values of r in formula (35). The relationship between r and k is shown graphically in Figure 26.

When r is	*k is*
1.00	0.0000
.90	.4359
.80	.6000
.70	.7141
.60	.8000
.50	.8660
.40	.9165
.30	.9539
.20	.9798
.10	.9950
0.00	1.0000

This graph shows that the strength of the relationship between X and Y is not directly proportional to the size of r. The coefficient of correlation is not a measurement on a scale of equal units. It cannot be interpreted directly as a percent of correlation. We cannot say, for instance, that an r of .50 means that there is one-half of a perfect correlation for when $r = .50$, k, which measures

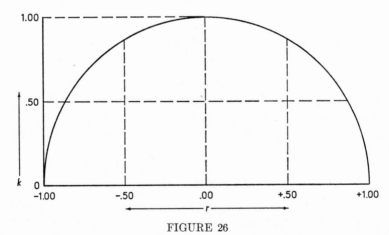

FIGURE 26

RELATION BETWEEN CORRELATION (r) AND ALIENATION (k)

lack of correlation, is .866. Similarly, it is incorrect to say that an r of .50 signifies twice as much correlation as an r of .25 since the k's corresponding to these values of r are .866 and .9682, respectively.

The interpretation of r is often based on the percent by which $S_{y \cdot x}$ is smaller than S_y for various values of r. Since $S_{y \cdot x} = k S_y$ this percent is given by

$$E = 100(1 - k) , \quad \text{where } E \text{ denotes the } \textit{index of forecasting efficiency} \quad (36)$$

Let us illustrate this interpretation of r by a particular example. The entering freshmen of a small liberal arts college were given a test of college aptitude, X. At the end of one semester, grade point indexes, Y, were computed for these same students. The following statistics were then obtained.

$$\bar{X} = 117.0 \qquad\qquad \bar{Y} = 163.4$$
$$S_x = 17.5 \qquad\qquad S_y = 28.6$$
$$N = 150$$
$$r_{xy} = .35$$

Suppose now that we are asked to estimate the grade point index of John Doe and that we know only that John is a member of this freshman class. Our best guess is that his grade point index is 163.4, since the mean is the "best fit" point on the Y-scale for this distribution. Of course, it is unlikely that his index is *exactly* 163.4; it may even be that none of the freshmen obtained an index of precisely this value. Nevertheless, our guess is the best possible because if we made a number of similar guesses for various freshmen our average error would be zero, since deviations about the mean of any distribution sum to zero.

Ordinarily we would not attempt to guess a precise numerical point on the Y-scale. Instead, we would attempt to "bracket" John Doe by specifying two numerical values between which his index is likely to be found. However, our guess runs a greater risk of error if these values are too close together. A convenient range for "bracketing" John's index is provided by the standard deviation of the distribution of indexes. Since about two-thirds of the usual distribution of scores lie within the range of $\bar{Y} \pm S_y$, we will expect to be right two-thirds of the time if we guess for each freshman that his index is somewhere between 134.8 and 192.0. Thus, our prediction of John's index can be expressed as an inequality:

$(\bar{Y} - S_y) < \bar{Y}' < (Y + S_y)$. In similar statements for all members of the class we would expect to be correct in two-thirds of our predictions.

Knowledge of the correlation between X and Y improves the estimate of Y in two respects: (1) Different values of Y' are predicted for different values of X. (2) The range of the bracket within which there are two chances in three of being right is narrower than it is if we do not know the correlation.

Knowing that John Doe had scored 137 on the aptitude test, we could use the regression line of Y' on X to improve our estimate of his grade point index. From formula (21), (24), or (26) we would simply compute the best fit Y' corresponding to his X-score.

$$z'_y = rz_x \quad z_x = \frac{137 - 117}{17.5} = +1.14$$
$$z'_y = (.35)(1.14) = +.399 \tag{21}$$
$$Y' = 163.4 + (.399)(28.6) = \underline{174.8}$$

$$y' = r\left(\frac{S_y}{S_x}\right)x \quad x = 137 - 117 = +20$$
$$y' = (.35)\frac{28.6}{17.5}(+20) = +11.4 \tag{24}$$
$$Y' = 163.4 + 11.4 = \underline{174.8}$$

$$Y' = r\left(\frac{S_y}{S_x}\right)X + \left(\bar{Y} - r\left(\frac{S_y}{S_x}\right)\bar{X}\right)$$
$$Y' = (.35)\frac{28.6}{17.5}(137) + 163.4 - (.35)\frac{28.6}{17.5}(117) = \underline{174.8} \tag{26}$$

Thus, if John's aptitude score was 137, we estimate his grade point index to be 174.8.

The error in this estimate is, of course, the difference between the predicted Y' and the grade point index which he actually earned. Suppose now that we were to make similar predictions for each of the 150 freshmen in the group. The overall extent of error in these predictions could be measured by $S_{y \cdot x}$, which is the standard deviation of observed values around the regression line. As in the frequency distribution, about two-thirds of the discrepancies between predicted and observed values of Y would not be greater than $S_{y \cdot x}$. Thus, the predicted grade point index is bracketed between $Y' - S_{y \cdot x}$

and $Y' + S_{y \cdot x}$. The prediction will be correct about two times in three if in every case we predict Y as

$$(Y' - S_{y \cdot x}) < Y < (Y' + S_{y \cdot x})$$

$S_{y \cdot x}$ is an overall measure of dispersion about the regression line which can be used to measure the range of error in a single prediction. To do this, however, we must assume dispersion about the regression line to be essentially the same for all values of Y'. This characteristic of equal dispersion of observed scores within the columns of the scatter diagram is known as *homoscedasticity*.

Ordinarily, before the assumption of homoscedasticity can be made, it is necessary to inspect the pattern of tallies in the scatter diagram. If there appears to be a systematic departure from homoscedasticity, a separate standard error of estimate can be computed for each column of the scatter diagram.

Returning now to our hypothetical freshman, John Doe, we can evaluate the accuracy of the estimated grade point index of 174.8. The standard error of estimate is given by formula (34).

$$S_{y \cdot x} = S_y \sqrt{1 - r^2} = 28.6 \sqrt{1 - (.35)^2} = 26.8$$

Assuming homoscedasticity, we can now state that the chances are two out of three that John's grade point index is between 148.0 and 201.6, a range of 53.6. Without knowing his aptitude test score we specified chances of two out of three that his index was between 134.8 and 192.0, a range of 57.2. Thus, where $r = .35$, predictions based on knowledge of X have a range of error 93.7 percent as great as predictions made without such knowledge. In other words, the r of .35 enables us to reduce the error of prediction by 6.3 percent. This illustrates the significance of the fact that when $r = .35$, $k = .937$, and $E = 6.3$ percent.

Before reaching this point in the discussion you may well have wondered why we are concerned with using r to predict Y' from X when the paired values of Y and X must already be known before r can be computed. There are two reasons. In the first place r defines the *best fit* regression line, an overall descriptive device which summarizes the group characteristics of the data and ignores the irregular chance variations found in particular pairs of observations. Secondly, on the assumption that natural events occur in a uniform and dependable fashion, it is possible to generalize from the coefficient of correlation computed from a set of paired observations to similar situations where only one of the variables has been measured. For example, if we can assume that next year's freshmen are similar to the present crop, this observed correlation between aptitude test and grades can be used as an aid in selecting and advising new students.

When we generalize in this way from the data of a sample to what is expected to occur in other samples, the standard error of estimate is correctly given by a slightly different formula. To distinguish this statistic from $S_{y \cdot x}$, we shall denote it by $s_{y \cdot x}$.

$$s_{y \cdot x} = \sqrt{\frac{\Sigma(y - y')^2}{N - 2}}$$

Comparing this with formula (17)

$$S_{y \cdot x} = \sqrt{\frac{\Sigma(y - y')^2}{N}}$$

we see that the following relationship holds.

$$s^2_{y \cdot x} = \frac{N}{N - 2} \cdot S^2_{y \cdot x}$$

Note that unless N is quite small, the factor $N/(N - 2)$ is so near unity that there is little difference between $s_{y \cdot x}$ and $S_{y \cdot x}$. The reason for introducing this refinement of the standard error of estimate will become clear in Chapters XIII and XIV, where we will consider the analysis of variance.

Correlation and Variance

A third way of interpreting r has to do with the proportion of the total variation in Y (measured by S^2_y) which can be predicted from a knowledge of variations in X. If $r = 0.00$, knowledge of X does not permit prediction of Y from a linear regression equation. When $r = \pm 1.00$, knowledge of X provides complete information about Y. For intermediate values of r, the amount of information about variations in Y which can be gained from knowing X is measured by r^2. It can be shown that the proportion of total variance in Y which can be predicted from X is equal to r^2.

We can see how this comes about by considering further the relationship between r and k.

From (34a) we find that

$$k = \frac{S_{y \cdot x}}{S_y}$$

$$k^2 = \frac{S^2_{y \cdot x}}{S^2_y}$$

In other words, k^2 is the ratio of two variances: $S^2_{y \cdot x}$, the variance of observed values of Y about the regression line, and S^2_y, the variance of observed values of Y about the mean of the Y-distribution. Now the denominator of this fraction, S^2_y, has nothing to do with the correlation of Y with any other variable. Only Y-scores enter into its computation. The numerator, however, is different for different values of r_{xy} since it is the variance of Y-scores about the regression line. Since $S^2_{y \cdot x} = S^2_y(1 - r^2)$, $S^2_{y \cdot x} = S^2_y$ when $r = 0.00$, and $S^2_{y \cdot x} = 0.00$ when $r = \pm 1.00$.

Thus, the ratio of these two variances is a function of the magnitude of the correlation between X and Y.

$$k^2 = \frac{S^2_{y \cdot x}}{S^2_y} = (1 - r^2)$$

In a similar manner r^2 can be shown to be a ratio of two variances: $S^2_{y'}$, the variance of predicted values of Y' about the mean of the Y-distribution, and $S^2_{y'}$. In order to demonstrate this, we shall first express the deviation of any observed Y from $\bar{Y}$ as the sum of its deviation from the regression line and the deviation of the regression line at this point from $\bar{Y}$. In raw scores

$$(Y - \bar{Y}) = (Y - Y') + (Y' - \bar{Y})$$

or, in deviation form

$$y = (y - y') + y'$$

Reference to Figure 27 (p. 118) will make this equation more meaningful.

A measure of variance can be obtained from each of these three deviations.

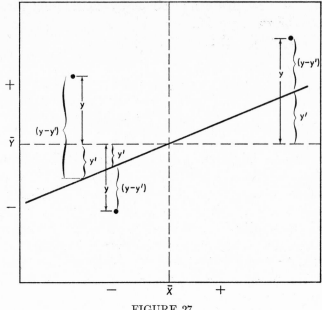

FIGURE 27

$$S^2{}_y = \frac{\Sigma y^2}{N}$$ a measure of deviations of observed scores from $\bar{Y}$

$$S^2{}_{y.x} = \frac{\Sigma(y - y')^2}{N}$$ a measure of discrepancies between predicted and observed scores

$$S^2{}_{y'} = \frac{\Sigma y'^2}{N}$$ a measure of deviations of predicted scores from $\bar{Y}$

Let us examine $S^2{}_{y'}$ in relation to the coefficient of correlation.

$$S^2{}_{y'} = \frac{\Sigma y'^2}{N}$$

But, since

$$y' = r\left(\frac{S_y}{S_x}\right)x\,,$$

$$S^2{}_{y'} = \frac{\sum\left[r\left(\frac{S_y}{S_x}\right)x\right]^2}{N}$$

$$= \frac{r^2\left(\frac{S^2{}_y}{S^2{}_x}\right)\Sigma x^2}{N}$$

$$= r^2 \left(\frac{S^2_y}{S^2_x} \right) \frac{\Sigma x^2}{N}$$

$$S^2_{y'} = r^2 S^2_y$$

It follows then that

$$r^2 = \frac{S^2_{y'}}{S^2_y}$$

Thus, r^2 is the ratio of the variance of predicted values of Y' to the variance of observed values of Y.

We have seen that

$$r^2 + k^2 = 1.00$$

Substituting variance ratios, we have

$$\frac{S^2_{y'}}{S^2_y} + \frac{S^2_{y \cdot x}}{S^2_y} = 1.00$$

It follows from this that

$$S^2_y = S^2_{y'} + S^2_{y \cdot x} \tag{37}$$

This equation means that the variance of observed values of Y is made up of two portions. One portion, represented by $S^2_{y'}$, is predictable from knowledge of X. The other, represented by $S^2_{y \cdot x}$, is unrelated to variations in X and is thus unpredictable.

Since the variance ratios corresponding to r^2 and k^2 add up to unity, they are proportions. The proportion of total variance in Y which is predictable from X is measured by r^2. The proportion unpredictable from X is measured by k^2.

The relationship of predictable variation in Y to the magnitude of r_{xy} is illustrated graphically in Figure 28. By following the broken line which extends from a given X to the regression line and then moving horizontally to the Y-scale you can find the predicted Y' for that X-score. The variation among predicted values of Y' is indicated by the width of the shaded histogram. This histogram can be compared with the distribution of observed Y to illustrate how predictable variation in Y' is related to the slope of the regression line.

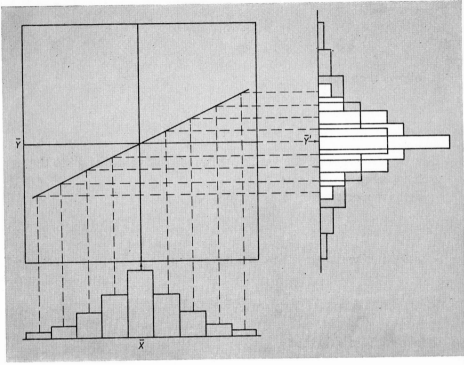

FIGURE 28
PREDICTABLE VARIANCE FOR $r = +.50*$

*To simplify the diagram identical distributions have been assumed for X and Y. The height of the histogram representing Y should not be taken to represent frequency because this histogram, although narrower in range, has been set equal in area to the Y histogram.

Regression and Correlation

Regression and correlation, although related ideas, are two different statistical concepts. The idea of regression is simpler, and more general, than that of correlation. Regression analysis deals with situations in which one variable is considered to be *independent* and the other *dependent*. The independent variable is manipulated by an experimenter or is carefully measured and selected by him to represent certain values along the scale of measurement. For example, an experimenter may subject various groups of rats to certain specified intervals of food deprivation so that he can observe a sample of measurements of general activity for each of these intervals. His interest is in discovering the regression function of general activity on food deprivation. At each point on the food deprivation scale observations of general activity form a frequency distribution over a range of activity characteristic of that degree of food deprivation. A measure, such as the mean, descriptive of these distributions of activity is then said to be a function of food deprivation. If this measure varies in a regular fashion with changes in the independent variable, that fact can be represented graphically by a regression line, and described by a particular regression equation. At no time does the experimenter attempt to describe hunger as dependent on general activity. In a similar manner, after administering a certain test to groups of children selected to represent various ages, an experimenter can describe by a graph or an equation the regression of "reading readiness" on age.

If there were any rational basis for doing so, it would be logically possible to reverse the direction of the inquiry and study the regression of age on reading readiness scores, but this would require a different approach. Groups of children would be selected according to points on a scale of reading readiness and a frequency distribution of age scores would be constructed for each group. In regression analysis this would lead to a description of age as a function of reading readiness. The experimental manipulation of one of the variables, or the selection of particular values of that variable, defines it as the *independent* variable in a regression analysis.

In correlational analysis there is no such distinction between the independent and the dependent variable. Neither variable is intentionally manipulated or selected by the experimenter to represent a certain set of points on the scale of measurement. Instances of paired observations of the two variables are recorded and used in computing the coefficient of correlation. In gathering the data no restrictions are imposed on either variable through experimental manipulation or through the selection of specified values. Since either variable can be considered to be independent, two regression lines are appropriate as descriptions of the data. If both regressions are linear, r is a measure of the degree of correlation (co-relation) between the two variables. Correlation refers to a *mutual relation* in which it is mathematically meaningful to express Y as a function of X, or X as a function of Y.

The coefficient of correlation is a *pure number*, a number which is not affected by changing the unit of measurement. The regression coefficients, $b_{y \cdot x}$ and $b_{x \cdot y}$, are *concrete* numbers because they will assume different values depending on the units of measurement. The relationship between r and the two regression coefficients is

$$r = \sqrt{b_{y \cdot x} \cdot b_{x \cdot y}}$$

This can be verified by referring to formulas (22) and (23).

Correlation and Causation

It is often useful and informative to interpret r^2 as the proportion of variance in Y which can be predicted from our knowledge of variations in X. In this way we can evaluate the relative importance of different factors which are thought to cause variations in Y. We must remember, however, that correlation alone, without other evidence, is no proof of causal relationship. For example, suppose we computed the correlation between weight and scores on a vocabulary test for a group of children whose ages range from six to fifteen years. The correlation would be high, but no one would be willing to assert that this finding establishes a causal relationship between weight and vocabulary. As another example, consider the correlation between the number of automobiles per capita and the consumption of cigarettes per capita in the U.S. The correlation over the period 1900 to 1962 is high, but are these two measures causally related? Obviously, a high correlation does not in itself constitute acceptable evidence of causal relationship. The assertion of a direct causal relationship is immediately rejected here because it does not appear reasonable.

Correlation between X and Y may have different meaning, depending upon the circumstances.

1. Variation in X may be the cause of variation in Y.
2. Variation in Y may be the cause of variation in X.
3. Variation in both X and Y may be caused by some other variable or variables.
4. Variation in X and Y may be causally related, but the *observed* correlation between them may be affected by the presence of some other variable or variables which in turn are causally related to X, or to Y, or to both.

The interpretation of data depends ultimately upon logical analysis and "common sense." Statistical method provides a useful and necessary tool for quantitative inductive inference, but uncritical use of statistics may, and often does, lead to preposterous conclusions.

Correlation and Prediction

The logical analysis of causal relationships is not necessary for prediction. Suppose, for instance, that the correlation between longevity and the diameter of the right big toe at the first joint were known to be $r = -.60$. Even though the causal connection between these variables remained undiscovered, measurements of toe diameter could be extremely useful to life insurance companies. The regression equation could be used to find life expectancy, and thereby the appropriate premium, for an applicant for insurance. A man's life expectancy could be predicted with 20 percent greater accuracy (pp. 112–13) than if it were simply assumed to be the mean life expectancy.

SUMMARY OF INTERPRETATIONS OF *r*

Three important meanings can be attached to the coefficient of correlation. The first two of these have to do with practical problems of prediction. The third is concerned with analyzing sources of variation in the dependent variable.

1. *Slope of the regression line.* r defines (in standard units) the rate at which one variable changes with changes in another. This assumes that the relationship between the two variables can be adequately described by a linear regression line.

2. *Accuracy of prediction.* r measures the accuracy of prediction from the regression line. The coefficient of alienation, k, indicates magnitude of the standard error of estimate in relation to the standard deviation of the dependent variable. This interpretation requires the assumption of linearity and homoscedasticity about the regression line.

3. *Predictable variance.* r^2 is the proportion of total variance in the dependent variable which is predictable from knowledge of the independent variable. This interpretation assumes linearity for the regression of the dependent variable. Here again, it must be remembered that predictability of one variable from knowledge of another should not be considered evidence of a direct causal connection between them.

There are a number of other ways in which r can be interpreted, but the three meanings described in this chapter are the most useful interpretations for the beginning student of statistics. In Chapter IX we will return to the coefficient of correlation in discussing the reliability of various statistics. Chapter XIV describes a different approach to the meaning of r and develops a statistical test of the assumption of linearity.

SUGGESTED READINGS

1. McNemar, Q. *Psychological Statistics,* chaps. viii, ix, and x. 3d ed. New York: John Wiley & Sons, 1962.
2. Walker, H. M. *Elementary Statistical Methods,* chaps. xii, xiii, and xiv. New York: Henry Holt and Co., 1943.

EXERCISES

1. If the standard deviation of scores on an arithmetic test is 25, and the correlation of this test with IQ is $r = .60$, what would you expect the standard deviation to be for a large group of pupils all of whom have the same IQ? Explain.

2. Given the following: $\bar{X} = 50$, $S_x = 5$; $\bar{Y} = 60$, $S_y = 10$; $r_{xy} = +.50$ —predict the score on Y of a person whose score on X is 55 in such a manner that your prediction has approximately two chances in three of being correct.

3. Given the same information (Problem 2), what Y-score would you predict if X were 50? What value of Y would you predict from this X if $r = 1.00$; if $r = -.33$; if $r = 0.00$? Explain.

4. If the predictions called for in the preceding problem were stated not as points on the Y-scale, but as *ranges* within which Y is expected to fall, how would they differ for the different values of r?

5. If $r = .63$, and $b_{y \cdot x} = 1.26$, what can you say about S_x and S_y?

6. If $r = -.50$, what value of z_y would you predict, knowing that $z_x = +1.5$?

7. The correlation between the score on an arithmetic test and the number of words correct on a spelling test was found to be $r = +.48$. What would you expect to be the approximate value of r if you computed for the same test papers the correlation between arithmetic scores and the number of words misspelled? Explain.

8. Suppose a person obtains a score on text X which is one standard deviation above the mean. What standard score would you predict for him on test Y if r_{xy} is known to be $-.60$?

9. After computing a regression equation of the form

$$y' = r\left(\frac{S_y}{S_x}\right) x$$

a student made several predictions of y'. Later, when asked to predict x' for several instances of y, he used the same equation. Criticize this procedure and indicate what he should have done in predicting x'.

10. Write three forms of the regression equation for predicting Y from X for the following data: $\bar{X} = 34.7$, $S_x = 4.3$, $\bar{Y} = 85.2$, $S_y = 15.1$; $r_{xy} = +.604$. Compute Y' in these three ways for each of the following X's: 28, 31, 36, 50.

11. Construct diagrams similar to Figure 28 for (a) $r = -.50$, (b) $r = +.75$, and (c) $r = -1.00$. What can you say about the sign of r from a comparison of (a) with Figure 28?

CHAPTER VIII

Probability and the Normal Distribution

The scientist is not satisfied with merely describing what he has observed. His work becomes meaningful only when he is able to make generalizations about past experience which permit prediction and control of future events. Knowledge of what has happened in the past, even though highly interesting, is of little practical value if it does not lead to prediction of the future. All of us predict future events in our own everyday lives whenever we behave as if we expect certain events to happen. We decide between possible courses of action because they seem likely to have different consequences, but as we learn through experience we continually modify and supplement the inductive generalizations which serve to guide our conduct.

Generalized scientific rules about the world in which we live are also continually changing. Scientific laws gradually supplant rules based on ignorance or superstition, and science itself changes from day to day, discarding old, worn-out laws and replacing them with more dependable generalizations. It is here that statistical inference and the theory of probability prove invaluable as a yardstick for deciding which laws to discard. The all-important test of any generalization is the risk of error one runs in using it to predict future events. Once this risk is known, we can select from a number of possible generalizations those which are most accurate, and discard those which do not lead to dependable predictions.

Statistical techniques useful in calculating the risk of incorrect predictions are based on the theory of probability. Because of this we must now consider some basic ideas of the mathematics of probability before proceeding to a discussion of the methods of statistical inference. It will be necessary to discuss probability in quantitative terms rather than on the level of everyday conversation, in which we often make loose statements such as, "It will probably rain tomorrow," or "There is a good chance that John will make the first team."

MATHEMATICAL PROBABILITY

If an event can occur in a known number of ways and can fail to occur in a known number of ways, and if all of the possible ways of occurring and of failing to occur are equally likely, the mathematical probability of the event can be specified.

If we let $m =$ the number of ways the event can occur and $n =$ the number of ways in which it can fail to occur, then the probability of its occurrence is

$$P = \frac{m}{m + n} \qquad (38)$$

The probability of its failure to occur is

$$Q = \frac{n}{m + n} \qquad (38a)$$

The numerical value of P, or of Q, is never greater than 1.00. But, since P and Q are *proportions*, they must always add to the total probability of unity.

$$P + Q = \left(\frac{m}{m + n}\right) + \left(\frac{n}{m + n}\right) = \frac{m + n}{m + n} = 1.00$$

This classical definition of probability has been severely criticized, mainly because it assumes the possible events to be "equally likely," which is the same as saying that they are "equally probable." Thus, probability is defined in terms of itself. Some critics have pointed out the difficulty of ever finding a real situation of the sort implied in the definition. For instance, how could anyone create a perfect coin and toss it under ideal circumstances so that heads and tails would be equally likely? These difficulties can be avoided if we recognize the theory of probability as an abstract mathematical model based on a set of arbitrary definitions and rules. Such models can be legitimately used as long as they are not contradicted by the results of real-life observations.

Suppose an ideal coin is tossed and that the two faces are equally likely to turn up. (We will assume that this coin cannot stand on edge.) The probability of tossing "heads" is

$$P = \frac{m}{m + n} = \frac{1}{1 + 1} = .5$$

As another example, suppose one card is drawn from a well shuffled bridge deck. The probability of drawing a spade is

$$P = \frac{m}{m + n} = \frac{13}{13 + (13 + 13 + 13)} = .25$$

The probability of not drawing a spade is

$$Q = \frac{n}{m + n} = \frac{13 + 13 + 13}{13 + (13 + 13 + 13)} = .75$$

Let us now consider a more complex problem. Imagine a large bowl which contains 200 marbles. Sixty of these are white, 50 blue, 55 green, and 35 red. If we thoroughly mix the marbles and then reach into the bowl and blindly draw one, the probabilities of drawing the various colors are

$$P(\text{white}) = \frac{60}{200} = .30$$

$$P(\text{blue}) = \frac{50}{200} = .25$$

$$P(\text{green}) = \frac{55}{200} = .275$$

$$P(\text{red}) = \frac{35}{200} = .175$$

The probability of drawing *either* white *or* green is given by

$$P(\text{white or green}) = \frac{m}{m + n} = \frac{60 + 55}{(60 + 55) + (50 + 35)} = .575$$

This figure is equal to the sum of the separate probabilities for white and green. This illustrates the *addition theorem* of probability: *The probability that any one of several mutually exclusive events will occur is the sum of their separate probabilities.*

Now suppose that we draw one marble, return it to the bowl and, after a thorough mixing, draw another. What is the probability that the first marble will be green and the second white? Again, the answer can be obtained by the use of

$$P = \frac{m}{m + n}$$

We must know (1) the total number of ways in which any combination of two marbles can be drawn and (2) the total number of ways in which the specified event can occur, namely: that the first marble is green and the second white.

Since there are 200 marbles in the bowl, there are 200 ways in which the first one can be drawn. After the first has been drawn and returned to the bowl, there are 200 ways of drawing the second. However, *any one* of these 200 possible second draws could follow *any one* of the possible first draws. Thus, there are 200×200, or 40,000 ways of drawing two marbles. This figure is equal to $m + n$ in our formula, since it includes all possible outcomes; possible failures to occur, as well as possible occurrences, of the specified event.

The first draw could be green in 55 ways, since there are 55 green marbles. Similarly, there are 60 ways in which the second draw could be white. Since any one of the 55 could occur with any one of the 60 to produce the specified event, there are 55×60, or 3300 ways of drawing green and white in that order.

The probability of green followed by white is thus

$$P(\text{green and white}) = \frac{m}{m + n} = \frac{3300}{40000} = .0825$$

This same result could have been obtained by multiplying together the separate probabilities for green and white in a single trial.

$$P = \frac{55}{200} \times \frac{60}{200} = \frac{3300}{40000} = .0825$$

This illustrates the *multiplication theorem* of probability: *The probability that a combination of independent events will occur is the product of their separate probabilities.*

If we were to predict the color of the marble for any single trial, our best bet would be "white" because in the long run we would expect to be correct 30 percent of the time. The risk of error in predicting any of the other three colors would be greater. Predicting "white or green," we would be right more than half of the time. Of course, if we predicted "white, blue, green, or red" we would always be right. Errorless prediction would be possible in this model situation because every possible outcome is known. *In practical applications of statistics we do not know all the possible results and the problem of prediction becomes more difficult.* Fortunately, however, sampling theory furnishes mathematical models which approximate the results of experimental observations even though the universe of possible outcomes is unknown. But before considering sampling theory we must first study some more complex examples of probability.

Let us now consider the number of ways two coins could fall. There are four possibilities.

Possible Ways			Probability of Each Way
Coin No. 1	Coin No. 2		(by Multiplication Theorem)
H..............T		(one head)	$\frac{1}{2} \times \frac{1}{2} = \frac{1}{4}$
H..............H		(two heads)	$\frac{1}{2} \times \frac{1}{2} = \frac{1}{4}$
T..............T		(no heads)	$\frac{1}{2} \times \frac{1}{2} = \frac{1}{4}$
T..............H		(one head)	$\frac{1}{2} \times \frac{1}{2} = \frac{1}{4}$

The probabilities for various numbers of heads are found by counting the different ways in which each could occur.

Specified Number of Heads	Ways Each Specified Number Could Occur	Probability
0................	1................	$\frac{1}{4}$
1................	2................	$\frac{1}{2}$
2................	1................	$\frac{1}{4}$

It is important here to note that all possible *arrangements* of the coins are equally likely to occur. However, the probability is *not* the same for different *numbers* of heads (or tails) to occur. For example, the probability of one head is the sum of the separate probabilities for the two ways in which one head could occur. This, of course, is another example of the *addition theorem*.

The probabilities of the various results from tossing three coins are shown on the next page.

The same results could be obtained by using the addition and the multiplication theorems. The probability of each coin turning heads is $\frac{1}{2}$. From the multiplication theorem the probability of three

Possible Arrangements of Three Coins			Specified Number of Heads	Ways Each Number Could Occur	Probability
Coin No.1	Coin No. 2	Coin No. 3			
H	H	H	0	1	⅛
H	H	T			
H	T	H	1	3	⅜
H	T	T			
T	H	H			
T	H	T	2	3	⅜
T	T	H			
T	T	T	3	1	⅛

coins turning heads is $(\frac{1}{2})^3$, or ⅛. Similarly, the probability is ⅛ for HTT, THT, and TTH. From the addition theorem, the probability that one or another of these three possibilities will occur is $\frac{1}{8} + \frac{1}{8} + \frac{1}{8} = \frac{3}{8}$.

Similar reasoning can be applied to find the probabilities of various outcomes for any number of coins, but in each case it is necessary to list the possible ways in which the specified outcome can occur. This involves a tremendous amount of work if there are more than three or four coins.

Permutations and Combinations

A much simpler way of finding the possible outcome of our coin tossing experiment is to make use of the mathematical formulas for *permutations* and *combinations*. *Permutations* refers to the number of separate orders in which a set of n distinct objects may be arranged. For instance, two objects, A and B, can be arranged in two permutations, AB and BA. For three objects there are six permutations: $ABC, ACB, BAC, BCA, CAB, CBA$. In general, the number of permutations in which n objects can be arranged is equal to the product of all of the successive whole numbers from n to 1, or $n \cdot (n–1) \cdot (n–2) \cdot (n–3)$, and so on. This product is known as *factorial n* and is designated by $n!$

Suppose now that there are ten members of a club from whom we must choose a committee of three and that we want to know how many different ways this selection could be made. Obviously we have ten possible ways of selecting our first name, and having chosen the first committee member, we have nine possible second choices. After the second has been selected, there are eight ways of choosing the third. The total number of permutations of three objects chosen from ten would thus be $10 \times 9 \times 8 = 720$. A convenient formula for the number of permutations of n objects, taken r at a time is

$$_nP_r = \frac{n!}{(n-r)!} \tag{39}$$

If all n objects are included in each ordered arrangement, the number of permutations becomes

$$P_n = \frac{n!}{(n-n)!} = \frac{n!}{0!} = n!$$

Here we must remember that $0! = 1$.

In the present example of selecting three committee members from ten people, the number of permutations would be

$$_{10}P_3 = \frac{10 \cdot 9 \cdot 8 \cdot 7 \cdot 6 \cdot 5 \cdot 4 \cdot 3 \cdot 2 \cdot 1}{7 \cdot 6 \cdot 5 \cdot 4 \cdot 3 \cdot 2 \cdot 1}$$
$$= 10 \cdot 9 \cdot 8 = 720$$

The 720 permutations include all possible sets of three members, each set arranged *in all possible orders*. But in considering the possible membership of the committee we are not interested in the particular order in which the members were selected. Our concern is with the number of different *combinations* of three which could be chosen from ten. *Combinations* refers to the various subsets of r objects which can be selected from a total of n objects if the *arrangement or order is ignored*. Since $_nP_r$ includes all possible sets of r objects in all possible orders, each set is included in the total as many times as there are different orders in which it can be arranged. Thus, to obtain the number of combinations we simply divide the number of permutations by the number of possible orders in which each set can be arranged. The number of combinations of n objects taken r at a time is in this way conveniently computed by

$$\binom{n}{r} = \frac{_nP_r}{P_r} = \frac{\dfrac{n!}{(n-r)!}}{r!} = \frac{n!}{r!(n-r)!} \tag{40}$$

In the present problem the possible memberships of the committee would be

$$\binom{10}{3} = \frac{10 \cdot 9 \cdot 8 \cdot 7 \cdot 6 \cdot 5 \cdot 4 \cdot 3 \cdot 2 \cdot 1}{(3 \cdot 2 \cdot 1)(7 \cdot 6 \cdot 5 \cdot 4 \cdot 3 \cdot 2 \cdot 1)}$$

$$= \frac{10 \cdot 9 \cdot 8}{3 \cdot 2 \cdot 1} = 120$$

EXERCISES

1. How many seating arrangements are possible in a row of six pupils?

2. A class of 24 second graders are to be seated at 12 tables, 2 children at each table. If a new teacher randomly assigns the children to their places, how likely is it that Bill and Jim, who have been "feuding" for several weeks, will sit at the same table?

3. A person claims that candy made from beet sugar does not taste as good as that made from cane sugar. He is allowed to taste six samples of candy which are identical except that two contain beet sugar. He is instructed to select the two made from beet sugar. What is the probability that he will choose correctly by chance even though he cannot really taste the difference?

4. If a date is named at random what is the chance that it will be a Sunday?

5. If two dates are named at random what is the chance that (a) the first will be a Sunday, (b) both will be Sunday, (c) the first will be a Sunday and the other some other day?

6. What is the probability of obtaining a total of 7 spots if we roll a pair of dice? Show how you use the addition and multiplication theorems in finding the answer.

The Binomial Distribution

The statistical methods used in answering many questions of probability are based on *theoretical distributions*. Such distributions are mathematical models which give the percentage of the time that various events are *expected* to occur. Since they are distributions of *expected* events they differ somewhat from the familiar frequency distribution, which describes *observed* events. One of the simplest theoretical distributions, the binomial distribution, can be understood through the *addition* and *multiplication theorems,* and the formula for combinations of *n* objects taken *r* at a time.

To illustrate the binomial distribution let us suppose that ten coins are thoroughly shaken in a cup and dumped onto a table. What is the probability that exactly four coins will turn heads?

In answering this question we will first suppose that each coin is stamped with a different number so that it can be identified. We can now ask, "What is the probability that coins No. 1, No. 4, No. 5, and No. 8 will be heads and the other six tails?" The probability of the combination of these ten independent events is, according to the multiplication theorem, the product of their separate probabilities, or $(\frac{1}{2})^4 (\frac{1}{2})^6 = \frac{1}{1024}$. But this is only one way in which exactly four heads could occur, and to find the chance of exactly four heads occurring in *any of the possible combinations of coins* we must add the separate probabilities. This is most easily accomplished by multiplying $\frac{1}{1024}$ by the number of combinations of ten coins taken four at a time. The probability of exactly four heads from ten coins is found in this way to be

$$P = \left(\frac{1}{2}\right)^4\left(\frac{1}{2}\right)^6\binom{n}{r}$$
$$= \frac{1}{1024} \cdot \frac{10 \cdot 9 \cdot 8 \cdot 7 \cdot 6 \cdot 5 \cdot 4 \cdot 3 \cdot 2 \cdot 1}{(4 \cdot 3 \cdot 2 \cdot 1)(6 \cdot 5 \cdot 4 \cdot 3 \cdot 2 \cdot 1)}$$
$$= \frac{210}{1024}$$

Our solution of this problem illustrates the application of a generalized formula for the probability that a certain event will occur r times in n trials.

$$P(r; n) = \frac{n!}{r!(n - r)!} P^r Q^{(n-r)} \tag{41}$$

$$\text{or} \quad P(r; n) = \binom{n}{r} P^r Q^{(n-r)}$$

in which P is the probability that the event will take place in one trial and $P(r;n)$ is the probability that it will occur exactly r times in n trials.

Let us now apply this formula to the problem of finding the probabilities of various numbers of heads when three coins are tossed.

The process of multiplication illustrates the fact that in expanding $(P + Q)^3$ we systematically take all of the possible combina-

$$(P + Q)^3 = (P + Q) \times (P + Q) \times (P + Q)$$

$$
\begin{array}{r}
(P + Q) \\
\underline{\times\ (P + Q)} \\
P^2 + PQ
\end{array}
$$

$$
\begin{array}{r}
PQ + Q^2 \\
\overline{P^2 + 2PQ + Q^2} = (P + Q)^2
\end{array}
$$

$$
\begin{array}{r}
(P^2 + 2PQ + Q^2) \\
\underline{\times\ (P + Q)} \\
P^3 + 2P^2Q + PQ^2
\end{array}
$$

$$
\begin{array}{r}
P^2Q + 2PQ^2 + Q^3 \\
\overline{P^3 + 3P^2Q + 3PQ^2 + Q^3} = (P + Q)^3
\end{array}
$$

tions of three factors, where each factor can be either P or Q. Each product of n factors, where the terms of the binomial represent probabilities, is the probability of a particular combination of n events (the multiplication theorem). By grouping these products according to the number of P's, or Q's contained in each we find the number of products which contain each possible combination of factors (the addition theorem). The numbers of the various products are the coefficients of the various terms of a binomial expansion. They are the frequencies which might be found by listing all possible combinations. Substituting the numerical values of P and Q, we can obtain the separate probabilities of the various combinations of factors. In the case of $(P + Q)^3$, where $P = \frac{1}{2}$ and $Q = \frac{1}{2}$, the probabilities are $\frac{1}{8}$, $\frac{3}{8}$, $\frac{3}{8}$, $\frac{1}{8}$.

The generalized formula for finding the terms of a binomial is

$$(P + Q)^n = P^n + \frac{nP^{n-1}Q}{1} + \frac{n(n-1)}{1 \cdot 2} P^{n-2}Q^2 + \ldots \qquad (42)$$

$$\ldots + \frac{n(n-1)n - 2 \ldots (n - r + 1)}{1 \cdot 2 \cdot 3 \ldots r} P^{n-r}Q^r + \ldots$$

$$+ \frac{nPQ^{n-1}}{1} + Q^n$$

Formula (41), however, is enough for most statistical applications of the binomial distribution, since it can be used to compute any separate term.

Thus far our illustrations of the binomial distribution have been situations in which $P = \frac{1}{2}$. This is not, however, a necessary restriction. Formula (41) and the binomial distribution can be used regardless of the value of P and Q. For example, the probability of guessing the correct answers for exactly fifteen four-alternative multiple choice items on a test consisting of twenty-five items is given by

$$P(r;n) = P(15;25) = \frac{25!}{(15!)(25-15)!}\left(\frac{1}{4}\right)^{15}\left(\frac{3}{4}\right)^{10}$$

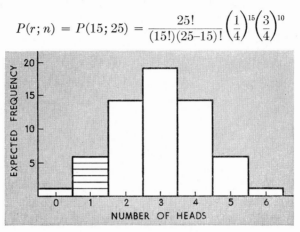

FIGURE 29

Graphical Representation of Probabilities

The theoretical probabilities of getting various numbers of heads when tossing six coins are represented graphically by the histogram of Figure 29. The expansion of $(P + Q)^6$ produces the coefficients 1, 6, 15, 20, 15, 6, 1. These numbers are represented by the heights of the rectangles of the histogram.

The total *area* of the histogram represents the sixty-four possible ways in which the six coins could turn up. Each separate way is represented by a small rectangle within the histogram. For example, one head could occur in these six particular ways:

		Coin			
No. 1	*No. 2*	*No. 3*	*No. 4*	*No. 5*	*No. 6*
H	T	T	T	T	T
T	H	T	T	T	T
T	T	H	T	T	T
T	T	T	H	T	T
T	T	T	T	H	T
T	T	T	T	T	H

The six different ways in which one head can occur are grouped together in the histogram over the portion of the X-axis which represents one head. The six small rectangles form a larger rectangle to represent the expected frequency of this score. Since the histogram is made up of sixty-four small rectangles to represent the sixty-four possible results, the *proportion* of the total area above any number of heads corresponds to the *probability* of that number. Thus, the probability of one head is $6/64$, or .0953125.

In this manner the area of a histogram can be used to represent probability as well as frequency. The proportion of the total area which lies above a specified interval on the X-scale is found by dividing the frequency in that interval by the total frequency.

The possible numbers of heads from six coins constitute a *discrete* series of seven X-values, the whole numbers from zero to six. It would be impossible to obtain a number of heads which is not included in this series. If ten coins were tossed, there would be eleven possible numbers of heads, the whole numbers from zero to ten inclusive. The probabilities in the case of ten coins are found from $(P + Q)^{10}$ to be

Number of Heads	Number of Ways for Specified Event to Occur	Probability
10	1	1/1024
9	10	10/1024
8	45	45/1024
7	120	120/1024
6	210	210/1024
5	252	252/1024
4	210	210/1024
3	120	120/1024
2	45	45/1024
1	10	10/1024
0	1	1/1024

A histogram drawn to represent these probabilities would have eleven bars, and the graph would appear somewhat smoother than the one for six coins. A histogram representing $(P + Q)^{100}$ would closely resemble a smooth curve.

EXERCISES

1. Compute the terms of the binomial $(P + Q)^5$, where $P = \frac{1}{3}$.

2. Assuming that 50 percent of all children born are boys, construct a histogram to show the expected percentage distribution of families of four children according to number of male births.

3. If the same face turned up on a die six times in ten trials would you suspect that it was loaded? (Hint: What is the probability of six or more trials being the same if $P = \frac{1}{6}$ for each face?)

4. Suppose a subject is asked to arrange six weights in rank order from the lightest to the heaviest. What is the probability that he will choose the correct order by pure guess work?

5. In a multiple choice test of six items, with four alternatives for each item, what is the probability of getting each of the following scores by pure chance: (a) exactly five correct, (b) from two to four correct, (c) three or more correct?

6. Compute the terms of the binomial $(P + Q)^5$, where $P = \frac{1}{10}$. (You can use the coefficients found in the first problem.) How does this distribution differ from the one obtained where $P = \frac{1}{3}$?

THE NORMAL DISTRIBUTION

One of the most useful theoretical distributions in statistics is the *normal distribution,* a bell-shaped curve which is the graph of a particular mathematical equation. The adjective "normal" does not mean that this particular form of distribution is a universal pattern or type which is always found with large masses of data. Frequency distributions can assume a great variety of forms of which the normal distribution is only one. Distributions which differ from the normal curve should not be considered as "abnormal" or distorted because no set of empirical data conforms exactly to this distribution.

The normal curve is an ideal, an abstract mathematical model. It is useful as a descriptive model because it approximates many observed distributions of concrete data, including most distributions of psychological and educational measurements. It can be used as an appropriate description of many observed distributions just as the mathematical model of a straight line was used in Chapters VI and VII to describe the correlation of Y with X even though the observed data did not fall exactly on this line. We shall see later that the normal distribution has many important applications to problems of statistical inference.

The normal distribution can be roughly described as "bell-shaped," "symmetrical," and *"asymptotic"* to the X-axis. This last means that as we move outward in either direction from the center, the curve approaches closer and closer to the base-line, but never quite touches it.

Because the normal curve derives mathematically from the theory of probability it is often called the *normal probability curve*. It is also sometimes referred to as the *curve of error* for it has long been known that the distribution of chance errors of observation and measurement in the physical sciences closely resembles this mathematical model.

The normal distribution is related to the binomial distribution, which we described in the preceding section. However, there are important differences between them, as can be seen by comparing the two curves in Figure 30. The graph of the binomial is a histogram, having definite upper and lower limits, and proceeding by discrete jumps from one frequency to the next. In contrast with this, the graph of the normal distribution is a continuous curve which is asymptotic to the X-axis, having no clear limiting value at either end.

Whereas the binomial expansion is useful in computing probabilities for a discrete series, the normal distribution is used with continuous series. Actually, the formula for the normal distribution can be derived mathematically as the limit approached by $P(r;n)$ as n becomes infinitely large, or as the discrete X-variable approaches a continuous series.

Figure 30 shows a histogram plotted to represent the expected frequencies of various numbers of heads in tossing ten coins. Upon this histogram is superimposed a normal distribution curve drawn to the same scale. In graphical terms, the normal curve is the limit of the histogram as the score intervals approach zero width and the total area of the figure remains unchanged.

The normal curve is precisely defined by the equation

$$y = \frac{N}{\sigma\sqrt{2\pi}} e^{-\frac{x^2}{2\sigma^2}} \tag{43}$$

In this equation

y is the ordinate, or height of the curve, at any point.

N is the number of cases in the distribution.

σ is the standard deviation.*

$\pi = 3.1416$, the ratio of the circumference of any circle to its diameter.

$e = 2.7183$, a mathematical constant.

x is any abscissa measured as a deviation from μ, the mean.*

---

* Since we are now dealing with an abstract model the Greek letters σ (sigma) and μ (mu) will be used to denote the standard deviation and mean.

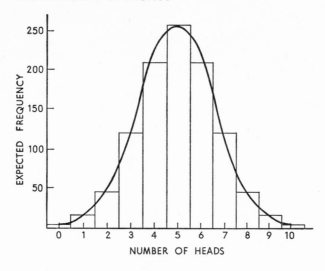

FIGURE 30

NORMAL CURVE SUPERIMPOSED ON HISTOGRAM OF BINOMIAL DISTRIBUTION

To see how the normal equation "works" let us set $N = 1$ and $\sigma = 1$. This gives us a numerical value for every term but x and y. Substituting these values in the equation, we have

$$y = \frac{1}{1\sqrt{2(3.1416)}} \, 2.7183^{-\frac{x^2}{2(1)^2}}$$

$$y = (0.3989)(2.7183)^{-\frac{x^2}{2}}$$

In this form of the normal equation it can be seen that the height of the curve varies as a function of the exponent, $-x^2/2$. The following definitions from elementary algebra will help you to understand the relationship of y to x defined by this equation

$$x^{-n} = \frac{1}{x^n}$$

$$x^0 = 1 \quad \text{(The 0th power of any number is 1.)}$$

At the mean of the distribution, $x = 0$, since $x = (X - \mu)$. Substituting this value for x in the formula, we have

$$y = (0.3989) \, (2.7183)^{-0/2}$$
$$y = (0.3989) \, (1)$$

Thus, we see that at the mean of a normal distribution of unit area ($N = 1$) and unit standard deviation ($\sigma = 1$), the ordinate is equal to .3989. From the above definition of a negative exponent we find that the ordinate at any other point will be less than the ordinate at the mean. As x increases (either positively or negatively) the exponent of 2.7183 becomes larger and the fraction becomes smaller. Thus, as x increases, the curve approaches the base line. It is asymptotic to the base line because any value of x, no matter how large, results in a value of y which is greater than zero.

The equation also specifies that the curve is symmetrical about the mean because the size of the exponent depends on x^2 and is thus the same for any value of x regardless of its sign.

Ordinates of the Normal Curve

The y-values in Table B of the Appendix have been computed by setting N and σ equal to 1.00 and substituting different values of x in the equation of the normal curve.

In order to understand the use of Table B you must have three points clearly in mind:

1. The origin, or reference point, of values on the X-scale is the *mean of the distribution.*
2. The unit of measurement on the X-scale is the *standard deviation of the distribution.*
3. The ordinates (y) of Table B are not frequencies. Frequency is associated with the *area* of a distribution curve. An ordinate of the curve refers to height, or distance above the base line. Since the area of a distance has no meaning, distance does not represent frequency.

One important use of Table B is in finding the approximate frequency within a class-interval of a particular normal distribution. This is done by finding the proportion of the total area under the curve which lies within the limits of that interval and converting this proportion to frequency. The total area of the curve is unity since N in the equation has been set equal to 1.00.

Example:

Suppose we wish to find the frequency contained in the class interval 35–39 of a normal distribution, where $\mu = 45$, $\sigma = 8$, and $N = 500$. Our problem is to find the area of this interval where the total area under the curve is 500 units of frequency. The area will be approximated if we consider the interval as a rectangle and multiply its width by its height at the mid-point.

The height, y, is found from Table B. But to use the table we must express the mid-point of the interval as a deviation in σ-units from the mean.

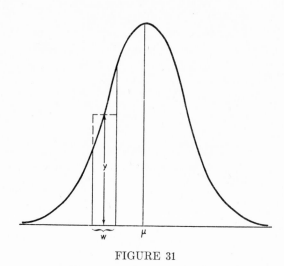

FIGURE 31

Mid-point of interval: $X = 37$

$$z = \frac{x}{\sigma} = \frac{X - \mu}{\sigma} = \frac{37 - 45}{8} = -1.00$$

y (at $x = -1.00$) $= .2420$ (from Table B). Area of c.i. (where $N = 1$) $= w \cdot y = \frac{5}{8}$ $(.2420) = .15125$. Frequency in c.i. (where $N = 500$) $= .15125$ $(500) = 75.62$. The interval contains 76 cases.

The generalized ordinate method for finding the frequency in any score interval of a normal distribution is

$$f = y \left(\frac{i}{\sigma}\right) N, \quad \begin{array}{l} \text{where } y \text{ is the ordinate at the} \\ \text{mid-point of the interval, and} \\ i \text{ is the size of the interval} \end{array} \quad (44)$$

This method is an approximation, since the area within a rectangle of a histogram does not exactly equal the area under the curve. The inaccuracy of this procedure becomes less as the width of the class interval decreases.

Areas of the Normal Curve

The exact area under a portion of the normal curve can be found through the use of integral calculus. Tables have been computed in this way which give the proportion of the total area included between μ and various z-values in the *unit normal curve* (where $\sigma = 1$ and $N = 1$). With such a table it is possible for you to compute the exact area of a portion of the normal curve even though you may have no knowledge of integral calculus. Table C in the Appendix can be used in this way.

The following typical examples will serve to illustrate the use of area tables.

Examples:

1. If $\mu = 100$, $\sigma = 10$, $N = 489$, how many cases in a normal distribution are above 109?

$$X = 109$$
$$z = \frac{109 - 100}{10} = .9$$

The proportion of the total area which lies between μ and $z = .9$ is found from Table C to be .3159.

Since .50 of the area is above μ, and .3159 is the proportion above μ but below 109, the proportion above 109 is $.50 - .3159 = .1841$. The total area represents 489 cases. This proportion (.1841) of the

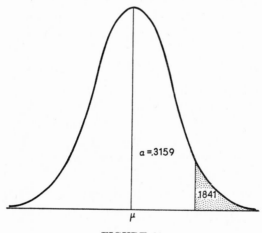

FIGURE 32

total represents $.1841 \times 489 = 90$ cases. Thus, 90 cases are above 109 in this normal distribution.

2. In the same distribution, how many cases are below 109?

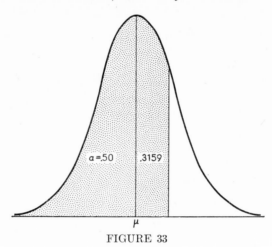

FIGURE 33

Proportion of area from μ to 109: .3159
Proportion of area below μ: .50
Proportion of area below 109:   .8159
Frequency below 109: .8195(489) = 400 cases

3. How many cases in this distribution have a score of 109? In attacking this type of problem, we must consider the limits of the score interval.

Limits of score interval: 108.5 and 109.5

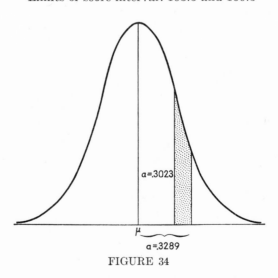

FIGURE 34

X	x	z	Area from μ
109.5	+9.5	+.95	.3289
108.5	+8.5	+.85	.3023

Area in interval = .3289 − .3023 = .0266
Frequency in interval = .0266 × 489 = 13

4. How many cases are within the class interval 99–102?

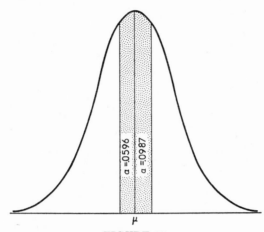

FIGURE 35
Limits of class interval: 98.5 and 102.5

X	x	z	Area from μ
102.5	+2.5	+.25	.0987
98.5	−1.5	−.15	.0596

Area in interval = .0987 + .0596 = .1583
Frequency in interval = .1583 × 489 = 77
(Note the importance in this problem of the
signs of x and z.)

5. How many cases are above a score of 109? This problem
differs in its solution from Example 1, which asked, "How many
cases in a normal distribution are above 109?" In order to be above
a *score* of 109, a case must be above 109.5, which is *the upper limit
of the score interval.**

$X = 109.5$
$z = .95$
Area from μ = .3289
Area above z = .1711
Frequency above z = .1711 × 489 = 83

---

* We would never have to decide in this situation what to do with a *score* of
109.5, because if such a measurement could occur in a set of data its score interval
would be 109.25 to 109.75.

In solving problems of this type we sometimes add the proportion of area obtained from Table C to .50 and we sometimes subtract it from .50. In some instances it is necessary to add two tabled proportions, in others to subtract one from the other. If you are not sure what to do in a particular problem, draw a rough diagram of a distribution curve, erect an ordinate at μ, and mark off the limits, roughly placed above or below μ, to indicate the interval for which the area is to be found. If you remember that Table C gives the area included between μ and z, you can determine from your diagram the appropriate procedure.

Deviates Corresponding to Areas of the Normal Curve

It is sometimes necessary to find the z above or below which a specified area lies. For instance, we might wish to know the score limits within which a certain proportion of the total number of cases is included. Table D has been constructed for this purpose. From this table we find, for example, that the middle 50 percent of the cases in a normal distribution fall within the range $\mu \pm .6745\sigma$. This follows from the fact that the z corresponding to .25 in the area column of Table D is .6745.*

From Table D we can find the percentile points of a normal distribution.

Examples:

1. What is the value of P_{84} in a normal distribution where $\mu = 67$ and $\sigma = 5.1$? P_{84} is the point below which there are 84 percent of the cases or .84 of the area. From Table D the z corresponding to an area of .34 is .9945. (Figure 36)

$$P_{84} = \mu + z\sigma = \mu + \frac{x}{\sigma}\sigma = 67 + .9945(5.1) = 72.1$$

2. Between what points will the middle 95 percent of the cases lie in a normal distribution where $\mu = 32.6$ and $\sigma = 4.3$? Since the normal curve is symmetrical, the required z is the point which marks off the distance above or below the mean to include 47.5 percent of the cases.

---

* One measure of the dispersion of a frequency distribution, which is seldom used today, is the *probable error*. It is defined as the distance, which, if measured off on each side of the mean, includes the middle 50 percent of a normal distribution. It is computed by P.E. $= .6745\sigma$.

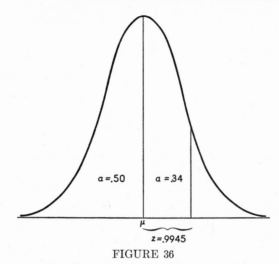

FIGURE 36

From Table D the z corresponding to an area of .475 is found to be 1.9600. The required limits are thus $\mu - 1.96\sigma$ and $\mu + 1.96\sigma$, or 24.2 and 41.0.

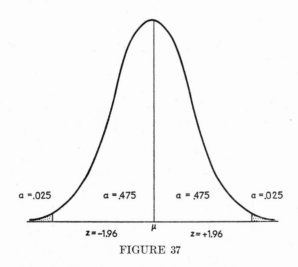

FIGURE 37

The Normal Approximation of the Binomial Distribution

Direct computation of probabilities by means of the binomial distribution becomes quite laborious in some situations. For instance, to find the probability of a student scoring above 50 by chance on a true-false examination containing 60 items, it is necessary to compute 10 terms of the expansion of $(\frac{1}{2} + \frac{1}{2})^{60}$, a time-consuming task.

Fortunately it is possible to obtain a very close approximation of the correct result by means of the normal distribution. To do this we make use of the mean and standard deviation of the binomial distribution, which are given by

$$\mu = nP \tag{45}$$

$$\sigma = \sqrt{nPQ} \tag{46}$$

For the particular binomial model of the chance distribution of scores on a 60-item true-false test,

$$\mu = 60(.5) = 30$$
$$\sigma = \sqrt{60(.5)\,(.5)} = \sqrt{15} = 3.87$$

On the assumption that the continuous normal distribution adequately approximates the discrete binomial in this situation, we take "above 50" in the discrete series to be the equivalent of "above 50.5" in the continuous series and proceed in the following manner to use the normal curve.

$$z = \frac{X - \mu}{\sigma} = \frac{50.5 - 30}{3.8} = +5.30$$

From Table C we find the area of the normal curve between the mean and $z = 5.0$ to be .49999971. The area beyond $z = 5.0$ is then $.5 - .49999971 = .00000029$. Scores above 50 deviate farther than $z = +5.00$, so we can state the probability of a chance score above 50 as $p < .00000029$, or as less than 3 chances in 10 million. If a student made such a score, it would be highly unlikely that he had done so by guessing!

From the binomial theory we compute the exact probability of six heads in ten tosses of a coin to be

$$P(r; n) = \binom{n}{r} P^r Q^{(n-r)}$$
$$= \frac{10 \cdot 9 \cdot 8 \cdot 7 \cdot 6 \cdot 5 \cdot 4 \cdot 3 \cdot 2 \cdot 1}{(6 \cdot 5 \cdot 4 \cdot 3 \cdot 2 \cdot 1)(4 \cdot 3 \cdot 2 \cdot 1)} \left(\frac{1}{2}\right)^6 \left(\frac{1}{2}\right)^4$$
$$P(6;10) = \frac{210}{1024} = .2051$$

The normal approximation of the binomial produces the following.

$$\mu = nP = 10(\tfrac{1}{2}) = 5$$

$$\sigma = nPQ = \sqrt{10(\tfrac{1}{2})(\tfrac{1}{2})} = \sqrt{1.58}$$

$$z_1 = \frac{5.5 - 5}{1.58} = .32, \quad \text{area from } \mu = .1255$$

$$z_2 = \frac{6.5 - 5}{1.58} = .95, \quad \text{area from } \mu = .3289$$

$$P = (\text{area between } z_1 \text{ and } z_2) = .2034$$

The results do not agree exactly, partly as a result of rounding; but the difference is slight—205 in 1000 as against 203 in 1000.

As n becomes smaller the approximation becomes less accurate, and generally when $n < 10$ direct computation of the binomial should be used rather than the normal approximation. Remember that the normal curve table provides an adequate approximation where nP (or nQ, whichever is smaller) is equal to or greater than 5. The reason for this rule-of-thumb will become apparent in a later chapter.

SUGGESTED READINGS

1. Cornell, F. G. *The Essentials of Educational Statistics*, chap. vi. New York: John Wiley & Sons, 1956.

2. Freund, J. E. *Modern Elementary Statistics*, chap. viii. 2d ed. New York: Prentice-Hall, 1960.

3. Guilford, J. P. *Fundamental Statistics in Psychology and Education*, chap. vii. 2d ed. New York: McGraw-Hill Book Company, 1950.

4. Walker, H. M. *Elementary Statistical Methods*, chap. xi. New York: Henry Holt and Co., 1943.

5. ———. *Mathematics Essential for Elementary Statistics*, chaps. xviii and xix. Rev. ed. New York: Henry Holt and Co., 1951.

EXERCISES

1. In a normal distribution what proportion of N falls within the range $\mu \pm \sigma$? $\mu \pm 2\sigma$? $\mu \pm 3\sigma$? (see p. 61.)

2. If the distribution in the example on page 73 were perfectly normal, what would be the frequencies of the following class intervals? (Assume $\sigma = S$ and $\mu = \bar{X}$.)
   a) 21–27
   b) 42–48
   c) 70–76

3. Find the following statistics for a normal distribution with $\mu = 73.2$ and $\sigma = 10.9$.
   a) Median
   b) Q_1
   c) Q
   d) P_{71}

4. If one score is randomly drawn from the distribution in Problem 3, what is the probability that it will be
   a) a score of 75?
   b) either 75 or 64?
   c) above Q_3?
   d) 100 or above?

5. Using Table B and formula (44), find the frequencies in class intervals of ten units for a normal distribution where $\mu = 250$, $\sigma = 24$, and $N = 1000$. (Use twelve intervals.)

6. Compute the frequencies required in Problem 5 by using Table C. Compare the results obtained by the two methods.

7. If in a normal distribution, Mdn $= 38.3$ and $Q_3 = 41.5$, what is the value of σ?

8. A manufacturer knows from past experience that on the average 2 percent of his product is defective. What is the probability that in a lot of 10 units of this product exactly 3 will be defective? Use the normal curve method and the direct method. How well do the results agree? Which do you consider more accurate?

9. Theoretically, in 10,000 bridge hands approximately 404 would have one suit of 7 or more cards. What is the probability that in playing 48 hands you would receive as many as 9 such "long suits"? Use the normal curve method.

10. In a multiple choice test of 50 items, each having 5 alternatives, how high a score would it be necessary for a student to make for you to feel reasonably sure that he was not merely guessing? How high for you to feel absolutely certain?

11. In a certain school district handicapped children, defined as IQ below 70, are placed in special classes. City-wide administration of a certain intelligence test has shown that one percent of fifth-grade pupils are below 70 IQ. It is now proposed that a new form of the test be used next year and this is administered on a trial basis to a sample of 200 fifth graders. For this sample, $\bar{X} = 102.8$ and $S = 19$. What would you expect would be the effect on the special education

classes if handicapped children are still defined as IQ below 70? What have you assumed in answering this question?

12. Last year the sixth-grade pupils in a school district were given a battery of achievement tests at the beginning of the school year. This year, just before they had completed the seventh grade, the tests were repeated. From the following data what can you say about their relative gains in the three types of achievement?

	Reading		*Composition*		*Arithmetic*	
	Mean	*S*	*Mean*	*S*	*Mean*	*S*
Sixth Grade.........	28.0	4.8	40.0	3.6	62.0	9.6
Seventh Grade......	31.6	4.0	52.2	4.5	77.8	8.7

On which test would the largest number of seventh graders fall below the sixth-grade mean? What percent of sixth graders are above the seventh-grade mean on each test? Would you feel more confident about your answers if you could inspect the frequency distributions of these results? Explain.

CHAPTER IX

Sampling and the Reliability of Statistics

STATISTICAL INFERENCE

Most empirical observations and experimental tests are conducted for the purpose of formulating generalizations concerning the *universe* from which a sample of data has been drawn. In statistics the terms *universe* and *population* are used to refer to all possible instances of a specified class of objects or events. The fundamental problem of statistical inference is that of making decisions and formulating generalizations about a population on the basis of the incomplete information contained in a sample. This chapter deals with methods of evaluating the dependability of information obtained from samples.

Here are some examples of populations which could be sampled and concerning which generalizations might then be made: annual income of home owners in the U.S.; ages of chamber of commerce members in cities of 50,000 or over; measurements of a certain person's reaction time to a standard auditory stimulus; size of speaking vocabulary of eight-year-old boys. These examples serve to illustrate that *a statistical population is really a universe of discourse*. It is the class of measurable objects or events about which a general statement is to be made. It can include almost anything so long as it is precisely defined.

The universes of interest to research workers are usually of some practical or theoretical significance. It would be quite legitimate, for instance, to study the universe of three-legged, cross-eyed, black tomcats weighing over seven pounds, but few researchers would be interested in doing so. On the other hand, such populations as schizophrenics between the ages of 25 and 30 who show "color-shock" on the Rorschach Test would be of interest to many psychologists.

It is theoretically possible to describe a sample drawn from a specified population with complete accuracy, and we can always compare the description with the original data in order to evaluate its accuracy. A statistical measure used to describe a sample, such as $\bar{X}$, S, or r, is known as a statistic. The numerical value of such sample statistics depends on the particular set of individual measurements which the sample contains. Consequently, such a measure as $\bar{X}$ will assume different values for different samples, even though the samples are all drawn from the same population.

The population value of a measure such as the mean or standard deviation, which is called a *parameter*, is generally unknown. To distinguish sample from population values, it is convenient to denote the latter by Greek letters. Thus, a population mean is designated by μ (mu), the population standard deviation by σ (sigma), and the coefficient of correlation for a population by ρ (rho). Greek letters are also used to symbolize the measures which describe a particular mathematical model even though they may have been assigned arbitrary numerical values. (As an aid to the student the Greek alphabet is shown in the Appendix.)

Statistical inference, a quantitative method of inductive reasoning, is usually concerned with (1) estimating the parameters of a population or (2) deciding to accept or reject some hypothetical statement about a population. Both of these objectives can be accomplished only through the use of incomplete and fallible information derived from a sample. Unlike statistical description, which can be entirely accurate for a particular sample, inductive inferences are always subject to possible error. They can seldom be known to be accurate because it is either impossible or impractical in most cases to observe the entire population.

Although the methods of statistical inference are among the most refined tools of scientific research, we should not conclude that the generalizations of the statistician are always right and that common sense generalizations are wrong. Both may be either right or wrong. The difference lies in the fact that common sense generalizations run an *unknown* risk of error whereas statistical inferences can be evaluated in terms of their *probability of error*. In fact, the central problem of all statistical inference is that of the risk of error incurred in accepting or rejecting various interpretations of observed data. Common sense sometimes leads us eagerly to accept generalizations which later turn out to be entirely wrong without our having realized the risk involved. The methods of statistical inference, on the other hand, lead to the possibility of acceptance or rejection in full awareness of the risk.

REPRESENTATIVE SAMPLES

An ideal sample, of course, would be a miniature of the population which it represents. The proportion of the population included within each interval of measurement would be exactly reproduced by the proportion of the sample contained in that interval. Thus, statistics computed from the sample would not differ from the parameters of the population. Moreover, a particular statistic would not differ from one to another of these ideal samples. However, in order to secure such a sample we would need to know so much about the population that there would be no point in observing a sample.

In some research, samples are carefully selected to represent proportionally the known relative frequencies of the population. Here, however, the variable under investigation is not the one carefully represented in the sample but one which is thought to be related to it. For example, a sample of pupils might be selected to represent the population distribution of IQ's of twelfth-grade students in the public schools. Such a sample could then be used to survey high school seniors' knowledge of U.S. history, and it might be a better sample for this purpose than one chosen by some other method. But it might not be particularly useful for studying the incidence of tooth decay because this variable is not known to be related to intelligence.

This same sample, chosen to represent IQ's of high school seniors, might well be used in an experiment designed to discover whether the intelligence of high school seniors could be raised by some sort of special training. Here again, however, the subject of the study would not be the population of IQ's so carefully represented in the sample, but rather the universe of changes in IQ which might be produced by the special treatment.

RANDOM SAMPLES

The most generally useful method for obtaining information concerning an unknown population is called *random sampling*. A simple random sample is a sample drawn in such a manner that each individual item in the population has an equal chance of being included in the sample. Moreover, the inclusion of one item must not affect the chances of any other item being included. Random samples are not necessarily "correct" samples. They may or may not give a representative picture of the population from which they were drawn since they come into being through the operation of chance influences. Their importance in statistics lies not in their representativeness, but in the fact that they make it possible to quantify the risk involved in basing decisions and generalizations on the incomplete information of a sample.

SAMPLING DISTRIBUTIONS

Variation among samples randomly drawn from the same population is of fundamental importance in statistical inference. The mathematical model used to describe the distribution of values of a statistic computed from all possible samples of size N which could be drawn from a particular population is known as the *sampling distribution* of that statistic. There is an important difference between population distributions and sampling distributions. The population distribution of a variable remains constant for a defined population, but the sampling distribution of a statistic computed from observations drawn from that population will be different depending on the size of the sample, the nature of the statistic, and the method used in obtaining the sample.

To illustrate the difference between these two kinds of distributions, we will imagine an infinite population consisting of only two classes, A and B, between which the items of the population are equally distributed with frequencies F_A and F_B. This is an example of a binomial population. The proportions of A's and B's can be thought of as relative frequencies, permitting us to deal with an infinite population without being concerned with the question of just how many A's and B's the population contains.

$$P_A \text{ (the proportion of } A\text{'s)} = \frac{F_A}{N}$$

$$\text{and } P_B = \frac{F_B}{N}$$

Suppose now that we define a variable X by the rule of measurement that $X = 0$ for all B's and $X = 1$ for all A's. The population distribution of X can then be represented by the following figure.

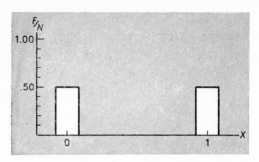

By using relative frequencies, we can compute the mean of this infinite population in the following manner.

X	F/N	$F/N \cdot X$
1	.5	.5
0	.5	0.0
Σ	1.0	0.5

$$\mu_x = \frac{\sum \frac{F}{N} X}{\sum \frac{F}{N}} = \frac{0.5}{1.0} = .5$$

The method is analogous to the computation of a sample mean.

$$\bar{X} = \frac{\Sigma fX}{N} = \frac{\Sigma fX}{\Sigma f}$$

Suppose now that an experimenter who does not know μ_x draws a random sample in an attempt to estimate this unknown parameter. Any sample which might be drawn will be described by the statistic $\bar{X} = (\Sigma fX)/N$. If he were to draw a sample of only one observation, he might find $\bar{X} = 0.00$, or $\bar{X} = 1.00$, the only possible values for a sample of this size. In this case the sampling distribution of $\bar{X}$ would be exactly the same as the population distribution of X. If he were to draw a sample of $N = 2$ observations, there would be three possible values of $\bar{X}$. The probabilities of these are shown by the following graph of the sampling distribution.

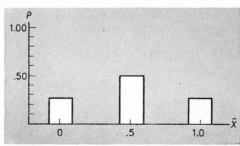

If $N = 3$ the sampling distribution of $\bar{X}$ is represented by the following figure.

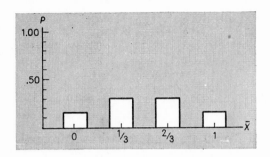

These sampling distributions will be recognized as graphs of the probabilities of the binomial distribution. Because of our rule of measurement for the variable X ($X = 1$ for all A's, and $X = 0$ for all B's), $\bar{X}$ for any sample is the same as the proportion of A's in the sample. Similarly, μ_x is identical with the proportion of A's in the population. For a finite sample of size N

$$\bar{X} = \frac{fX}{N} = P$$

since

$$\frac{fA}{N} = P_A$$

For the infinite population

$$\mu_x = \frac{\sum \frac{F}{N} X}{\sum \frac{F}{N}} = \frac{\frac{F_A}{N}}{1} = P_A$$

Let us now consider an infinite population in which a variable, X, can take 5 different numerical values: 1, 2, 3, 4, or 5. We will assume that these various values occur with equal frequency in the population. Then, for any value of X, $F/N = .20$, which is also the probability that a single randomly drawn observation of X will be any one of the possible values.

The mean of this hypothetical population is easily obtained.

X	$\dfrac{F}{N}$	$\dfrac{F}{N} \cdot X$
5	.20	1.0
4	.20	0.8
3	.20	0.6
2	.20	0.4
1	.20	0.2
Σ	1.00	3.0

$$\mu_x = \frac{\sum \dfrac{F}{N} \cdot X}{\sum \dfrac{F}{N}} = \frac{3.0}{1.00} = 3.0$$

If samples of $N = 2$ are randomly drawn from this population, there are 25 different pairs of values which can occur, since any one of the 5 might be obtained on the first draw, and this first X might be paired with any one of the 5 possible values on the second draw. The probability of any one pair's being drawn is the product of the separate probabilities of its members, $(.20)\,(.20) = .04$. Since the population is assumed to be infinite, we do not have to replace the first X before drawing the second for this statement of probability to be correct.

We can easily find the values of $\bar{X}$ which would be produced by the 25 combinations by constructing a square table.

VALUES OF $\bar{X}$ FOR ALL POSSIBLE SAMPLES OF $N = 2$

$$\bar{X} = \frac{X_1 + X_2}{2}$$

Possible Values of X_1 (First Draw)	Possible Values of X_2 (Second Draw)				
	1	2	3	4	5
1	1.0	1.5	2.0	2.5	3.0
2	1.5	2.0	2.5	3.0	3.5
3	2.0	2.5	3.0	3.5	4.0
4	2.5	3.0	3.5	4.0	4.5
5	3.0	3.5	4.0	4.5	5.0

In this way we find that $\bar{X}$ can have nine different numerical values when samples of $N = 2$ are drawn from this population. However, the different values are not equally likely to occur. For instance, we find from the table that $\bar{X} = 5.0$ could happen in only one way, while there are five different ways in which $\bar{X} = 3.0$. By constructing a frequency distribution of the possible results and computing the relative frequency of each $\bar{X}$ we obtain the sampling distribution.

Possible Values of $\bar{X}$	Number of Ways	Probability $\left(\dfrac{F}{N}\right)$	$\dfrac{F}{N} \cdot X$
5.0................	1	.04	.20
4.5................	2	.08	.36
4.0................	3	.12	.48
3.5................	4	.16	.56
3.0................	5	.20	.60
2.5................	4	.16	.40
2.0................	3	.12	.24
1.5................	2	.08	.12
1.0................	1	.04	.04
Σ	25	1.00	3.00

$$\mu_{\bar{x}} = \frac{\Sigma(F/N)\bar{X}}{\Sigma F/N} = \frac{3.00}{1.00} = 3.00$$

Note that $\mu_{\bar{x}}$, the mean of the sampling distribution of $\bar{X}$, is the same as μ_x, the mean of the population distribution of X. The forms of these distributions, however, are quite different.

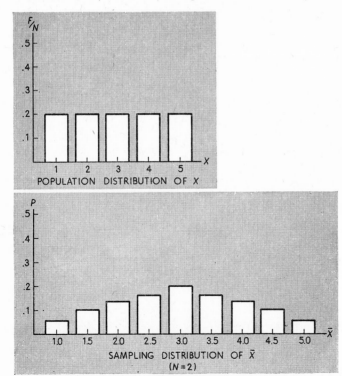

POPULATION DISTRIBUTION OF X

SAMPLING DISTRIBUTION OF $\bar{X}$
(N = 2)

If $n = 3$, there would be 125 possible values of $\bar{X}$. If $n = 4$, the number of possible values would be 625. In each case, however, regardless of the size of N, it can be shown that $\mu_{\bar{x}} = \mu_x$. Although the mean of a large number of $\bar{X}$'s computed from samples of any size is expected to be equal to μ_x, the form of the sampling distribution of $\bar{X}$ will be different for samples of different size. The examples we have described illustrate two important facts: (1) As N increases, the sampling distribution of $\bar{X}$ becomes more bell-shaped, and (2) As N increases, the dispersion of the sampling distribution of $\bar{X}$ decreases. The mean of a larger sample is a more reliable statistic than is the mean of a small sample. As N increases $\bar{X}$ is less likely to differ greatly from μ. Where $N = 2$ the probability is $\frac{2}{25}$ that $\bar{X}$ will be either 1 or 5, a sampling error of ± 2. If $N = 3$ the probability of an error this large is $\frac{2}{125}$. What is the probability of this large an error in $\bar{X}$ computed from a random sample of 10 cases?

Let us turn now to a simple mathematical model of random sampling. We will specify the universe of numbers of heads turning up in single tosses of a set of three coins. It will be recalled that this population is described by the binomial distribution $(P + Q)^3$. The possible outcomes of a single trial are 3, 2, 1, or 0 heads; and the probability of each of these, which is its proportion in the sampling distribution, is given by substituting these values for r in formula (41), the formula for $P(r;n)$, where $P = .50$. The mean of this population distribution is $\mu = nP = 1.5$. The distribution of numbers of heads for separate trials, X, is shown below.

X (Number of Heads)	Proportion in Population
3	$\dfrac{1}{8}$
2	$\dfrac{3}{8}$
1	$\dfrac{3}{8}$
0	$\dfrac{1}{8}$

$$\mu_x = 1.5$$

Assume that the population is not known and that we are going to try to discover its mean from a random sample of actual coin tossing. Suppose that we set out to estimate μ_x from a sample of one trial. How good an estimate would this be? We know that no sample of $N = 1$ could produce $\bar{X} = 1.5$, which is the exact value of μ_x. However, since a great many $\bar{X}$'s computed in this way would be expected to follow the population distribution, $\bar{X}$ would be expected to be either 1 or 2 for 75 percent of samples where $N = 1$. Another way of stating this is

$$P(\bar{X} = 1, \text{ or } 2) = .750, \text{ where } N = 1$$

Now consider what will be expected to happen if for each sample $N = 2$. Possible values for ΣX would be 6, 5, 4, 3, 2, 1, 0. Each of these, when divided by N, gives a possible value for $\bar{X}$. The sixty-four possible outcomes would be distributed according to the value of $\bar{X}$ as in the following table.

$\sum_{i-1}^{2} X_i$	$\bar{X}$	Proportion in Population
6	3.0	$\frac{1}{64}$
5	2.5	$\frac{6}{64}$
4	2.0	$\frac{15}{64}$
3	1.5	$\frac{20}{64}$
2	1.0	$\frac{15}{64}$
1	0.5	$\frac{6}{64}$
0	0.0	$\frac{1}{64}$

This distribution leads to the following statement about $\bar{X}$.

$$P(\bar{X} \geq 1, \text{ or } \bar{X} \leq 2) = \frac{50}{64} = .781, \quad \text{where } N = 2$$

If $N = 3$, the 512 possible outcomes produce the following sampling distribution.

$\sum_{i=1}^{3} X_i$	$\bar{X}$	*Proportion in Population*
9	3	$\dfrac{1}{512}$
8	$2\dfrac{2}{3}$	$\dfrac{9}{512}$
7	$2\dfrac{1}{3}$	$\dfrac{36}{512}$
6	2	$\dfrac{84}{512}$
5	$1\dfrac{2}{3}$	$\dfrac{126}{512}$
4	$1\dfrac{1}{3}$	$\dfrac{126}{512}$
3	1	$\dfrac{84}{512}$
2	$\dfrac{2}{3}$	$\dfrac{36}{512}$
1	$\dfrac{1}{3}$	$\dfrac{9}{512}$
0	0	$\dfrac{1}{512}$

From this distribution we can derive a third statement concerning the expected values of $\bar{X}$.

$$P(\bar{X} \geq 1, \text{ or } \bar{X} \leq 2) = .820 , \quad \text{where } N = 3$$

We now have three probability statements, each describing the expected distribution of $\bar{X}$ under a set of specified conditions. Thus, knowledge of the distribution of expected values of a sample statistic makes it possible for us to specify the risk of error involved in taking a sample statistic as descriptive of a population. To quantify risk in this way we must always make use of an abstract mathematical model, assuming that it is a reasonable approximation of the real-life circumstances in which our data were observed. Statistical inference makes use of a variety of probability models, each specifying a certain set of conditions which must be assumed to be satisfied by those who apply the model to empirical data. These required assumptions will be discussed where appropriate in the following pages as we consider a number of the more common methods of statistical inference.

ERRORS IN SAMPLING

It often happens that an experimenter unintentionally violates one or both of the conditions of random sampling: (1) that each item of the population has an equal chance of being included in the sample and (2) that the drawing of one item has no effect on the chances of drawing any other. Samples which give a systematically distorted reflection of the population as a result of failure to meet these requirements are said to be *biased*.

One of the most common errors in sampling, which is really an error of interpretation, occurs when a sample drawn from one population is used as a basis for generalized statements concerning a quite different one. An example of this is the all too frequent generalization of results from psychological experiments performed on members of sophomore classes in general psychology. You will have no difficulty in finding many instances of this.

Another common source of error in sampling, one which is much more difficult to detect, occurs when the method used in drawing the sample changes the probability that certain items in the population will be drawn. For example, a public opinion poll conducted by telephone might produce a biased sample of voters' opinions. It would be more representative of the opinions of people who subscribe to telephone service. For this reason it might be biased with respect to economic level and other factors associated with subscription to telephone service if these factors are related to the opinions being studied. Similarly, the use of psychological interview data obtained from a sample of volunteers might lead to serious error if used to represent a population including people who do not volunteer for such interviews. These simple examples serve to illustrate the kinds of precautions which must be observed in drawing samples and in interpreting statistics computed from samples.

Sampling errors should be clearly distinguished from *errors in sampling*. Sampling errors refer to chance variations among the values of a descriptive statistic for a number of samples randomly drawn from the same population. Quantitative estimates of the magnitude and distribution of such variations provide useful tools of statistical inference. On the other hand, errors in sampling constitute an ever-present threat to the validity of conclusions drawn from empirical observation. Such errors, which all too often remain undetected, can be avoided only through careful planning and execution of research with attention constantly directed towards the task of discovering all possible sources of bias. Comprehensive treatments of the problems of experimental design and the control of error are available to the student who has acquired an understanding of the basic principles of statistical inference.

EXERCISES

1. Each member of the class is to toss three coins for three trials, recording the number of heads for each trial and computing $\bar{X}$. If the class is small, each student should obtain several $\bar{X}$'s in this way so that N is near 50.

   a) Construct a frequency distribution of the $\bar{X}$'s grouped according to the ten possible values. How well does this agree with the theoretical distribution shown on page 162?

   b) Compute the mean of the obtained $\bar{X}$'s and compare it with μ_x.

2. The standard deviation of the binomial was given on page 148 as $\sigma = \sqrt{nPQ}$, formula (46). If this is applied to the binomial $(P + Q)^3$, where $P = .50$, which describes the expected distribution of heads for tosses of three coins, $\sigma = \sqrt{.75} = .866$.

   a) Compute σ from the theoretical distribution shown on page 131 by using formula (8), page 58. (Your answer should be .866.)

   b) Each member of the class is now to toss three coins for ten trials and compute S from formula (46). Construct a frequency distribution for the S's obtained in this way and find the mean. How does this compare with the theoretical value of .866?

   c) Repeat (b) with twenty trials for each member of the class and compare the results with those obtained in (b) and with the theoretical value of .866.

   d) Construct frequency polygons for the class distributions of S obtained in (b) and (c). Compare these distributions with respect to central tendency, dispersion, and shape.

3. Construct a graph to represent the population distribution for the occurrence of "five" in casts of a single die. Construct graphs of the sampling distributions of the proportion of "fives" in samples of $N = 1, N = 2, N = 4$ and $N = 6$.

4. Assume a binomial population consisting of equal proportions of $X = 1$ and $X = 2$. If samples of $N = 6$ were randomly drawn from this population, how would you expect $\bar{X}$ to be distributed? Compute the probabilities of the possible values of $\bar{X}$ and draw a graph to represent the sampling distribution. (See Figure 29, page 136, but remember that the axes of your graph will be labeled and numbered differently if it represents the sampling distribution of $\bar{X}$.)

5. If an infinite population contains equal proportions of $X = 1$, $X = 2$, and $X = 3$, what are the possible values of $\bar{X}$ for samples of $N = 3$? What are the probabilities of obtaining each of the possible values of $\bar{X}$? Construct a graph to represent this sampling distribution.

6. Suppose that an infinite population of X is distributed in the following manner:

X	$\dfrac{F}{N}$
0	.10
1	.40
2	.30
3	.20

a) What is the value of μ_x for this population?

b) Construct the sampling distribution of $\bar{X}$ for samples of $N = 2$. (Begin by considering the possible values of $\bar{X}$. Next, consider the probability of each possible combination of X_1 and X_2.)

RELIABILITY OF STATISTICS

Knowledge of the dispersion of the sampling distribution enables us to evaluate the degree of confidence we can have in a measure, such as the mean, obtained from a single sample. A statistic is said to be more reliable as the variability of its sampling distribution decreases. *Reliability,* then, refers to the degree of consistency expected among the results of many samples from the same population.

In general, as N increases, the variability of a sampling distribution decreases. Thus, large samples produce more reliable results. Large samples, however, do not correct biases introduced by errors in sampling. But, even though incorrect, a statistic computed from a large biased sample would still be said to be reliable if it were consistent from sample to sample. It is the degree of consistency and not the "correctness" of a statistic which increases as N increases.

The reliability of a statistic depends also upon the consistency of the individual measurements within the sample. Thus, if a sample contained a variety of measurements we would consider its mean much less dependable than if the measurements were quite similar to each other. Variation within a sample reflects the degree of variation existing within the population. This, in turn, determines the range of values which a statistic such as $\bar{X}$ can assume.

This suggests that N, together with some measure of variation within the sample, can be used to evaluate the reliability of a sample statistic. Actually, however, this is not quite the case because any measure of variation within a sample is itself subject to chance variation from sample to sample, and to a systematic bias depending on the size of N. Consequently, depending upon which of the possible samples we might get and the size of the sample, we would arrive at different answers to the question of reliability. It is shown mathematically that the reliability of many statistics can be specified exactly if we know N and the variability of the population from which the sample was drawn. But the practical utility of this is limited by the fact that while N is always known the variability of the population is usually not. Suitable *estimates* of the reliability of most statistics can be computed, however, from N and an *estimate* of the population variability.

Standard Errors of Statistics

The *standard error* of a statistic is an *estimate* of the standard deviation of the sampling distribution of that statistic. The standard deviation of a population is symbolized by σ without a subscript, or by σ_x, σ_y, σ_i, etc., where the subscript denotes the variable under consideration.* Standard errors are symbolized by $s_{\bar{x}}$, s_s, s_r, etc., where the subscript denotes a statistic.

The Variance of Statistics

Often it is convenient to work with the variance, rather than the standard deviation of a sampling distribution. The variance of a mean, for instance, is the variance of the sampling distribution of $\bar{X}$ for samples of a given size. The estimate of the variance of a sampling distribution is simply the square of the estimated standard error of a statistic, such as $s^2_{\bar{x}}$, etc.

Means of Large Samples

The mathematical theory underlying statistical method demonstrates that means of random samples drawn from a normal universe are themselves normally distributed about μ regardless of the size of N. Moreover, when N is large the sampling distribution

---

* In some instances we will need to distinguish population standard deviations of sampling distributions from the estimates necessarily used in problems of statistical inference. We will denote these population values by σ. Thus, $S_{\bar{x}}$ is an *estimate* of $\sigma_{\bar{x}}$, the unknown parameter.

of means is in most cases approximately normal even though the population distribution of X is not.

It can also be shown mathematically that the standard deviation of the sampling distribution of the means of all possible samples of a given size which might be drawn from a very large universe is

$$\sigma_{\bar{x}} = \frac{\sigma}{\sqrt{N}} \tag{47}$$

Furthermore, it is known that the means of samples are distributed normally around a mean equal to μ if the population from which the samples are drawn is itself normally distributed. Even when samples are drawn from a non-normal population, the sampling distribution of $\bar{X}$ approaches the normal distribution more closely as N becomes larger (pp. 156–60).

Formula (47) requires knowledge of σ, the population standard deviation, and since this is seldom known, the formula has little practical utility. However, a good estimate of σ^2 can be computed from the sample by

$$s^2 = \frac{\Sigma x^2}{N - 1} \tag{48}$$

This *variance estimate,* denoted by s^2, must be clearly distinguished from S^2, the descriptive variance of a sample. s^2 is an *unbiased estimate* of σ^2. That is, if s^2 were computed from many random samples of size N drawn from a normal population, the mean of these unbiased estimates would approach closer and closer to σ^2 as we increase the number of samples.

To illustrate the difference between s^2 and S^2, let us again consider an infinite population in which the 5 possible numerical values of X (1, 2, 3, 4, and 5) each occur with equal frequency. We found (p. 158) that there are twenty-five different samples of $N = 2$ which can be drawn from this population and that there are 9 possible values for $\bar{X}$ computed from these samples. We will now consider the possible values of s^2 and S^2 for these 25 samples in order to compare the sampling distributions of these two statistics and to see how well they serve as estimators of σ^2.

The variance σ^2 of our hypothetical population is easily computed. We have already found that $\mu = 3.0$ (p. 158).

X	$\dfrac{F}{N}$	$(X - \mu)$	$(X - \mu)^2$	$\dfrac{F}{N}(X - \mu)^2$
5	.20	$+2$	4	.8
4	.20	$+1$	1	.2
3	.20	0	0	0.0
2	.20	-1	1	.2
1	.20	-2	4	.8

$$\sum \frac{F}{N} = 1.00 \qquad\qquad \sum \frac{F}{N}(X - \mu)^2 = 2.0$$

$$\sigma^2 = \frac{\displaystyle\sum \frac{F}{N}(X - \mu)^2}{\displaystyle\sum \frac{F}{N}} = 2.0$$

The values of s^2 and S^2 for each of the possible samples of $N = 2$ are shown below.

Values of s^2 and S^2 for All Possible Samples of $N = 2$

$$s^2 = \frac{\Sigma(X - \bar{X})^2}{N - 1}$$

$$S^2 = \frac{\Sigma(X - \bar{X})^2}{N}$$

X_1 (First Draw)		X_2 (Second Draw)				
		1	2	3	4	5
1	$\bar{X}$	1.0	1.5	2.0	2.5	3.0
	s^2	0.00	.50	2.00	4.50	8.00
	S^2	0.00	.25	1.00	2.25	4.00
2	$\bar{X}$	1.5	2.0	2.5	3.0	3.5
	s^2	.50	0.00	.50	2.00	4.50
	S^2	.25	0.00	.25	1.00	2.25
3	$\bar{X}$	2.0	2.5	3.0	3.5	4.0
	s^2	2.00	.50	0.00	.50	2.00
	S^2	1.00	.25	0.00	.25	1.00
4	$\bar{X}$	2.5	3.0	3.5	4.0	4.5
	s^2	4.50	2.00	.50	0.00	.50
	S^2	2.25	1.00	.25	0.00	.25
5	$\bar{X}$	3.0	3.5	4.0	4.5	5.0
	s^2	8.00	4.50	2.00	.50	0.00
	S^2	4.00	2.25	1.00	.25	0.00

Sampling distributions for s^2 and S^2, where $N = 2$, are obtained by finding the relative frequency for each of the possible values of these statistics. The mean S^2 is smaller than σ^2, but the mean s^2 is exactly equal to σ^2.

Sampling Distributions of s^2 and S^2

Possible Values of s^2	$\dfrac{F}{N}$	$\left(\dfrac{F}{N}\right)s^2$	Possible Values of S^2	$\dfrac{F}{N}$	$\left(\dfrac{F}{N}\right)S^2$
8.00	$\dfrac{2}{25}$	$\dfrac{16}{25}$	4.00	$\dfrac{2}{25}$	$\dfrac{8}{25}$
4.50	$\dfrac{4}{25}$	$\dfrac{18}{25}$	2.25	$\dfrac{4}{25}$	$\dfrac{9}{25}$
2.00	$\dfrac{6}{25}$	$\dfrac{12}{25}$	1.00	$\dfrac{6}{25}$	$\dfrac{6}{25}$
0.50	$\dfrac{8}{25}$	$\dfrac{4}{25}$	0.25	$\dfrac{8}{25}$	$\dfrac{2}{25}$
0.00	$\dfrac{5}{25}$	0	0.00	$\dfrac{5}{25}$	0

$$\sum\frac{F}{N} = 1 \qquad \sum\left(\frac{F}{N}\right)s^2 = 2 \qquad\qquad \sum\frac{F}{N} = 1 \qquad \sum\left(\frac{F}{N}\right)S^2 = 1$$

$$\text{Mean } s^2 = \frac{\sum\left(\dfrac{F}{N}\right)s^2}{\sum\dfrac{F}{N}} = 2 \qquad\qquad \text{Mean } S^2 = 1$$

For any sample of data, $S^2 < s^2$. However, the difference between them becomes smaller and the means of their sampling distributions approach equality as N increases.

By taking the square root of s^2 we can obtain a useful estimate of σ. This estimate is sufficiently accurate for all ordinary statistical applications.

$$\text{est. } \sigma = s = \sqrt{\frac{\Sigma x^2}{N - 1}} \tag{49}$$

Unfortunately, statistics textbooks do not agree regarding the symbols and formulas used for standard deviations. In most of the older books σ was used for standard deviations of samples as well as populations. No symbol was used for the unbiased estimate of σ^2 because its mathematical basis was as yet unknown. In using other statistics books for further study or reference you should check carefully the definition of each symbol. The main point to watch for is whether the author has divided the sum of squares by N or by $N - 1$. If we divide by N, the sample variance is on the average too small. It is a *biased* estimate of σ^2. When $N - 1$ is used as the divisor the sample variance is an *unbiased estimate* of σ^2. For this reason many statisticians advocate the use of $N - 1$ as the divisor in all cases regardless of whether the objective is the description of a sample or the estimation of σ^2.

Older textbooks often give the following as an estimate of the standard error of $\bar{X}$

$$\sigma_m = \sigma_{\bar{x}} = \frac{\sigma}{\sqrt{N-1}}, \quad \text{where } \sigma = \sqrt{\frac{\Sigma x^2}{\iota N}}$$

In our notation this would be

$$s_{\bar{x}} = \frac{s}{\sqrt{N}}, \quad \text{where } s = \sqrt{\frac{\Sigma x^2}{N-1}} \tag{50}$$

Both methods give the same result because the sum of squares is divided by N and by $N - 1$. The order in which these divisions are performed does not affect the final result.

The sampling distribution of $\bar{X}$ can often be assumed to be normal without introducing serious error. It is *always* normal for means of random samples drawn from a normal population of X. It is *approximately* so for means of large samples, regardless of the population distribution of X. However, if the population distribution of X is not normal the sampling distribution of $\bar{X}$ departs farther from the normal curve as N becomes smaller. In fact, if $N = 1$ the sampling distribution of $\bar{X}$ is *identical* with the population distribution of X, no matter what its form might be.

This raises the awkward question of deciding in many particular applications of statistics whether or not we can reasonably act on the assumption that $\bar{X}$ is normally distributed. Each case must be decided on its merits, but ordinarily this assumption will not lead to serious error when $N > 30$.

Where it is reasonable to assume a normal sampling distribution the means of samples can be represented on a scale of z, where

$$z = \frac{\bar{X} - \mu}{\sigma_{\bar{x}}}$$

These new values are normally distributed with a mean of zero and a variance of 1.00. (It was shown in Chapter V that $M_z = 0$, and $S_z = 1.00$.) This is the same as transforming raw X-scores into x/S-units with origin equal to $\bar{X}$. Since only the unit of measurement is changed, the shape of the distribution remains the same as the distribution of $\bar{X}$. This will be true no matter what value is assigned to μ in the formula for z.

Since $\sigma_{\bar{x}}$ is never known, we find it necessary in practice to use an estimate derived from a sample. When N is large the estimate approximates a normal sampling distribution with a mean equal to the true value of $\sigma_{\bar{x}}$. It can be shown that for large samples the sampling distribution of z, obtained by dividing the normally distributed values of $\bar{X} - \mu$ by the approximately normally distributed $s_{\bar{x}}$, is itself an approximately normal distribution. This fact permits the use of the normal distribution as a model for statistical inferences from the means of large samples.

Estimating μ

When the assumption of normality is reasonably justified, which is usually the case with large samples, the incomplete information contained in a sample can be used to estimate the mean of the population from which the sample was drawn. To illustrate the method we will use the data of Table 1, p. 14. When tabulated as in Table 11, p. 46, these data yield $\bar{X} = 42.8$ and $S = 20.3$. Although the sample distribution appears to be somewhat positively skewed, we nevertheless decide that since $N = 90$ the sampling distribution of means for the population can be considered to be approximately normal. An estimate of $\sigma_{\bar{x}}$ is computed by

$$s_{\bar{x}} = \frac{S}{\sqrt{N-1}} = \frac{20.3}{\sqrt{89}} = 2.15$$

Now, if means of samples where $N = 90$ are normally distributed around μ with a standard deviation of 2.15, the probability is .6827 that our sample $\bar{X}$ is within a range defined by $\mu \pm 2.15$. This is deduced from the fact that in any normal distribution .6827 of the total area lies within the range defined by $\mu \pm \sigma$. Since Table C shows .025 of the area to be beyond 1.96σ in one tail of the normal curve, we can state the chances as only one in 20 that this $\bar{X}$ differs more than 4.2 score units from μ in *either* direction. ($1.96\ S_{\bar{x}} = 4.2$). It appears very unlikely that $\bar{X}$ differs as much as 10 score units from μ because that would be a deviation of 4.65 σ-units in a normal distribution.

Let us now assume for the moment the tentative hypothesis that $\mu = 50$. If this were true, means of random samples where $N = 90$ would be distributed as in the following figure, and we can find from Table C the chances of obtaining an $\bar{X}$ as low as 42.8, or lower.

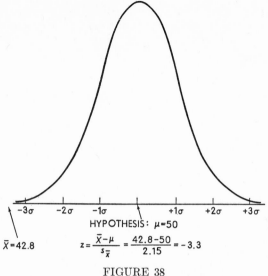

FIGURE 38

$(\bar{X} - \mu)/s_{\bar{x}} = -3.3$, and the probability is approximately .0005. Thus, with only about one chance in 2,000 of obtaining a sample $\bar{X}$ as low as this one, we reject the hypothesis that $\mu = 50$.

Any hypothesized value of μ can be tested in this manner, but since the number of possible hypotheses about a continuous variable is unlimited, it would be an endless task to attempt to discover all the acceptable ones by this method. We can, however, establish points below and above $\bar{X}$ to define a range which includes all possible hypothetical values of μ which we are willing to accept as plausible. The choice of these limiting values is an arbitrary matter of custom and convenience because such hypotheses differ from each other on a continuous scale of plausibility.

Confidence Intervals

The upper and lower limits of a range within which we can feel reasonably certain that a parameter such as μ is located are known as *confidence limits*. The range included between those points is called a *confidence interval*. Because the expression "reasonably certain" means different things to different people, such intervals are precisely denoted as a 95 percent confidence interval, a 98 percent confidence interval, etc. A 95 percent confidence interval, for example, is one computed by a procedure which would in the long run lead to correct conclusions 95 percent of the time. In applying this method to a great many samples we would expect to be wrong 5 percent of the time in inferring that such an interval includes the parameter. The confidence interval will differ from sample to sample and it is impossible to know that the inference from any particular sample is either right or wrong. A statistical inference can be evaluated only in terms of its probability of error. Since there is no method for finding the exact value of a parameter from the results of a sample, we can only specify limits which are, at a specified level of probability, likely to "bracket" the unknown parameter.

Let us return now to the sample of personality test scores from Table 1 (p. 14), for which $\bar{X} = 42.8$ and $S_{\bar{x}} = 2.15$. The observed $\bar{X}$ may be either above or below μ. From Table C we find that .025 of the area of a normal distribution is above $\mu + 1.96\sigma$. Similarly, .025 of the area is below $\mu - 1.96\sigma$. Thus, the probability is .05 that our sample mean is farther than 1.96 $\sigma_{\bar{x}}$ above or below μ. The probability is .95 that it is *not* farther than this distance from the population mean.

The distribution of sample means about μ is shown in Figure 39. The probability is .95 that our sample mean lies within the shaded area under the curve. If a very large number of random samples were obtained, 95 percent of them would be expected to produce means within the range of the shaded area.

Now, if we happen to obtain a sample mean from the shaded area, the two points found from $\bar{X} \pm 1.96\sigma_{\bar{x}}$ will bracket the mean

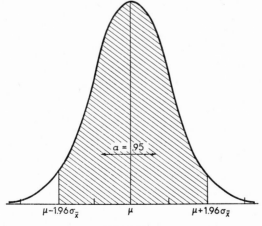

FIGURE 39

of the population from which our sample was drawn. This will happen 95 percent of the time because 95 percent of $\bar{X}$'s lie within this range. Thus, although we can never know its precise value, we can make the following statement about μ.

$$\bar{X} - 1.96s_{\bar{x}} < \mu < \bar{X} + 1.96s_{\bar{x}}$$

Since we run the risk of being wrong in about 5 out of 100 such statements, this expression is known as the 95 percent confidence interval for the population mean. It is a statistical estimate of μ, subject to error, as is any estimate. This estimate, however, is better than others because we have used a method which allows us to state the probability that it is correct.

Using this method we can now make the following statement regarding the population from which the sample of personality test scores in Table 1 was drawn. This is a statement of the probability that our computed interval contains the unknown population mean.

$$P[42.8 - 1.96(2.15) < \mu < 42.8 + 1.96(2.15)] = .95$$

In working with confidence intervals remember that the population mean, although unknown, is a fixed value which does not vary from sample to sample. Statements are sometimes made about confidence intervals which erroneously imply that the interval is marked off by two fixed values between which the population mean will fall 95 percent of the time. This interpretation is incorrect because μ, though unknown, is an absolute value. *It is the confidence interval which varies from sample to sample* and which, in any particular sample, either does or does not include μ. We call it a 95 percent confidence interval because the method used in computing it is expected to be successful 95 times in 100.

The population mean can be estimated from large samples with any desired degree of confidence by finding the appropriate z from Table D and substituting it in

$$\bar{X} - zs_{\bar{x}} < \mu < \bar{X} + zs_{\bar{x}} \tag{51}$$

For instance, the 98 percent confidence interval for μ is given by

$$\bar{X} - 2.33s_{\bar{x}} < \mu < \bar{X} + 2.33s_{\bar{x}}$$

Putting 1 percent of the area into each tail of the normal curve, we find the z corresponding to an area of .49 between μ and z. Since this is 2.33 we expect 98 percent of sample means to lie within the range $\mu \pm 2.33s_{\bar{x}}$. This leads us to conclude that for a random sample of this size the chances are 98 in 100 that $\bar{X} \pm 2.33s_{\bar{x}}$ includes the population mean. Similarly we estimate the 99 percent confidence interval for μ by

$$\bar{X} - 2.58s_{\bar{x}} < \mu < \bar{X} + 2.58s_{\bar{x}}$$

In estimating such confidence intervals from the normal distribution we must remember that the method is entirely accurate only when $\bar{X}$'s are normally distributed and the true value of $\sigma_{\bar{x}}$ is used in the formula. When N is large the sampling distribution of $\bar{X}$ is reasonably normal and s^2 provides a good estimate of σ^2. Although the method we have described is strictly correct only when σ is known, most statisticians agree that it is a reasonably good approximation when $N > 30$.

An exact method for estimating μ. In recent years, beginning with the work of W. S. Gosset,* who wrote under the pseudonym "Student," mathematical statisticians have developed an exact theory of sampling which applies to means from samples of any size. Since the methods based on small sample theory are applicable to samples of any size they are gradually supplanting the older, less exact procedures, which can be used only with large samples. We have described the older procedure only as an aid to the student who will find many instances in which experimenters have used large sample theory in reporting their findings.

"Student" recognized the important fact that an adequate mathematical model for the sampling distribution of $\bar{X}$ must take into account the variability of $s_{\bar{x}}$ from sample to sample. Student's t, defined by formula (52) actually has many sampling distributions —one for each value of $(N - 1)$. When N is small these distributions differ considerably from one another. As N increases, they become more alike, and as $N \longrightarrow \infty$ the distribution of t approaches the normal curve as a limit.

$$t = \frac{\bar{X} - \mu}{s_{\bar{x}}} \tag{52}$$

An alternative formula is

$$t = \left(\frac{\bar{X} - \mu}{s_x}\right)\sqrt{N} \tag{52a}$$

If the descriptive standard deviation S is used instead of the unbiased estimate s, the formula becomes

---

* "Student," "Probable Error of Mean," *Biometrika*, Vol. 6 (1908).

$$t = \left(\frac{\bar{X} - \mu}{S_x}\right)\sqrt{N - 1} \tag{52b}$$

A similar formula for the normally distributed z would be

$$z = \frac{\bar{X} - \mu}{\sigma_{\bar{x}}} = \left(\frac{\bar{X} - \mu}{\sigma_x}\right)\sqrt{N}$$

The similarity of these formulas suggests that the sampling distribution of t resembles the normal curve. This is indeed the case when N is large, but as N decreases the t distribution differs more and more from the normal curve because the difference between $\sqrt{N}$ and $\sqrt{(N - 1)}$ becomes larger and the variation of s from sample to sample increases.

Let us now consider how the sampling distribution of s varies with N in order to understand better the nature of the t-distribution. If N were as small as two, s would vary widely from sample to sample, but most of the time it would be too small in comparison with σ because the probability is low that any single sample of $N = 2$ would represent the range of variation in the population. As N increases, the probability becomes greater that any given sample will include a representative range of variation. Because of this, s^2 has a skewed sampling distribution, even though it is an unbiased estimate of σ^2. This can be illustrated by reference to the sampling distribution of s^2 described earlier in the chapter (p. 168).

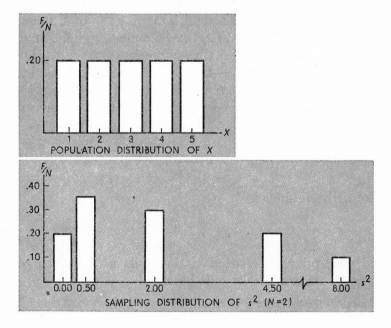

POPULATION DISTRIBUTION OF X

SAMPLING DISTRIBUTION OF s^2 (N = 2)

The sampling distribution of s has several important features:

1. Its mean is equal to σ. (s is an unbiased estimate of σ.) *
2. It is positively skewed for all finite values of N, but the skewness becomes less and it approaches the normal distribution as N increases.
3. As N increases, the variation of s from sample to sample decreases.

The diagram below is a schematic representation of the form of the sampling distribution of s for a small value of N.

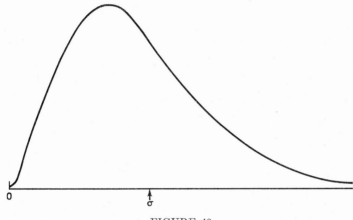

FIGURE 40

Note that in this skewed distribution more than half of the area is to the left of σ. This means that $\sigma_{\bar{x}}$ will be underestimated by $s_{\bar{x}}$ more often than it is overestimated. Consequently, the t-ratio will exceed a given value on the scale of the normal distribution more often than would the z-ratio computed from the true value of $\sigma_{\bar{x}}$.

The ideal normal distribution of z is independent of the size of N, but the probability of t differing from zero in either direction by a given amount becomes greater as N becomes smaller. This reflects the fact that as N becomes smaller there is increasing probability that $s_{\bar{x}}$ will underestimate $\sigma_{\bar{x}}$, while, at the same time, $s_{\bar{x}}$ varies more widely from sample to sample. The distribution of t differs more and more from the normal distribution as N becomes smaller. With increasing probability that $s_{\bar{x}}$ will underestimate $\sigma_{\bar{x}}$ there is a corresponding increase in the probability that $(\bar{X} - \mu)/s_{\bar{x}}$ will exceed any specified value. Thus, whereas the probability is .05 that the normal z will deviate in either direction from μ by more

---

* Actually, s is slightly biased as an estimator of σ, but a full discussion of this is too complex for an introductory textbook.

than 1.96, the probability that t will exceed this value is greater than .05 by an amount which depends on the sample size.

Actually, the distribution of t depends on the number of *independent* measures of variability from which $s_{\bar{x}}$ is computed. For any sample of size N, there are only $(N-1)$ independent measures of $(X - \bar{X})$. This results from the fact that $\Sigma(X - \bar{X}) = 0$ (p. 38). If we set out to assign numerical values to a set of N measures of $(X - \bar{X})$, we can choose $(N-1)$ such values with complete freedom as to their direction and magnitude. We would have no freedom of choice in assigning a value to the one remaining deviation—it must be the unique value which satisfies the requirement that $\Sigma(X - \bar{X}) = 0$.

In general, *degrees of freedom*, symbolized by df, refers to the number of independent observations from which a statistic is computed. Student's t, as defined by formula (52), has $df = N - 1$ because the sum of squares used in estimating $\sigma_{\bar{x}}$ is computed from $N - 1$ independent measures of deviation.

The following figure illustrates the nature of the difference between the distribution of t and the normal curve. As $df \longrightarrow \infty$ the sampling distribution of t approaches the normal curve as a limit. With decreasing df the t-distribution becomes more leptokurtic.

Sampling distributions of t have been mathematically derived for various numbers of df. Table E in the Appendix gives values of t which will be exceeded, in both directions from the mean, at five

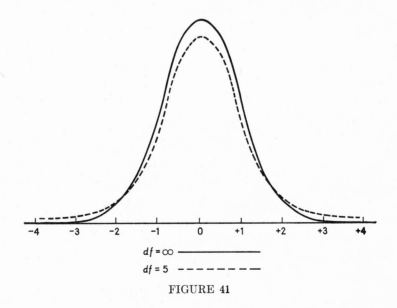

FIGURE 41

levels of probability. The five values in each row are taken from a complete distribution of t for the number of df represented by that row. The row corresponding to $df = \infty$ contains the normal curve values of z which would be used in finding the .90, .95, .98, .99, and .999 confidence intervals for μ. (Compare these entries with Table C.)

For example, to compute the 99 percent confidence interval for μ where $N = 24$, we find from Table E that the required value of t for $p = .01$ and $df = 23$ is 2.807. Using this value, we can make the following statement about the unknown μ.

$$P(\bar{X} - 2.807s_{\bar{x}} < \mu < \bar{X} + 2.807s_{\bar{x}}) = .99$$

But if $N = 5$, the 99 percent confidence interval would be

$$\bar{X} - 4.604s_{\bar{x}} < \mu < \bar{X} + 4.604s_{\bar{x}}$$

Both intervals have the same probability of bracketing μ ($p = .99$), but the one computed from a sample having twenty-three degrees of freedom is much narrower than the one based on only four. In general, then, confidence intervals at any desired degree of confidence can be computed from the following formula by substituting the appropriate value of t from Table E.

$$\bar{X} - ts_{\bar{x}} < \mu < \bar{X} + ts_{\bar{x}} \tag{53}$$

Comparison of t *and* z. Although the normal distribution of z is often used as a model for computing confidence intervals for large samples, *it is better practice to use the* t-*distribution for samples of any size.* When N is small, t *must* be used because the error in using z becomes large.

Limitations of the t-*ratio.* Both t and z depend on the assumption that *the sampling distribution of* $\bar{X}$ *is normal.* [This is the same as assuming the sampling distribution of $(\bar{X} - \mu)$ to be normal.] Now we have seen that the sampling distribution of means can safely be considered normal in most cases if N is large. When N is small, on the other hand, $\bar{X}$ is normally distributed only if the sampled variable is itself normally distributed. Thus, t, *when used with small samples,* assumes that the sample is randomly drawn from a normal universe.

When it is either impossible or uneconomical to obtain large samples, it is the research worker's responsibility to assure himself that there is a reasonable basis for assuming that the conditions necessary for valid application of his statistical method have been met. In many instances the assumption of normality is very difficult because the only available evidence comes from the sample under scrutiny. If the sample is small, the evidence is likely to be inadequate.

EXERCISES

1. Find the 95 percent confidence interval for each of the following, using the normal distribution of z. Find the same intervals from the distribution of t. Explain the difference in results.

   a) $\bar{X} = 47, s = 3.1, N = 28$

   b) $\bar{X} = 39.3, s = 4.8, N = 125$

2. From the distribution of t find the 99 percent confidence interval for μ for each of the following distributions. In each case decide if it is reasonable to consider that the assumptions underlying this procedure have been met.

   a) Twenty trout were dipped from a large pond. Their lengths in mm. were:

27	56	22	79
91	33	70	19
47	54	82	119
87	97	94	58
50	129	195	89

   b) Twelve ball bearings turned out by a certain machine had the following diameters in mm.

20.01	20.00
20.02	20.01
19.95	20.01
20.01	20.00
20.00	19.97
20.00	19.98

   c) The following reaction times to an auditory stimulus were obtained from one subject. What can be inferred concerning this subject's mean reaction time? (What is your best guess concerning the form of the population distribution of reaction times for a single subject?)

215ms.	223	212
247	221	210
214	218	208
230	220	219
256	201	203

3. A test of college aptitude has been standardized so that $\bar{X} = 500$ and $S = 100$. An entering class of 200 freshmen at a certain college group of freshmen?

4. In Problem 3, which standard deviation, 100 or 102.1, did you decide to use in estimating $\sigma_{\bar{x}}$? Compare the relative merits of these two ways of estimating the reliability of the sample mean.

5. What kinds of considerations should lead one to choose a 95 percent, 98 percent, or 99 percent confidence interval when estimating μ? Can you think of situations where you would be willing to use a 90 percent interval? Describe a situation where you would require a 99.75 percent interval.

6. Suppose that a sample of measurements produced a standard deviation of 20. How large a sample would be required to estimate μ at the 95 percent level of confidence within an interval not greater than had a mean score of 556.8 and a standard deviation of 102.1. Evaluate the hypothesis that this freshman class is a random sample from the universe of applicants for admission to colleges upon which the test was standardized. Would the director of admissions of this college be justified in claiming that he has been able to select a superior 6.5 points on the scale of measurement? Why is it impossible for you to give more than an *approximate* solution?

7. The national mean on an achievement test for high school seniors has been reported as $\bar{X} = 86.2$, and $S = 16.5$. A high school principal claims that his senior class of eighty-three pupils is superior to the national norm because for this class $\bar{X} = 89.1$. How would you evaluate his claim?

8. If the mean IQ for a certain intelligence test is reported as 102.4 for high school students, and S is 15.0, what would you conclude if the mean IQ for a high school of 672 pupils was found to be 105.8?

Reliability of the Median

The standard error of the median for large samples drawn from a normal universe is

$$\sigma_{\text{Mdn}} = \frac{1.253\sigma}{\sqrt{N}} \tag{54}$$

Here, again, σ is unknown and we must use the estimate. This formula indicates that the median is a less stable statistic than the mean. A confidence interval for the population median will be larger than the corresponding confidence interval for μ obtained from the same sample.

Reliability of Measures of Dispersion

For large samples drawn from a normal universe, the sampling errors of measures of dispersion are safely estimated by

$$\sigma_s = \frac{.707S}{\sqrt{N}} \tag{55}$$

$$\sigma_{\text{M.D.}} = \frac{.756 \text{ M.D.}}{\sqrt{N}} \tag{56}$$

$$\sigma_Q = \frac{1.166Q}{\sqrt{N}} \tag{57}$$

Comparison of these formulas shows that s is more reliable than the other measures of dispersion. If N is 100 or more, these standard errors can be interpreted in relation to the normal distribution. For example, the 95 percent confidence interval for σ is given by $s \pm 1.96\sigma_s$. The limits of the 99 percent confidence interval for the population Q are given by $Q \pm 2.58\sigma_Q$.

These formulas should not be used when $N < 100$. For estimating the dispersion of a population from samples of *any size* there is a very useful procedure for computing confidence intervals for σ^2. This makes use of the F-ratio, which will be discussed in Chapter XI.

Reliability of Proportions, Percents, and Frequencies

It is often impossible for the research worker to measure on a graduated scale the variable which he is studying. In such cases the data are frequencies classified according to presence or absence of some attribute. Sometimes this is simply the result of our inability to measure the variable in anything but crude intervals as in rating pupils as "cooperative" or "uncooperative." In other cases the observations naturally fall into discrete categories, such as "television" or "no television" in the home.

Sampling problems of this type can often be handled by the binomial distribution, or its normal approximation. If we were to classify each of a group of 15 children as "cooperative" or "uncooperative" and if we knew the proportion of uncooperative children in the universe from which the sample was drawn, the sampling distribution of frequencies of uncooperative children in samples of this size could be computed from $(P + Q)^{15}$. This binomial tells us the expected frequencies of the various possible numbers of uncooperative children which could occur in samples of 15.

The formula for the standard deviation of the binomial distribution was given earlier as $\sigma = \sqrt{nPQ}$. When applied to sampling problems such as this one it is called the *standard error of a frequency* and is written

$$\sigma_f = \sqrt{NPQ} \tag{58}*$$

Instead of working with frequencies it is possible to carry the computation through in terms of proportions. Since a proportion is found by dividing frequency by the size of the sample, σ_p is easily obtained from (58).

$$\sigma_p = \frac{1}{N} \sigma_f$$

$$= \frac{1}{N} \sqrt{NPQ}$$

$$\sigma_p = \sqrt{\frac{PQ}{N}} \tag{59}*$$

The standard error of a percentage can be computed from

$$\sigma_\% = 100\sigma_p = 100\sqrt{\frac{PQ}{N}} \tag{60}*$$

This follows from the fact that proportions can be converted to percentages by multiplying by 100. Using formula (58), (59), or (60) and the normal curve table we can compute confidence intervals for population proportions, frequencies, or percentages by the procedure used for estimating μ.

Example:

Out of 100 voters interviewed in a public opinion poll, 61 stated that they plan to vote for candidate A. What is the 95 percent confidence interval for the proportion in the voting population?

---

* Note that P and Q in the above formulas refer to population values. Sample proportions will be designated by p and q. We have used σ to designate these standard errors because they are computed from the parameter of the binomial distribution, and do not require an estimate of σ.

$$\sigma_p = \sqrt{\frac{(.61)(.39)}{100}} = .0488$$
$$p - 1.96\sigma_p < P < p + 1.96\sigma_p$$
$$.514 < P < .706$$

We would run the risk of 5 chances in 100 of being wrong if we state the population proportion to be between .514 and .706. If the election were to be held at this time (and if every qualified voter participated) the chances are very good that candidate A would have a majority.

This method is only an approximation which can lead to incorrect conclusions if used uncautiously. One source of error is the fact that formula (59), as well as (58) and (60), is based on the population value of P, but since this is unknown, we are forced to substitute the sample proportion in the formula. A second source of error is that sample proportions, frequencies, and percentages are not normally distributed. Their sampling distribution is the discrete binomial, which can be approximated by the normal curve only under certain conditions.

The observed proportion, p, cannot be greater than 1.00 or less than 0.00. Thus, the sampling distribution of p, unlike the normal curve, has definite points at which it must reach the base line. Moreover, if the parameter, P, is near 1.00 or 0.00, the distribution of sample proportions must be skewed as a result of these limits. The degree of skewness, however, becomes less as P is closer to .50. The degree of skewness in the sampling distribution of P is also a function of the size of N. As N increases, the amount by which p is likely to deviate by chance from P becomes less and the sample values become more alike. For this reason, as N becomes larger, P can be nearer the limits of 1.00 or 0.00 without introducing a serious degree of skewness in the sampling distribution.

The two requirements, (1) that N be large enough and (2) that P be near enough to .50 can be combined in a single statement of the condition which must be fulfilled if the normal curve is used to approximate the sampling distribution of p. This requirement is that $NP \geqq 5$, and $NQ \geqq 5$.

Figure 42 shows graphically the 95 percent confidence interval for P computed from the binomial distribution for various observed proportions. To use this graph for estimating a confidence interval, locate along the base line the observed p or $(1 - p)$, whichever is smaller. The limits of the 95 percent confidence interval are then obtained from the vertical scale for the points at which the ordinate above p crosses the two curves corresponding to N. If $1 - p$ is used, the confidence limits must be subtracted from 1.00.

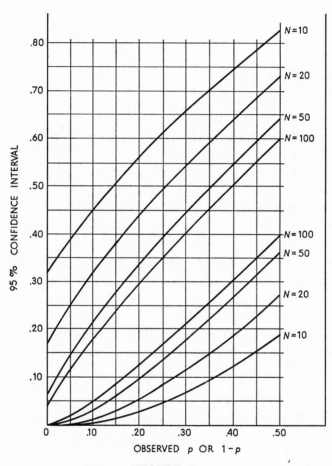

FIGURE 42

95 PERCENT CONFIDENCE INTERVAL FOR THE BINOMIAL DISTRIBUTION

Examples:

1. Problem: to estimate from Figure 42 the 95 percent confidence interval for P where $p = .60$ and $N = 20$. Above $p = .40$ we find the curves for $N = 20$ to be at .19 and .70. By subtracting both of these from 1.00, the required interval can be stated as

$$.30 < P < .81$$

2. The 95 percent confidence interval in the example on page 183 was found by the normal curve approximation to be

$$.514 < P < .706$$

Graphical approximation gives

$$.29 < 1 - P < .49$$

which is then restated as

$$.51 < P < .71$$

The two methods agree fairly closely because N is large and the sample proportion is near .50.

3. For $p = .10$ and $N = 20$, the normal approximation, using p as an estimate of P in the formula, leads to the following estimate of the 95 percent confidence interval.

$$.00 < P < .23$$

The lower confidence limit is taken as .00 because P could not be negative. Graphical approximation gives the following.

$$.01 < P < .31$$

Here the two methods give quite different results. The graphical method is better in this case because it takes into account the skewness of the sampling distribution.

The Standard Error of r

Many of the older textbooks in statistics give formulas for σ_r, the standard error of r. These are of extremely limited utility because in most cases the sampling distribution of r cannot be approximated by the normal distribution. Since r cannot assume values outside of the range -1.00 to $+1.00$, its sampling distribution becomes greatly skewed when the universe value, ρ, differs from 0.00. Moreover, as N decreases, the degree of skewness increases (if $\rho \neq 0$). The skewness is often so great as to invalidate the use of the normal curve. Because the use of σ_r can lead to serious errors we shall limit our discussion to a more modern procedure which does not suffer from such limitations.

The z transformation of r. R. A. Fisher has provided a method of transforming values of r to another statistic which follows very closely the normal distribution. He denotes these transformed values by z. However, in order to avoid confusion of Fisher's z with normal deviates, which are commonly designated by the same symbol, we shall use the symbol z_r for this transformation.

$$z_r = \tfrac{1}{2} \log_e(1 + r) - \tfrac{1}{2} \log_e(1 - r) \tag{61}$$

$$\text{or} \quad z_r = 1.1513 \left[\log_{10} \frac{1 + r}{1 - r} \right] \tag{61a}$$

Tables *F* and *G* in the Appendix make it possible for you to transform r to z_r, or z_r to r, without using the formulas.

In Table *F* values of z_r increase by progressively greater steps as r increases by equal amounts in either direction from 0.00. As r approaches ±1.00, z_r approaches ∞. Consequently, very slight differences in r in the region of ±1.00 produce tremendous changes in z_r. As a result of this progressively greater "stretching" of the scale of z_r as r becomes larger, the possible sampling variation of z_r has no upper and lower limit, as does that of r. Thus, the sampling distribution of z_r is symmetrical regardless of the size of z_ρ (the z corresponding to the population value of the coefficient of correlation). Moreover, it is very close to the normal distribution for any value of z_ρ. Finally, for a specified *N*, the sampling distribution is exactly the same for any value of z_ρ.

The standard error of z_r is given by

$$\sigma_{z_r} = \frac{1}{\sqrt{N - 3}} \tag{62}*$$

Confidence Intervals for *r*

The following procedure provides an easy and accurate method for obtaining confidence intervals for r.

1. Transform the observed r to a value of z_r by using Table *F*.
2. Find σ_{z_r} from formula (62).
3. Compute $z_r \pm 2.58\sigma_{z_r}$ (or the appropriate values for any desired level of confidence). This gives the confidence interval for z_ρ.
4. Find the values of r in Table *G* which correspond to the confidence limits for z_ρ. These limits define the confidence interval for ρ.

---

* Note that this formula, unlike most standard error formulas, does not call for the estimate of a parameter.

Example:

To find the 95 percent confidence interval for ρ when $r = .79$ and $N = 50$.

$$z_r = 1.071 \quad \text{(from Table } F\text{)}$$

$$\sigma_{z_r} = \frac{1}{\sqrt{50 - 3}} = .1459$$

$$z_r - 1.96(.1459) < z_\rho < z_r + 1.96(.1459)$$
$$.785 < z_\rho < 1.357$$

The confidence limits for ρ are found from Table G as

$$.66 < \rho < .88$$

EXERCISES

1. It has been claimed that body build and intelligence are not correlated. In a sample of seventy-five male college freshmen, the correlation between height-weight ratios and intelligence test scores was found to be $r = +.16$. Does this result agree with the hypothesis that $\rho = 0.00$?

2. If the weights of 100 rats used in a certain experiment had a standard deviation of 4.7 grams, compute the 96 percent confidence interval for σ.

3. Find the 95 percent confidence interval for the population from which each of the following was drawn.
   a) $r = -.62,\ N = 20$
   b) $r = +.53,\ N = 125$
   c) $p = .372,\ N = 200$
   d) $p = .807,\ N = 25$
   e) Mdn $= 67.8,\ S = 9.2,\ N = 63$ $(df = ?)$
   f) $p = .25,\ N = 12$

4. If the population of public opinion were evenly split on a particular question, how likely is it that in a random sample of 100 there would be 63 in favor of the proposal? Justify the estimate of P which you use in formula (59).

5. If a manufacturer can tolerate no more than 8 percent defects in the output of his factory, and a sample of 50 includes 5 defective units, should he stop production in order to track down the source of the difficulty? Describe three methods which might be used and justify your preference for one of them.

6. Suppose that you want to take a public opinion poll on a certain issue. You hope to be able to conclude that people are generally opposed to the issue, but you cannot afford to take too great a risk by acting on this conclusion when it might be wrong. You have reason to believe that that opinion is almost evenly divided. What will you do to guard yourself against running a large risk of error?

7. On the basis of a sample of 200 cases, which produced $r = .45$, a test publisher claims that his test of academic aptitude is a good predictor of grades in social studies courses. Evaluate his claim, using the material of this chapter and of Chapter VII.

8. For the situation described in Problem 6, how could you obtain data which would permit you to conclude that $\sigma_p \leq .02$? (Hint: Under what conditions will σ_p be as large as possible for a given N?)

SAMPLING DISTRIBUTIONS

In this chapter we have seen how knowledge of sampling distributions enables us to formulate at any desired level of confidence inductive inferences concerning the parameters of the universe from which a sample was drawn. We have considered three kinds of probability distributions which have many applications in problems of statistical inference: the binomial distribution, the normal curve, and the distribution of t. Two others, the F-distribution and the distribution of chi square will be discussed in later chapters.

In general, a sampling distribution is a *theoretical* probability distribution of the values of some statistic, such as a mean or proportion, which summarizes the possible outcomes of samples of N observations randomly drawn from a specified population. We must clearly distinguish *sampling distributions* from two other kinds of distributions of interest to statisticians. The first of these, which was described in Chapter III, is the observed *sample distribution,* or frequency distribution. This is simply a summary or description of the data contained in a particular sample. The other is the *theoretical* population distribution, which describes the relative frequencies in the universe of the possible observations which fall into the various measurement intervals or categories of classification.

After *assuming* a specified population distribution, it is possible to derive mathematically the theoretical sampling distribution of any statistic which might be used to describe samples. Clearly, the number of different sampling distributions is extremely large, depending on how many different kinds of populations we can imagine and how many different kinds of statistics we can invent to describe samples. Furthermore, as we have seen, the sampling distribution of a particular statistic randomly drawn from a specified population is different for different values of N.

In using statistical methods we can choose a descriptive statistic (or invent one) which serves our purpose. We also can usually choose how large a sample to use and take the necessary precautions to be reasonably satisfied that it is a *random* sample. The nature of the population distribution, on the other hand, is not under our control and it is usually unknown. Consequently, we must select from available theoretical distributions a mathematical model which can be assumed to be a reasonably good approximation of the real population distribution.

Fortunately, when N is large the sampling distributions of many statistics are known to be relatively insensitive to differences in the population distribution and we can use these measures with large samples drawn from a variety of populations. With small samples, however, most methods of statistical inference must be applied with caution.

Sampling distributions, it must be remembered, are abstract mathematical models. They are derived as the logical consequence of certain carefully stated assumptions. To the extent that these assumptions are not true in any situation where statistical inferences are drawn from observed data, the inferences are subject to error. Such errors, unlike errors of random sampling, do not lend themselves to quantitative statements in terms of probability. In fact, such errors are often unrecognized and, for that reason, they constitute a serious hazard.

The research worker must always recognize the possibility that the assumptions required by his statistical analysis are not met by his method of research or by the nature of the universe he is studying. He can never know enough about all of the factors present in a particular research situation to be sure that the assumptions are completely fulfilled. For that reason he must be alert to discover instances of failure to fulfill assumptions. If such instances are discovered, he need not necessarily conclude that the particular statistical method must not be used. He should rather consider carefully what effect this failure to meet assumptions is likely to have on the sampling distribution and what the practical consequences might be.

Abstract mathematical models are seldom, if ever, exactly realized in practice. They must be considered as ideals which only approximate the actual data of observation. The important question is whether or not the abstract model is an *adequate* approximation.

There is no rule of thumb for determining how close the approximation must be to be considered adequate. This often can be decided on the basis of the consequences of an erroneous inference. The mean and standard deviation of tensile strength in runs of steel wire produced by a factory must be estimated much more precisely if the wire is to be used for suspension bridge cables than if it is to be used for fencing poultry.

SUGGESTED READING

1. Walker, H. M., and Lev, J. *Statistical Inference,* chap. ii. New York: Henry Holt and Co., 1953.

CHAPTER X

Testing Hypotheses by Single Samples

Inferences about the universe from which a sample has been drawn are of two types: (1) the definition of a confidence interval for a parameter and (2) the decision of whether to accept or reject a particular statement about the universe. The statistical theory underlying these two types of inference is the same but the methods used in applying the theory are not the same because the questions to be answered are different. In the first type of problem we must find two values which define the limits of an interval to be used in *estimating a parameter*. In the second our purpose is to decide from the evidence of the sample whether to accept, or reject as implausible, a particular hypothesis. Here our problem is that of *making a decision*.

Decisions to accept or to reject a hypothesis are always subject to error except in the rare, and perhaps never attained, situation where an entire population is measured without error. But even though subject to error, such decisions are valuable if we know the likelihood of their being wrong. Judgments which cannot be so evaluated are dangerous because they can lead the unwary to preposterous conclusions. On the other hand, judgments made in full awareness of their probability of error keep us on guard and preserve a healthy attitude of skepticism.

As a result of the nature of inductive inference we usually can have more confidence in the judgment that a hypothesis is false than in the judgment that it is true. In fact, convincing proof of the truth of a hypothesis is seldom possible because a statistic computed from any random sample is always within the expected range of sampling variation from a number of hypothetical population values, any of which might be true. In contrast with this, a sample of data can differ so greatly from a preformulated specific hypothesis that no reasonable person would be willing to argue that the hypothesis is true.

For example, suppose someone asserts that $\mu = 4$ feet for the population of mean heights of adult males in the U.S. It is likely that a random sample of 500 such measurements would lead us to reject the hypothesis. However, it is rather unlikely that the same sample would persuade us to reject the hypothesis that $\mu = 5$ feet 8.5 inches. But would such a result prove that the population mean is exactly 5 feet 8.5 inches? Might not the mean height actually be 5 feet 8.39 inches, or 5 feet 8.6 inches, etc.? Even if the sample mean turned out to be 5 feet 8.5 inches, in exact agreement with the hypothesis, that result could not be accepted as proof because it might well be a sampling deviation from any one of a large number of reasonably acceptable hypothetical values.

The only way to prove a particular hypothesis is to measure accurately every individual in the universe. Otherwise, there always remains a possibility that the addition of one more case to the sample will change the result. For this reason, evidence concerning the truth of a hypothesis is usually stated as a confidence interval. On the other hand, even a small sample is sufficient to cast reasonable doubt on many hypotheses about the universe from which it was drawn.

THE DECISION MAKING PROCESS

The objective procedure usually followed in arriving at statistical decisions having a known risk of error can be viewed as a sequence of four separate steps: (1) precise statement of the hypothesis to be tested, (2) selection of an appropriate statistical test, (3) computation of the risk of error, (4) decision to accept or reject the hypothesis. These will now be considered in some detail as we apply this decision making process to an experimental problem.

The Experiment

A man asserts that he senses a vague feeling of restlessness whenever someone is staring at him. In order to test his claim we will ask him to sit for 30 minutes in a room equipped with a one-way visual screen. He can be seen through this screen, but he cannot see through it. Near the end of each successive three-minute period a buzzer will sound in the room, whereupon the subject is to record on a sheet of paper whether or not he feels restless. He will be informed before the experiment that there are to be 10 reports and that five of them will come at times when someone is staring at him through the one-way screen. Before the experiment begins we will determine by some random procedure, such as rolling a die, which five periods these will be.

Formulating the Hypothesis

On the surface the experiment seems to test the hypothesis that the man is sensitive to staring, and that actually is our reason for performing the experiment. But this hypothesis is unsatisfactory for statistical purposes because it is too vague and ambiguous to permit precise testing. Does it mean that the subject is always sensitive? If so, one failure on his part would lead to rejection, and this decision would run no risk of error. Experimental evidence could not possibly prove this hypothesis because no finite number of trials could exhaust the possibility of failure on the next one. Suppose, the hypothesis states that he is sensitive 95 percent of the time. This could be tested by our method, but it is only one of an infinity of similar hypotheses and there is no obvious reason why this particular statement should be singled out for special treatment.

The ultimate object of an experimental test—in this case the hypothesis that our subject is sensitive to staring—is often referred to as the *experimental hypothesis.* Since it is usually stated in terms which do not lead directly to a statistical test, we must formulate another statement which can be tested. This testable statement is known as a *null hypothesis,* and is denoted by H_0.

The essential nature of a null hypothesis is found in Fisher's statement, "Every experiment must be said to exist only in order to give the facts a chance of disproving the null hypothesis."[*] In our experiment the null hypothesis is that the subject's judgments are not influenced by the fact that someone is staring at him.

Our H_0 can be stated in different ways, all of which are logically equivalent. For example: "The proportion of the subject's judgments which are correct differs only by chance from the hypothesis that $P = .50$" or "The population mean of sample differences between the observed proportion and .50 is zero." The null hypothesis is formulated in slightly different ways depending on the particular problem being studied. In most general form, however,

---

[*] R. A. Fisher, *The Design of Experiments* (4th ed.; London: Oliver and Boyd, 1947), p. 16.

H_0 is a statement of no difference between a population of experimental observations and some meaningful frame of reference.

Selecting an Appropriate Test

The choice of a statistical test can be made best before the experiment is performed. Knowing the assumptions and conditions required for legitimate use of different mathematical models, the research worker can design an experiment which fits the model he intends to use. In this way he can avoid the embarrassment of discovering too late that a laboriously acquired mass of data defies meaningful interpretation. In planning an experiment it is always desirable to consider the various ways it might turn out and to decide how each possible outcome will be interpreted. The subject's task in the present experiment will be to designate the 5 reports which are called for while someone is staring at him. There are 6 possible results: he might get none, 1, 2, 3, 4, or 5 correct. Probabilities of the possible results are easily computed from the numbers of ways in which the various scores can occur. There is only one way of getting a score of 5 correct. Similarly, there is only one way to obtain a score of 0. Four correct judgments can occur in 25 different ways. This is ascertained by reasoning as follows: There are 5 correct choices from which the subject must select 4. The number of ways in which he could do this is simply $\binom{5}{4}$, computed by formula (40). But to get a score of 4 he must have 4 correct *and 1 wrong*. For each possible combination of 4 right there are 5 possible ways of doing this. Thus the total ways in which he could get 4 right *and 1 wrong* is given by $5 \cdot 5 = 25$. Similar reasoning leads to the conclusion that there are 100 possible ways of getting 3 right and 2 wrong.

These and other possible outcomes of the experiment can now be brought together in the form of a *sampling distribution*. This abstract mathematical model, the sampling distribution, enables us

Score (No. right)	Possible Ways	Probability
5	1	1/252
4	25	25/252
3	100	100/252
2	100	100/252
1	25	25/252
0	1	1/252

to decide which of the 252 possible outcomes of the experiment we will be willing to accept as evidence that the subject's score differs significantly from pure chance.

The Risk of Error and the Decision

A score of four correct is rather weak evidence for rejecting H_0 because scores this high or higher are expected to happen by chance slightly more often than once in ten experiments like this one, ($26/252$). Thus, if we decide on a score of four or better to reject H_0 and to accept the alternative hypothesis that our subject possesses some degree of sensitivity to being stared at, our risk of error is $P > .10$. The decision to reject H_0 if the subject makes a score of five is more defensible because that decision is expected to be wrong only once in 252 experiments. Many experimenters are willing to take such a risk. Scores of 1, 2, 3, or 4 are so likely to happen by chance that none of these would persuade us to reject H_0, and for that reason they would not lend support to the experimental hypothesis that the subject feels uneasy when someone stares at him.

It should be noted that any of these results, regardless of our decision, require cautious qualifications concerning the universe of individuals who might do the staring, because our experiment has not been designed to provide a random sample of starers.

Five of the six possible outcomes permit reasonably clear interpretations. One constitutes evidence for rejection of H_0 and acceptance of the experimental hypothesis, and the chances of this decision being wrong are $1/256$. Four of the possible results are so likely to happen by chance that we would decide not to reject H_0. But what about the remaining possibility—a score of 0? If this should happen we will have to reject H_0 in order to be consistent with our decision to reject for a score of 5; but unlike a score of 5, this result offers no support for the experimental hypothesis. This type of problem will be considered when we compare one-tailed and two-tailed tests.

It may rightly be argued that a result expected to occur once in 252 trials by chance is not conclusive, but no experiment can lead to completely conclusive results. It can only support an interpretation which seems reasonable to expert opinion in the area under investigation.

The probability of incorrectly deciding to reject H_0 is commonly denoted by α (alpha). The question of how small α must be to justify rejection of the null hypothesis is not easily answered. In fact, the answer may be different for different experiments, depending on the circumstances. It is not possible to set a criterion which allows no error. The risk of being wrong, however, is not an insurmountable difficulty. If we recognize the fact that the results of any experiment may lead to an incorrect inference, it becomes apparent that experimental results must be interpreted, not in isolation, but in the light of many considerations outside of the data themselves. Some of the more important of these are (1) how well the mathematical model fits the experiment, (2) the adequacy of experimental controls, (3) the results already known from similar experiments, and (4) the possible loss which might result from accepting certain interpretations which turn out later to be incorrect.

Although there is no magical probability figure for the decision to reject H_0, many statisticians follow the practice of describing results which reach a standard of .05 or less as *significant* and those which reach .01 or less as *very significant.* It is better practice for the experimenter to decide in each case on an appropriate value of α to be required for rejecting H_0 *before performing the experiment,* carefully considering the consequences of such a decision and its alternative. The decision to reject or not to reject H_0 always rests ultimately on the common sense judgment of the experimenter. *Careful research customarily reports not only conclusions, but the probability of error as well* so that readers will have an objective basis for evaluating the interpretation.

EXERCISES

1. If the experiment described in this section consisted of twelve trials, the subject being instructed to select the five periods during which someone stares at him, how would you interpret the six possible results?

2. Suppose ten trials were used and the occurrence or non-occurrence of staring determined by tossing a coin just before each trial. The subject would be required to respond "yes" or "no" to each trial. Compute the probability distribution of the possible results. (According to H_0, the probability of a correct response on each trial is $P = .5$.)

TESTING HYPOTHESES

The simplest form of experiment, illustrated by the preceding example, is one in which a single sample is secured under carefully specified circumstances for the purpose of testing some previously formulated hypothesis about the population value of a statistic. If the sampling distribution of the test statistic is known, assuming H_0 to be true, the risk of error in rejecting H_0 can be specified. The probability of error in deciding to reject H_0 is sometimes computed exactly, as in the preceding example, where we used the *exact probabilities* of the possible results. But it is more convenient in most cases to *estimate* α by using mathematically derived sampling distributions, such as the normal curve or the t-distribution. Other sampling distributions and their applications will be discussed in later chapters.

Decision Errors and the Choice of a Criterion

In deciding whether or not to reject H_0 the two possible decisions have different logical implications. For this reason, statisticians distinguish two types of decision errors. If we reject the null hypothesis when it is actually true we have committed a *type 1 error*. If we decide to accept that hypothesis when it is actually false we have committed a *type 2 error*.

In choosing a criterion for rejection at a certain level of significance, $p = \alpha$, we specify the risk of a type 1 error which we are willing to accept. The criterion α is simply the proportion of a large number of samples from a universe *for which the null hypothesis is true* which would in the long run lead erroneously to rejection of this true hypothesis.

The probabilities of the two types of error are inversely related. If the null hypothesis were never rejected, regardless of how the experimental data turned out, the probability of a type 1 error would be zero, but the probability of a type 2 error would be maximum. If in every experiment we should decide to reject, there would be no risk of a type 2 error but the probability of a type 1 error would be maximum. Thus, the choice of a criterion of significance is not an arbitrary or simple matter. We shall consider briefly some of the more important factors upon which it should be based.

It is easy to specify precisely α, the probability of a type 1 error, because this sort of error can occur *only if the null hypothesis is true*. This is illustrated by the following figure, which represents the expected distribution of sample means. The mean of this sampling distribution, μ, is the same as the hypothesis being tested

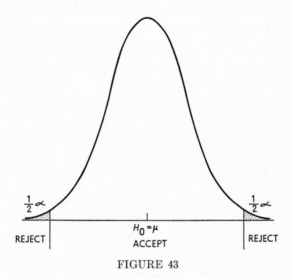

FIGURE 43

because a type 1 error would otherwise be impossible. The probability of a type 1 error is equal to the shaded proportion in both tails of the sampling distribution. Here we have decided that deviations in either direction can disprove H_0. The choice of a particular value of α, however, is not all that is involved in setting up a criterion for accepting or rejecting H_0. We must also consider the question of type 2 errors.

Now, a type 2 error can occur *only if the null hypothesis is not true*. In this case μ is not the same as the hypothesis being tested. Figure 44 represents by a solid curve the mathematical model of the distribution of sample means if H_0 is true. The broken curve represents what might be the actual distribution of sample $\bar{X}$'s around μ if H_0 is false. The shaded portion of Figure 44, usually denoted by β, represents the probability of a type 2 error if μ is actually at the point indicated in the diagram because any result in the shaded region would support the incorrect decision to accept H_0. But, of course, μ might be at *any point* other than H_0. By imagining the broken curve at various locations on the base line where $\mu \neq H_0$, it can be seen that β varies with the magnitude of the difference be-

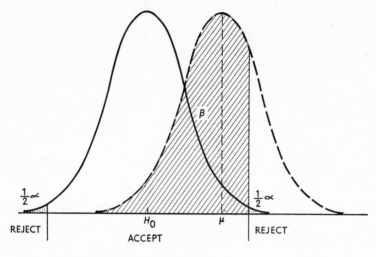

FIGURE 44

tween μ and H_0. If this difference is small the probability of a type 2 error is great. As this difference becomes larger, we are less likely to accept a false H_0 and thus commit a type 2 error. Another factor which influences the risk of a type 2 error is the value chosen for α. It can be seen from the diagram that by increasing α we can reduce β. Thus, although α, the probability of a type 1 error, can be made as small as we wish, this can be done only at the expense of increasing β.

Suppose that we have completed our experiment on sensitivity to staring and that we are now ready to interpret the results. We must choose among three possible courses of action. We can (1) reject H_0, (2) accept H_0, or (3) withhold judgment. This third choice, which is not subject to error, usually implies that we are simply postponing the decision until more data are collected or the entire experiment is repeated. This decision is often described as a failure of the experiment to disprove the null hypothesis.

If we actually decide either to accept or to reject H_0, there are four possible outcomes of that decision, each having different logical implications. These are represented by the *decision table* on the next page.

In setting up the model for the statistical test we assumed that the subject's responses were pure guess-work. If this assumption were true, the probability of a type 2 error—cell (C) of the decision table—would be zero because such an error would be possible only

DECISION TABLE

Our Decision	What Is Really True	
	He is sensitive to some degree. (H₀ is false.)	He is not sensitive. (H₀ is true.)
He is sensitive. (Reject H₀.)	(A) We are correct.	(B) We are wrong (type 1 error). $P(\text{error}) = \alpha$
He is not sensitive. (Accept H₀.)	(C) We are wrong (Type 2 error). $P(\text{error}) = \beta$	(D) We are correct.

if he were sensitive to some degree and we failed to discover that fact. If H_0, the assumption of our model, were true, the only way in which we could be wrong is shown in cell (B) of the table. The risk of being wrong in this way was freely decided by us when we chose the value of α upon which we based our decision rule.

On the other hand, should our subject really possess *some degree* of sensitivity to being stared at, the type 1 error would be impossible and the only way we could make a wrong decision is shown in cell (C) of the table. The risk of error in this situation, however, is not directly under our control. It depends on how sensitive the subject really is. In order to evaluate β we must consider what the situation would be if our subject possessed such a degree of sensitivity that he could discriminate correctly say 60 percent of the time, or 52 percent, or 79 percent, etc. For any *specified* degree of sensitivity we can compute the probability that the experimental result will fall in the acceptance region defined by our decision rule. This probability, which must be separately stated for any *specified alternative* to H_0, is β, the probability of a type 2 error.

Cell (A) of the decision table is of special interest. It represents the situation in which the experimental hypothesis is true and we correctly reach that conclusion by deciding to reject H_0. Research workers are often interested in knowing how effective their experiment is in discovering slight differences from H_0 which might really exist. For instance, if our subject really possesses even a slight degree of sensitivity to being stared at, the discovery of that fact would be an extremely important event for psychology.

The probability that a statistical test will correctly lead us to reject H_0 when it is false is known as the power of the test. Power can be described as the sensitivity of a test in detecting differences between H_0 and what is really true of the universe from which the sample was drawn. Power is defined precisely as the probability of *correctly* rejecting the null hypothesis. It is computed by

$$\text{Power} = (1 - \beta)$$

For a given decision rule β will have different values depending on the actual difference between H_0 and what is true of the universe. Similarly, the power of a test will be different for various possible alternatives to H_0 because Power $+ \beta = 1.00$. The power function of a test is a graph which shows the probability of rejecting H_0 when various alternatives to H_0 are actually true. The power of a test is not a fixed value. It is a variable which changes depending upon what alternative to H_0 is actually true.

A detailed treatment of power functions is outside the scope of an introductory text. However, it is important for the beginning student to understand the concept of power and to remember that *the power of any test can be increased by increasing N*. Increasing N reduces the variability of the sampling distribution of a statistic. This narrows the region for acceptance of H_0. These two changes decrease the likelihood that for a given difference between H_0 and what is actually true the result of an experiment will fall in the region which leads to incorrectly accepting H_0. This means that the probability of a type 2 error can be reduced by increasing the size of the sample without increasing the risk of a type 1 error. Here we can have our cake and eat it too. The sensitivity of an experiment in detecting small differences from the null hypothesis can always be increased by using a larger sample.

One-Tailed and Two-Tailed Tests

For any precise statement of H_0 the sample statistic can deviate above or below that value, and a large enough deviation in either direction constitutes a basis for deciding to reject H_0. In this case, where the value of H_0 is stated precisely, we have what is known as a two-tailed test because α is the sum of two areas, one from each tail of the sampling distribution.

In some cases, however, it is meaningful to state H_0 somewhat less precisely as an inequality, specifying that the population parameter is not greater than, or not less than a particular value. If we wish to test the hypothesis that μ *is not greater than a certain value,* μ_0, H_0 is stated as

$$\mu \leq \mu_0$$

The decision will be to reject only if $\bar{X} > \mu_0$. Thus α, the critical region of the sampling distribution is entirely in the upper tail of the curve, which is the reason for the expression "one-tailed test." These two types of test are illustrated below. In both cases the critical region α is the same in value, but the location of α is different.

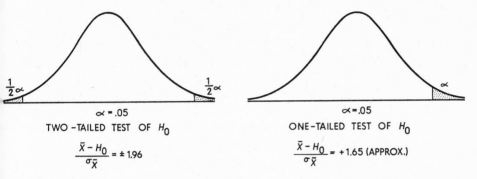

TWO–TAILED TEST OF H_0 ONE–TAILED TEST OF H_0

$\alpha = .05$ $\alpha = .05$

$$\frac{\bar{X} - H_0}{\sigma_{\bar{X}}} = \pm 1.96$$

$$\frac{\bar{X} - H_0}{\sigma_{\bar{X}}} = +1.65 \text{ (APPROX.)}$$

FIGURE 45

If an experimenter is interested in the probability of a deviation exceeding a given value in one direction and if his null hypothesis states that the sample mean is not significantly greater than (or less than) the population mean, the hypothesis is properly evaluated by a one-tailed test. Of course, this hypothesis must be formulated independently of the data which provide the test. It would not be logically sound to collect data and then, only after having discovered the direction of deviation, to apply a one-tailed test. If this were done with a large number of samples drawn from the same population 10 percent of those samples would be expected to exceed the 5 percent point of significance. The effect of this would be to make the actual risk of a type 1 error twice as great as that implied in the stated value of α.

If, on the other hand, an experiment is exploratory and there is no independent reason for expecting deviations in one direction rather than the other, the appropriate null hypothesis is simply that the sample was drawn from a specified universe. Deviations in *either* direction provide evidence concerning the tenability of this hypothesis. The significance of such deviations is properly evaluated by a two-tailed test.

Before illustrating these two types of test by numerical examples, we will first define in general terms the statistic used in evaluating hypotheses according to the normal distribution model.

The "Critical Ratio"

The ratio obtained by dividing the deviation of a statistic from the hypothetical parameter by the standard deviation of its sampling distribution is called a *critical ratio*. This ratio, often denoted by C.R., is actually the z of the normal distribution. Since it is interpreted with reference to that distribution it should be used only when the sampling distribution of the test statistic is reasonably normal. In general, critical ratios are of the form

$$\text{C.R.} = z = \frac{\text{test statistic} - \text{hypothetical parameter}}{\sigma \text{ of sampling distribution}} \tag{63}$$

When N is large hypotheses regarding μ can be tested with reference to tables of the normal distribution by

$$z = \frac{\bar{X} - \mu_0}{s_{\bar{x}}} \tag{64}$$

Because this method is only an approximation, which can lead to serious errors of interpretation when N is small, most experimenters now use the t-ratio, which can be used with samples of any size.

Although the critical ratio has been superseded in many instances by more modern techniques, it is still used with test statistics which are known to be normally distributed, or which are so distributed that the use of the mathematical model of the normal distribution does not introduce serious error.

For instance, medians of *large* samples drawn from a *normal population* can be assumed to have a normal sampling distribution. A good estimate of the standard deviation of this normal distribution is provided by

$$s_{\text{Mdn}} = \frac{1.253s}{\sqrt{N}} \tag{54}$$

Thus, hypotheses regarding the median of a normal population can be tested with large samples by

$$z = \frac{\text{Mdn} - \text{Mdn}_0}{s_{\text{Mdn}}}$$

The standard error of a proportion was given earlier by

$$\sigma_p = \sqrt{\frac{PQ}{N}} \tag{59}$$

Our earlier discussion (pp. 182–86) showed that the sampling distribution of p can be considered approximately normal when both NP and NQ are greater than 5. Thus, when these conditions are met hypotheses about P can be tested by

$$z = \frac{p - P_0}{\sigma_p}$$

It is important to note that the value of P in (59) should be the hypothesized population proportion and not the proportion observed in the sample.

Examples:

A widely used test of college aptitude has been standardized so that $\bar{X} = 500$ and $S = 100$. Suppose that in a certain college the entering class of 216 freshmen made a mean score of 512 on this test. Having noted that this class apparently differs from the standard, we might ask, "Does the mean of this class *differ significantly* from the population upon which the test was standardized?"

$$H_0 : \mu = 500$$
$$S_{\bar{x}} = \frac{100}{\sqrt{215}} = 6.7$$
$$z = \frac{512 - 500}{6.7} = +1.8$$

From Table C we find that .072 of the area under the normal curve lies outside of the range $\mu \pm 1.8\sigma$. Since one out of fourteen means of random samples of this size is expected to deviate this much or more from 500, the evidence does not seem sufficient to reject the null hypothesis. Thus we conclude that the mean of this class is not significantly different from 500.

Now, suppose that apart from the sample of test scores there are reasons to believe that this college attracts superior students. If so, we might ask, "Is the mean of this class *significantly higher* than 500?" The experimental hypothesis is that this class is a sample from a population with $\mu > 500$. This leads to a statement of H_0 as

$$\mu \leq 500$$

The C.R. is computed as above. From Table C we find that .036 of the area under the normal curve is *above* $\mu + 1.8\sigma$. The probability is thus .036 that the mean of a random sample this size would deviate this much or more *above* 500. Since there is less than one chance in twenty-five that a random sample would have this *high* a mean, we might conclude that this is a superior group of freshmen.

In a random sample of 100 qualified voters, 63 state that they are opposed to a bond issue to be voted upon one week hence. What is likely to be the result of the election if public opinion does not shift between now and election day?

$$H_0 : P = .50$$

$$\sigma_p = \sqrt{\frac{PQ}{N}} = \sqrt{\frac{(.5)(.5)}{100}} = .05$$

$$z = \frac{p - P_0}{\sigma_p} = \frac{.63 - .50}{.05} = 2.6$$

We find from Table C that $p < .01$ for a two-tailed test. Thus, we decide to reject H_0 and to predict that the measure is unlikely to pass.

Here, we have used a two-tailed test of H_0, and although it now appears reasonable to predict the direction of the majority, we should not use the α of the one-tailed test as a measure of the risk incurred because the direction was predicted only *after the outcome of the poll was known.*

The *t*-ratio

The best test of any hypotheses about μ, and the one which is especially appropriate when N is small, is the t-ratio. The normally distributed z is an acceptable approximation when N is large, but as N decreases the normal distribution systematically under-estimates α, the probability of a type 1 error, because the error in estimating σ is systematically related to N. This error can seriously distort the estimate of α when $N < 30$. Table E lists for various df's the critical values which t must reach for a two-tailed test to be significant at the .10, .05, .02, .01, and .001 levels.

When t is used as a one-tailed test the values in the columns correspond to the .05, .025, .01, .005, and .0005 probability points.

It is customary to represent the estimate of $\sigma_{\bar{x}}$ in the t formula by $s_{\bar{x}}$.

$$t = \frac{\bar{X} - \mu_0}{s_{\bar{x}}}, \quad \text{where} \quad s_{\bar{x}} = \frac{s}{\sqrt{N}}, \quad \text{and} \quad s = \sqrt{\frac{\Sigma x^2}{N-1}}$$

Testing the significance of r. The r obtained from a sample can be tested against the H_0 that $\rho = .00$. The t-ratio provides a convenient test of this hypothesis, where

$$t = \frac{r}{\sqrt{\dfrac{1-r^2}{N-2}}} \tag{65}$$

The t-ratio computed from formula (65) is interpreted in relation to the values in Table E for $N-2$ degrees of freedom, where N is the number of pairs of observations. This test may be applied to samples of any size.

It must be remembered that the t-ratio provides a test of whether the observed r differs significantly from $H_0:\rho = .00$. Even though r proves to be significantly different from zero, it may be of little value either in reducing errors of prediction or in accounting for variance in Y.

EXERCISES

DATA *F*: SCORES OF 198 COLLEGE FRESH-
MEN ON THE ACE PSYCHOLOGICAL EXAMI-
NATION, 1944 EDITION, SEPTEMBER, 1947

Score	Frequency
175–179	2
170–174	0
165–169	1
160–164	8
155–159	10
150–154	19
145–149	14
140–144	14
135–139	22
130–134	25
125–129	30
120–124	26
115–119	17
110–114	1
105–109	3
100–104	1
95– 99	3
90– 94	1
85– 89	1

1. The authors of the ACE Psychological Examination report that 29,781 freshmen in 187 colleges had a distribution of scores with $M = 106.44$. Test the hypothesis that the scores in Data F were randomly drawn from a population having that mean.

2. The authors report further that the standard deviation for these 29,781 freshmen was 26.65. Test the hypothesis that Data F were drawn from a population having that σ. [Use formula (55).]

3. Suppose $r = .32$. How large must N be for us to reject at the .01 level the hypothesis that the true correlation is zero?

4. If $N = 25$, how large must r be for us to reject at the .05 level the H_0 that $\rho = .00$?

5. Apply the t-ratio formula (65) to Exercise 1, p. 188 and compare the result with that obtained by using z_r and σ_{z_r}.

6. A public opinion poll of 300 voters showed that 183 favored a proposed legislation. Test at the .05 point of significance the hypothesis that this bill will receive *at least* 50 percent of the vote.

7. It is known that the mortality rate for a certain disease is at least 15 percent. In a sample of 100 patients suffering from this disease who were treated with a new drug, 92 recovered. State the appropriate hypothesis to be used in testing the effectiveness of the drug and the probability of a type 1 error. Does this call for a one- or two-tailed test?

8. In 50 trials with two weights which differ only slightly, a blindfolded subject correctly selects the heavier one 32 times. Test the hypothesis that the subject is unable to discriminate this slight difference.

9. In a mental telepathy experiment a subject is told that a box contains 1 of 5 objects and that he is to try to guess which object it is. He is given a total of 25 trials, in which the objects occur in a random order. (They do not necessarily appear an equal number of times.) How many trials must he get right in order to convince you that his judgments are influenced by something other than chance factors?

10. Suppose that r is computed for the following data.

Subject	X	Y
A	15	10
B	23	16

Would r be the same value for any sample where $N = 2$ and there is variation in both X and Y? Explain the connection between this and the fact that $df = N - 2$ when the t-ratio is used to test the hypothesis that $\rho = .00$.

11. Given: $r = .61$ and $N = 65$, test the following hypotheses about ρ: (a) $\rho = .00$, (b) $\rho = .70$, (c) $\rho = .60$.

LIMITATIONS OF THE SINGLE-SAMPLE EXPERIMENT

In this chapter we have discussed the more common statistical methods for testing hypotheses by means of a single sample. Although single samples are adequate for some purposes, such as testing the prediction deduced from a carefully formulated theory or discovering significant deviations from established standards in the product of a factory, most psychological problems can be handled better by experiments designed to compare two or more groups of data. Such comparisons require the use of statistical methods devised for testing the significance of differences between the values of a statistic computed from different samples. These methods will be discussed in the next chapter.

To illustrate the source of error which often invalidates experimental tests based on a single sample, we shall again describe an imaginary experiment. Suppose an instructor announces to his class that an experiment in mental telepathy is about to be performed. He proposes to toss a coin 5 times and to concentrate for 30 seconds on the outcome after each toss. At the end of each period of concentration the students are instructed to record on a sheet of paper their guess as to the outcome of the preceding toss. The papers are collected and at the next class period the instructor announces the mean number of correct guesses for the 100 students in the class to be 3.02.

If the probability is assumed to be .5 for a correct guess in a single trial, the mean number correct in 100 sets of 5 trials is expected to be $np = 2.5$. The standard deviation of the population of sets of 5 is $\sqrt{npq} = 1.118$ and $\sigma_{\bar{x}}$ for samples of 100 sets is .1118.* The critical ratio is found to be $z = \dfrac{3.02 - 2.5}{.1118} = 4.6$, and H_0 is rejected.

---

* Here, $\sigma_{\bar{x}}$ is computed exactly as $\sigma/\sqrt{N}$ because we are dealing with a theoretical sampling distribution rather than an estimate obtained from a sample.

The decision to reject H_0 may run a risk considerably greater than the value of α associated with $z = 4.6$ because our original assumption may be invalid. We have used a model which assumes that a student's guess is equally likely to be "heads" or "tails" for each trial, and that the coin is equally likely to fall either way. If the assumption is correct, the four possible combinations of guess and coin are equally likely to occur, and since there are two possible ways for them to agree, the probability of agreement is .5. A critical assumption of our model is that each guess in the series of five is *independent*. It is reasonable to assume independence for the five separate tosses of the coin since "the coin has no memory," but it is known that the responses of a human being in a series of this sort are not independent. Each guess is affected by the individual's preceding responses and by his knowledge that the series consists of five trials. When asked to guess how a coin will turn in such a series, people show much greater preference for a sequence such as HTHHT than for TTTTH, although both are equally probable in the actual tossing of an unbiased coin. If a preferred sequence should occur by chance in the tosses of the coin, H_0 will be rejected, and properly so. But rejection of H_0 does not constitute evidence for the experimental hypothesis of mental telepathy. *The statistical test of H_0 does not identify the factors responsible for significant results.*

Of course, a single-sample experiment could be used here if we know the correct probability values for the different sequences of guesses, but even if these were known computation would present a formidable problem. A better way of attacking most research problems in psychology is to compare data collected under control conditions with observations obtained in the presence of the experimental variable.

SUGGESTED READINGS

1. Dixon, W. J., and Massey, F. J. *Introduction to Statistical Analysis,* chap. xiv. New York: McGraw-Hill Book Co., 1951.
2. Siegel, S. *Nonparametric Statistics for the Behavioral Sciences,* chaps. ii and iii. New York: McGraw-Hill Book Co., 1956.
3. Smith, K. "Distribution-free Statistical Method and the Concept of Power Efficiency," in Festinger, L., and Katz, D. (eds.). *Research Methods in the Behavioral Sciences.* New York: The Dryden Press, 1953.

EXERCISES

1. Could the illustrative experiment discussed at the beginning of this chapter be improved by designing it for the comparison of two samples of data? Describe how this might be done and compare the two designs.

2. Suppose a pupil answers fifteen questions correctly on a multiple choice examination containing a total of forty questions. Each question has four choices, only one of which is correct. How would you test the hypothesis that the pupil knows nothing about the subject matter of the examination? State as many as you can of the assumptions required by your statistical test and indicate how a decision to reject H_0 should be qualified.

CHAPTER XI

Group Comparisons

Although it is sometimes useful to test with a single sample some hypothetical value of a parameter, a more common experimental problem is that of discovering possible relationships between two variables. Experiments of this type endeavor to answer questions such as: Is there a difference between high school boys and girls in mechanical aptitude? Is reaction time affected by the loudness of an auditory stimulus? Is the proportion of Republicans greater among men in the highest 10 percent of annual income than among the lowest 10 percent? Is the correlation between IQ and grade in a freshman mathematics course higher among boys than among girls? Is social adjustment in the first grade affected by prior nursery school experience?

In experiments such as these, one characteristic, the *dependent variable* (Y), is sampled under two or more conditions defined by systematically varying the *independent variable* (X). The data lead to a decision as to whether or not observed differences in the dependent variable can reasonably be asserted to be greater than expected chance variation from sample to sample where the independent variable remains constant.

A simple form of this type of experiment is one in which Y is measured for only two levels of X. Such experiments are designed to test whether or not X and Y are significantly related without attempting to describe the nature of the relationship. The experimental hypothesis is the simple statement that Y is greater for one level of X than for the other and H_0 states that the population difference between the values of a statistic computed from the two distributions of Y is zero. The X-classification can be made according to qualitative categories, presence or absence of a certain attribute, or a numerical measurement.

If observations of Y have been secured under a number of conditions of X, and if X and Y can be described by interval scales, the relationship between them can often be represented by the graph of a mathematical equation. We have seen how r can be used to describe such data by a *linear equation* and how the question of whether X and Y are linearly related can be answered by testing the H_0 that $\rho = .00$. Of course, the form of the relationship cannot be discovered if only two levels of the independent variable are used.

TESTING A MEAN DIFFERENCE BETWEEN TWO EXPERIMENTAL CONDITIONS

The *t*-ratio

In an experiment designed to discover if muscle tension affects rote memorization, twelve subjects memorized nonsense syllables under normal conditions, and while squeezing on a hand dynamometer. Two lists of syllables, of equal difficulty, were randomly assigned to the control and tension condition for each subject, and a coin was tossed to determine the order in which the two conditions were to be presented. The following table shows for each subject the number of correct anticipations in six trials.

Subject	Tension	Control	D (Tension-Control)
A	78	68	10
B	38	30	8
C	81	57	24
D	61	46	15
E	55	38	17
F	61	39	22
G	82	65	17
H	51	53	−2
I	55	37	18
J	69	44	25
K	55	41	14
L	59	76	−17

$$\Sigma D = +151$$
$$\bar{D} = +12.6$$

It appears that memorization scores are higher under tension than under the control condition. The mean difference, $\bar{D}$, is $+12.6$, and in only two instances out of twelve is the tension condition inferior. Reasonable as it may appear, however, such a conclusion should be accompanied by a statement of the probability of a type 1 error.

The null hypothesis to be tested is that the mean difference in the population from which the sample was drawn is zero. Since the sample is small we choose the t-distribution rather than the normal curve. The method of computation is shown below.

Subject	Tension	Control	D	D^2
A	78	68	10	100
B	38	30	8	64
C	81	57	24	576
D	61	46	15	225
E	55	38	17	289
F	61	39	22	484
G	82	65	17	289
H	51	53	-2	4
I	55	37	18	324
J	69	44	25	625
K	55	41	14	196
L	59	76	-17	289

$$\bar{D} = \frac{151}{12} = 12.58 \qquad \Sigma D = +151 \quad \Sigma D^2 = 3465$$

$$S_D = \frac{1}{12} \sqrt{12(3465) - (151)^2} = 11.4$$

$$s_{\bar{D}} = \frac{11.4}{\sqrt{12 - 1}} = 3.43$$

$$t = \frac{\bar{D} - H_0}{s_{\bar{D}}} = \frac{12.58}{3.43} = 3.67$$

Entering Table E with 11 df, since there are eleven independent observations of $(D - \bar{D})$, we find $p < .01$.

Before deciding whether to accept or reject H_0, we must satisfy ourselves that the model is appropriate for this particular experiment. In other words, we must ask whether the sample of data was obtained in a manner which does not seriously violate the mathematical assumptions of the theoretical distribution of t. For the present problem these assumptions can be stated as

1. $\mu = 0$ (this is the null hypothesis which is being tested).
2. Random samples of any given size would yield a normal sampling distribution of $\bar{D}$, having a mean equal to μ. This requires for small samples that the differences, themselves, are normally distributed.
3. The data constitute a random sample.

Now, if all three assumptions are correct, t-ratios computed from experiments of this sort will have a known probability of exceeding the values shown in Table E. In the present experiment, *if all three assumptions are correct,* we have obtained a result which would occur less than once in 100 similar experiments. Thus, if the second and third assumptions are correct, we can reject H_0 at the $p < .01$ level of significance. On the other hand, if there is reason to doubt the correctness of the second or third assumption, we cannot estimate α by this method. Ordinary care in designing experimental projects is usually sufficient to justify the assumption of random sampling. But the assumption of normality is extremely difficult to justify when working with small samples since they do not contain enough information.

The critical assumption implied in this application of the *t*-ratio is clearly that the data are drawn from a normal universe. In some cases this appears reasonable in view of what is known from other studies of the phenomenon being investigated. In other instances, particularly in exploratory and pioneering research, adequate information is not available, and sometimes the evidence leads to serious doubt concerning this assumption.

Another assumption of the *t*-ratio, which is implied when we assume that $\bar{D}$ has a normal sampling distribution, is that the original measurements are points on an interval scale. Even though this is not strictly true, it is usually justifiable to consider the sampling distribution of $\bar{D}$ to be approximately normal and to use the *t*-distribution for this type of problem.

Sometimes the original data are known to be on an ordinal scale of measurement which does not even remotely resemble an interval scale. Sometimes it is known that the population of possible measurements differs so much from the normal distribution that the sampling distribution of $\bar{D}$ cannot be taken as approximately normal. Fortunately these conditions are rare, but when they occur it is necessary to use other methods.

The Sign Test

In recent years mathematical statisticians have devised procedures known as "nonparametric statistics," or more appropriately as "distribution-free statistics." The models used in these tests make fewer or less restrictive assumptions about the population than are required by the *t*-distribution and the normal curve.

One of the simplest distribution-free methods is the sign test, which is applicable in all cases where the same subjects have been observed under a control and an experimental condition. In using this test only two basic assumptions must be met. First it is assumed that the difference for each pair of scores is randomly drawn from a universe of differences with median equal to zero. This is the H_0 which is to be tested. (Another way of stating H_0 is to specify equal probability that the experimental or the control measurement will be higher for each subject.) The second assumption is that each difference between paired measurements is independent of all the others. This requirement is ordinarily easy to meet. Nothing is assumed about the scale of measurement beyond the ordinal relationship required for us to perceive differences and to specify their direction.

We will now apply this test to the data of the experiment on muscle tension. Each difference is given a sign depending on its direction, the number of each kind of sign is counted, and the null hypothesis will be rejected if the proportion of positive signs differs significantly from .50. The appropriate model is the binomial distribution, which was described in Chapter VIII.*

Subject	Tension	Control	Sign
A	78	68	+
B	38	30	+
C	81	57	+
D	61	46	+
E	55	38	+
F	61	39	+
G	82	65	+
H	51	53	−
I	55	37	+
J	69	44	+
K	55	41	+
L	59	76	−

Expected proportion of +'s: $P_{hyp} = .50$

$$\sigma_p = \sqrt{\frac{PQ_{hyp}}{N}} = \sqrt{\frac{(.5)(.5)}{12}} = .144$$

Observed proportion of +'s: $p = 10/12 = .83$

$$\text{C.R.} = z = \frac{.83 - .50}{.144} = 2.29\dagger$$

---

* It is customary to discard cases in which ties occur, although if there are a large number of ties they should be handled by methods described in more advanced treatments.

† A simpler computational scheme is given by formula (79), p. 241.

From Table C, using the normal approximation, we find the probability of a difference this large in either direction to be $p = .022$. A more accurate figure is obtained if we consider the discrete number 10, the observed number of $+$'s, as having a lower limit at 9.5. With this correction for continuity, $p = .79$ and the critical ratio is 2.01, which gives the probability of a difference this large in either direction as $p = .044$. Either of these results supports the decision to reject H_0 at the 5 percent level of significance.

Although H_0 is evaluated by using either the binomial distribution or the normal curve, the sign test is still distribution free because *very little is assumed about the population sampled by the basic experimental operations.* The validity of a sampling distribution for evaluating significance depends on the statement of H_0 and not necessarily on assumptions about the population of original data. It is important to note that the assumptions made in using any statistical test are of two kinds. One kind concerns the hypothesis which the experiment sets out directly to test. The other assumptions are descriptions of the mathematical model of the sampling distribution which provides a probability statement for decision errors. We actually decide to reject the sampling model when an unlikely result occurs. But rather than rejecting the entire model as incorrect, we want to disprove a particular aspect of it, namely H_0. This can be done only if we are able to accept all other assumptions implied by the model as essentially correct approximations of the sampling distribution. Thus, it is necessary for the user of statistics to be aware of these assumptions and to be constantly on guard lest he unwittingly fail to meet their requirements. The mathematical models used in distribution-free tests make fewer and less restrictive assumptions concerning the *population of data* than do the older parametric methods.

The increased applicability of the sign test is gained only at the expense of sacrificing another desirable quality. It is generally true that distribution-free methods are less effective in avoiding type 2 errors when testing data drawn from a normal population than are tests based on the normal curve or the t-distribution. For this reason the sign test should not be used simply to achieve greater ease of computation when the assumptions of the t-ratio can be met. Where both tests are applicable, and with samples of the same size, the t-ratio is capable of detecting small differences to which the sign test is insensitive. However, if circumstances do not warrant the use of t, the power of the sign test can be increased by increasing N.

THE VARIANCE OF A SAMPLING DISTRIBUTION OF DIFFERENCES

Let us turn now to a generalized formula for the standard deviation of differences between paired observations. Suppose there are two distributions, X_1 and X_2, and that each X_1 is paired with a certain X_2. D will stand for the difference $(X_1 - X_2)$ for any pair.

$$\bar{D} = \frac{\Sigma D}{N} = \frac{\Sigma (X_1 - X_2)}{N}$$
$$\bar{D} = \bar{X}_1 - \bar{X}_2$$

The mean difference is equal to the difference between the two means.

The deviation of a single difference from the mean difference is equal to the difference between the deviations of the two paired measurements from their respective means.

$$D - \bar{D} = (X_1 - X_2) - (\bar{X}_1 - \bar{X}_2)$$
$$D - \bar{D} = x_1 - x_2$$

The variance of a distribution of D's is thus

$$S^2_D = \frac{\Sigma (D - \bar{D})^2}{N}$$
$$S^2_D = \frac{\Sigma (x_1 - x_2)^2}{N}$$
$$S^2_D = \frac{\Sigma x^2_1}{N} + \frac{\Sigma x^2_2}{N} - 2\frac{\Sigma x_1 x_2}{N}$$

The first two terms of the above expression are the S^2's of X_1 and X_2. The third term can be expressed in terms of r_{12} because its numerator is the sum of cross products of deviations from the means.

$$r_{12} = \frac{\Sigma x_1 x_2}{N S_1 S_2}$$
$$\frac{\Sigma x_1 x_2}{N} = r_{12} S_1 S_2$$

It is thus possible to express the standard deviation of a distribution of differences between paired scores as

$$S_D = \sqrt{S^2_1 + S^2_2 - 2r_{12}S_1S_2} \tag{66}$$

The correlation between X_1 and X_2 is reflected in the variance of the distribution of differences between paired measurements, and sometimes it is convenient to compute r by

$$r_{12} = \frac{S^2_1 + S^2_2 - S^2_D}{2S_1S_2} \tag{67}$$

The importance of the correlation between samples is illustrated by the following example, where the same values for X_1 and X_2 are paired in three different ways. Although the correlation between X_1 and X_2 (and the variation among the differences) is not the same, $\bar{X}_1 = 13$, $\bar{X}_2 = 8$, and $M_D = 5$ for all three arrangements.

X_1	X_2	D	X_1	X_2	D	X_1	X_2	D
15	10	5	15	6	9	15	8	7
14	9	5	14	7	7	14	7	7
13	8	5	13	8	5	13	10	3
12	7	5	12	9	3	12	6	6
11	6	5	11	10	1	11	9	2

This illustrates the fact, expressed by formula (66), that the standard deviation of a distribution of differences varies with the correlation between the paired measurements.

The Standard Error of a Difference between Two Measures

Suppose now that we draw a large number of samples of size N from the same population. From each sample we will compute a certain statistic denoted as A. Following the reasoning which led us to formula (66), we can express the standard deviation of the sampling distribution of differences between paired observations of this statistic by a similar formula.

$$\sigma_{A_1-A_2} = \sqrt{\sigma^2_{A_1} + \sigma^2_{A_2} - 2\rho_{A_1A_2}\sigma_{A_1}\sigma_{A_2}} \tag{68}$$

In general, if the standard deviation of the sampling distribution of a statistic A is known it is possible to express the standard error of the difference between two such measures ($A_1 - A_2$) by means of this type formula. The practical applications of this statistic are limited by the fact that a good estimate of ρ_{A1A2} is often unavailable, and even where this correlation can be estimated adequately it is difficult to justify the assumption that $(A_1 - A_2)$ has a normal sampling distribution. The standard error of the difference can be computed if satisfactory estimates are available for the required σ's and the coefficient of correlation. If, in addition, the sampling distribution of differences is known to be adequately approximated by the normal curve or the t-distribution, the significance of an observed difference can be evaluated.

Testing Differences in Dispersion

If differences between standard deviations of large samples are randomly drawn from a normal universe the S.D. of the sampling distribution of such differences is

$$\sigma_{s_1-s_2} = \sqrt{\sigma^2{}_{s_1} + \sigma^2{}_{s_2} - 2\rho_{s_1s_2}\sigma_{s_1}\sigma_{s_2}} \tag{69}$$

By substituting estimates for the unknown parameters, we can approximate the value of this standard error when N_1 and N_2 are both 100 or more by using the following estimates.

$$\text{est. } \sigma_s = \frac{S}{\sqrt{2N}} \qquad \text{est. } \rho_{s_1s_2} = r^2{}_{12}$$

If the samples are independent, $\rho = 0.00$, and the formula becomes

$$\sigma_{s_1-s_2} = \sqrt{\sigma^2{}_{s_1} + \sigma^2{}_{s_2}}$$

As in testing differences between means, the observed difference between standard deviations is divided by the standard error and the resulting C.R. is interpreted in relation to the normal distribution of z.

Since the sampling distribution of S is appreciably skewed when $N < 100$, the distribution of $(S_1 - S_2)$ is also skewed, but to a somewhat lesser degree. However, the departure from normality is still so great that formula (69) should be used with considerable caution.

These tests are mentioned here only because they have appeared in much of the older psychological literature. For contemporary problems it is much better to use the more modern methods of the t-ratio and the variance ratio, which are described later in this chapter.

Differences between Means

The assumptions of formula (66) can be reasonably well met when we are dealing with differences between means. If all possible pairs of means for random samples of a specified N were drawn from a population of X, the standard deviation of the sampling distribution of differences between paired means would be

$$\sigma_{\bar{x}_1 - \bar{x}_2} = \sigma_{\bar{D}} = \sqrt{\sigma^2_{\bar{x}_1} + \sigma^2_{\bar{x}_2} - 2\rho_{\bar{x}_1 \bar{x}_2}\sigma_{\bar{x}_1}\sigma_{\bar{x}_2}} \qquad (70)$$

If N is large, or if the distribution of X is symmetrical and approximately bell-shaped, the sampling distribution of differences between means is reasonably approximated by the normal curve.

By substituting estimates for the unknown parameters in formula (70) we can obtain a formula which is very useful in testing the significance of the difference between the means of experimental and control observations.

$$\text{est. } \sigma_{\bar{x}} = \frac{S}{\sqrt{N-1}} \qquad \text{est. } \rho_{\bar{x}_1 \bar{x}_2} = r_{12}$$

$$s_{\bar{x}_1 - \bar{x}_2} = \sqrt{s^2_{\bar{x}_1} + s^2_{\bar{x}_2} - 2r_{12}s_{\bar{x}_1}s_{\bar{x}_2}} \qquad (71)$$

It was shown above that $\bar{D} = (\bar{X}_1 - \bar{X}_2)$. Since these two measures are identical, their standard errors must be the same. Thus, we can use either $s_{\bar{D}}$ or $s_{\bar{x}_1 - \bar{x}_2}$ in testing a difference between correlated means. The two statements of H_0 are equivalent. One asserts that the mean of the differences is zero; the other asserts that the difference between means is zero.

To illustrate the comparability of these two methods we will now apply formula (71) to the muscle tension data. The final result is the same (except for differences in rounding) as that which we obtained earlier by computing S_D directly from the differences between obtained scores.

It is important to note that both of these methods require us to have some rational basis for arranging the two sets of data in pairs. In this case both scores in each pair were obtained from the same subject.

Subject	X_1 Tension	X_2 Control	X^2_1	X^2_2	$X_1 X_2$
A	78	68	6084	4624	5304
B	38	30	1444	900	1140
C	81	57	6561	3249	4617
D	61	46	3721	2116	2806
E	55	38	3025	1444	2090
F	61	39	3721	1521	2379
G	82	65	6724	4225	5330
H	51	53	2601	2809	2703
I	55	37	3025	1369	2035
J	69	44	4761	1936	3036
K	55	41	3025	1681	2255
L	59	76	3481	5776	4484
Sums	745	594	48173	31650	38179

$$\bar{X}_1 = \frac{745}{12} = 62.1$$

$$S_1 = \frac{1}{12}\sqrt{12(48173) - (745)^2} = 12.7$$

$$s_{\bar{x}_1} = \frac{12.7}{\sqrt{11}} = 3.8$$

$$\bar{X}_2 = \frac{594}{12} = 49.5$$

$$S_2 = \frac{1}{12}\sqrt{12(31650) - (594)^2} = 13.7$$

$$s_{\bar{x}_2} = \frac{13.7}{\sqrt{11}} = 4.1$$

$$r_{12} = \frac{12(38179) - (745)(594)}{\sqrt{12(48173) - (745)^2}\,\sqrt{12(31650) - (594)^2}} = +.62$$

$$s_{\bar{x}_1 - \bar{x}_2} = \sqrt{(3.8)^2 + (4.1)^2 - 2(.62)(3.8)(4.1)} = 3.4$$

$$* \text{ C.R.} = \frac{62.1 - 49.5}{3.4} = 3.7 +$$

Unless there is some reason for finding the correlation between the paired measurements, $s_{\bar{D}}$ is usually computed directly from the differences.

The estimate of $\sigma_{\bar{D}}$ (or $\sigma_{\bar{x}_1 - \bar{x}_2}$) must be computed by one of the methods which we have just illustrated whenever the two groups of data are correlated, as they are in any experiment which compares two means obtained from the same subjects.

---

* C.R. and t have the same numerical value when computed in this way if $N_1 = N_2$. The t-table should be entered with df equal to one less than the number of pairs.

Using the same group of people for the two experimental conditions reduces the amount by which two means are likely to differ by chance since individual differences among subjects are held constant. For this reason experiments should be designed in this way whenever possible.

The same individuals cannot always be used for both sets of measurements because the first test may cause subjects to react quite differently to a second testing. However, it is often possible to match two groups of subjects with respect to some variable which is correlated with individual differences in the performance under investigation. For example, pupils are often matched on IQ for methods experiments in education. Subjects are sometimes matched according to preliminary scores on the dependent variable obtained under similar conditions for both groups *before the experimental and control conditions are introduced.* The matching need not be exact and can often be done by pairing individuals according to rank orders within the groups. In education experiments it is possible to match pupils on the basis of the past year's grades in courses related to the experimental course. In some learning experiments subjects can be assigned to matched pairs according to their scores at the end of a certain number of trials before introducing the independent variable and without interrupting the course of learning.

It is obviously incorrect to match subjects on the basis of the scores which are to be tested for significant differences. This would introduce an *artificial* correlation and thus lead to an incorrect estimate of sampling errors through reducing variation among the observed differences.

In general, the efficiency of an experiment can be greatly increased by using matched pairs of subjects. However, H_0 can be tested by the t-ratio only if the correlation produced by matching is taken into account in the computation.

Testing Differences between Uncorrelated Means

In some experiments a suitable matching variable is not available. In others the logic of the experiment is such that matching is not appropriate. For example, a school superintendent in a large city might want to compare the mean IQ's of freshmen in two high schools. With no information beyond the IQ's of pupils in the two classes he would have no reasonable basis for pairing them. It might lead to serious error if he were to pair IQ's in some chance fashion and test the significance of the difference by either of the methods discussed in the last section. Any chance arrangement might happen to produce a high correlation in either the positive or the negative direction. In the first case he might judge the difference to be significant when it really is not. In the other he might decide to accept the null hypothesis when there actually is a significant difference.

Because there is no reasonable basis for assuming the samples to be correlated in this type of experiment, the proper method is to use formula (68) assuming that $\rho_{\bar{x}_1\bar{x}_2} = 0.00$. The standard error of the difference between means of *uncorrelated* groups thus becomes

$$s_{\bar{x}_1-\bar{x}_2} = \sqrt{s^2_{\bar{x}_1} + s^2_{\bar{x}_2}} \tag{71a}$$

The critical ratio obtained by dividing the observed difference between the means by this standard error can be interpreted with reference to the normal distribution. *If the two samples are the same size* this ratio is numerically the same as the t-ratio with $(N_1 + N_2 - 2)$ degrees of freedom and can be evaluated with reference to Table E. The degrees of freedom here are equal to the number of *individual observations* in the sample which are free to vary by chance. Because two sample means are used as points of reference for measuring our sample of variations, the total degrees of freedom are $(N_1 - 1) + (N_2 - 1)$.

When uncorrelated means are to be compared it often happens that $N_1 \neq N_2$. In such cases it is necessary to compute the t-ratio by a different method. This procedure uses an estimate of σ^2 obtained by *pooling the separate sums of squares* and *dividing by the combined degrees of freedom* for the two samples. In the following formula note that the same s^2, the unbiased estimate of σ^2, is used for both groups in the denominator of the ratio.

$$t = \frac{\bar{X}_1 - \bar{X}_2}{\sqrt{\dfrac{s^2}{N_1} + \dfrac{s^2}{N_2}}}, \quad \text{where} \quad s^2 = \frac{\Sigma(X_1 - \bar{X}_1)^2 + \Sigma(X_2 - \bar{X}_2)^2}{N_1 + N_2 - 2} \tag{72}$$

In order to use the pooled sums of squares in this way we must assume that both samples are drawn from universes having the same variance. If this assumption is correct the combination of the two samples provides a more dependable estimate of σ^2 than could be obtained from either of the smaller samples alone. If inspection of the data, or any other consideration, suggests that the samples do not represent populations having the same variance the assumption of homogeneity of variance should be tested by means of the F-ratio, which is considered in the next section. This assumption of homogeneous variance often causes difficulty because many of the independent variables used in education and psychological experiments affect the variance of scores as well as the mean level of performance. If the two sample variances differ significantly, or if there are other reasons for believing that the populations differ in variance, an approximation of t can be computed by using formula (71a) as the denominator. Taking $df = (N_1 + N_2 - 2)$, a reasonable decision to accept or reject H_0 can usually be based on the normal distribution or the critical values of t.

The problem of homogeneity of variance arises only when the t-ratio is applied to independent samples. When the samples are correlated we are actually dealing with only one sample, a sample of differences between paired observations, and it is not necessary to pool two sums of squares in order to estimate σ^2. This fact, plus the additional experimental control resulting from pairing subjects, suggests that experiments should be designed wherever possible so that the statistical analysis can be carried out with differences between paired scores.

Here again we must assume that the numerator of the t-ratio $(\bar{X}_1 - \bar{X}_2)$ has a normal sampling distribution. And of course the further assumption of the null hypothesis is required in order to evaluate the observed difference. The problem is simplified somewhat by the fact that in most psychological and educational applications of this test the sampling distribution of $(\bar{X}_1 - \bar{X}_2)$ is approximately normal. This is the case even when the populations from which the individual measures are drawn differ considerably from the normal distribution. So unless there is evidence to the contrary, it is fairly safe to assume the condition of normality to be adequately met.

Even though it is known that a sample of data does not meet all of the requirements assumed by the mathematical model of the distribution of t, it is still permissible to use that distribution in deciding whether or not to reject H_0. The effect of the moderate departures from normality and homogeneity of variance commonly found in psychological and educational measurements is to increase slightly the probability of a type 1 error. Moreover, this effect rapidly diminishes as N increases above ten. Even with small samples serious errors of decision can be avoided by requiring a smaller value of α than would be used in working with large samples.

Example:

A group of six subjects is tested under condition A and another group of eight under condition B. Is there a significant difference between the means?

Condition A		Condition B	
X_A	$X^2{}_A$	X_B	$X^2{}_B$
8	64	20	400
15	225	12	144
12	144	25	625
8	64	18	324
7	49	19	361
9	81	16	256
		23	529
		10	100

$$\Sigma X_A = \overline{59} \ \ \Sigma X^2{}_A = \overline{627} \qquad \Sigma X_B = \overline{143} \ \ \Sigma X^2{}_B = \overline{2739}$$

$$\bar{X}_A = \frac{59}{6} = 9.83 \qquad\qquad \bar{X}_B = \frac{143}{8} = 17.88$$

$$\Sigma(X_A - \bar{X}_A)^2 = 627 - \frac{(59)^2}{6} = 46.83*$$

$$\Sigma(X_B - \bar{X}_B)^2 = 2739 - \frac{(143)^2}{8} = 182.87*$$

$$s^2 = \frac{46.83 + 182.87}{6 + 8 - 2} = 19.14$$

$$t = \frac{17.88 - 9.83}{\sqrt{\dfrac{19.14}{6} + \dfrac{19.14}{8}}} = 3.41$$

$$df = 12, \quad p < .01$$

In group comparisons, as well as in one-sample tests of hypotheses, H_0 is stated differently for a one-tailed and a two-tailed test. The preceding example was a two-tailed test of the H_0: $\mu_A - \mu_B = 0$. If the objective of the experiment had been to discover if performance was better under condition B, H_0 would have been stated $\mu_A \geqq \mu_B$. The significance of the difference would then have been reported as

---

* This is a convenient method for computing a sum of squares. The formula (75) is developed on p. 231.

$p < .005$, and would have been accompanied by a clear statement that a one-tailed test had been used. Without such a statement it is generally understood in reporting experiments that two-tailed values of α have been used.

EXERCISES

1. Measurements of the heights of people belonging to two different national groups produced the following results.

$$N_1 = 130 \quad \bar{X}_1 = 67.2 \text{ in.} \quad S_1 = 3.1 \text{ in.}$$
$$N_2 = 69 \quad \bar{X}_2 = 64.1 \text{ in.} \quad S_2 = 4.8 \text{ in.}$$

Is it reasonable to conclude that these two samples were drawn from populations having the same distribution of height?

2. An educational experiment was conducted using two matched groups of ten pupils each. The same teacher taught both groups in a course in U.S. history. The same method of teaching was used in each class, except that pupils in class A were given no information concerning their work until the final grade, while those in group B were informed of their rank in class after every written exercise. The following grades were made by the members of the two classes on a standardized test at the end of the term. What can you say concerning the effectiveness of giving information of success in this experiment? Apply two different tests to the results and in each case evaluate the appropriateness of the test for data of this type.

Matched Pairs of Students	Score in Group A	Score in Group B
A	50	56
B	86	83
C	74	88
D	32	41
E	55	68
F	47	47
G	90	85
H	27	38
I	43	50
J	46	57

3. A group of students was given an aptitude test on two successive Saturdays. From the data below what would you conclude concerning the effect of practice on this test performance?

Student	First Score	Second Score	Student	First Score	Second Score
A	27	34	G	37	43
B	35	33	H	39	34
C	42	53	I	40	45
D	50	50	J	38	39
E	39	41	K	30	45
F	32	37	L	45	47

4. In a mirror star-tracing experiment twenty subjects were arranged in ten matched pairs according to the time they required to trace a star with the non-preferred hand. Following this, the control subject of each pair was given one additional trial with the same hand. He then read for five minutes, after which he was tested with the non-preferred hand. The experimental subjects were given one trial with the non-preferred hand. This was followed by five trials with the preferred hand, after which they were tested with the non-preferred hand. Results in terms of the time required to trace a star are shown for the second and the final trials with the non-preferred hand.

MATCHED PAIRS	CONTROL		EXPERIMENTAL	
	Second Trial	Final Trial	Second Trial	Final Trial
1	60 sec.	35 sec.	62	35
2	38	30	40	28
3	95	62	95	36
4	87	70	85	50
5	70	45	75	45
6	110	70	105	37
7	165	120	165	63
8	90	70	90	47
9	70	55	65	47
10	50	55	57	41

State the appropriate null hypothesis for the experimental hypothesis that practice with the preferred hand improves performance with the non-preferred hand. Apply the appropriate statistical test.

5. From Data *B*, p. 31, test the hypothesis that there is a difference in the ages of men and women who enroll in the course.

6. Fifty subjects were randomly divided into two groups. Use the following information to test the appropriate hypothesis if the experimental group was tested under conditions which were expected to impair performance.

	Control	Experimental
$\bar{X}$	30.70	26.93
Σx^2	27.82	50.14
N	21	29

State the assumptions of the test you select and decide how well they are met.

COMPARING VARIABILITIES

The *t*-ratio for Differences between Correlated Variance Estimates

Correlated measures of dispersion often occur in psychological and educational research. A common problem is that of comparing the extent of individual differences within the same group of subjects at different stages of practice, at different ages, or under different experimental conditions. When two forms of a test are administered to the same group we may wish to test the hypothesis that the dispersions are equal. Measures of dispersion must be considered to be correlated when matched groups are compared.

A satisfactory test of $H_0 : (\sigma^2_1 - \sigma^2_2) = 0$, which can be used with correlated samples of any size, is given by

$$t = \frac{(S^2_1 - S^2_2)\sqrt{N - 2}}{\sqrt{4S^2_1S^2_2(1 - r^2_{12})}}, \quad \begin{array}{l} \text{where} \quad N = \text{the number of paired scores} \\ \text{and} \quad S^2 = \frac{\Sigma(X - \bar{X})^2}{N} \text{ for each sample} \end{array} \quad (73)$$

This statistic can be evaluated as a two-tailed t-ratio having $N - 2$ degrees of freedom.

The Variance Ratio

Before continuing with the problem of testing differences in dispersion let us briefly consider the question of single-sample tests. A method which can be applied to samples of any size, is provided by the variance ratio F—a ratio computed by dividing the s^2 obtained from a sample by the σ^2 for the population. Since the sampling distribution of this ratio is known we can calculate the probability of obtaining a given value of s^2 from a normal population having some hypothetical value of σ^2 which we wish to test.

The utility of the variance ratio has been greatly increased by generalizing it to include the case where two s^2's are compared to test the null hypothesis that they both were drawn independently from the same population. This generalized variance ratio is defined

$$F = \frac{s^2_1}{s^2_2}, \quad \begin{array}{l} \text{where} \quad s^2 = \frac{\Sigma x^2}{N - 1} \\ \text{and} \quad s^2_1 > s^2_1 \end{array} \quad (74)$$

Because of the stipulation that the larger s^2 is to be divided by the smaller, the sampling distribution of F has a lower limit of 1.00. The relative frequency with which F computed from random samples will be greater than 1.00 by various amounts depends on the degrees of freedom upon which the s^2's are based. The df for a variance estimate is equal to $N - 1$.

Table H shows for given df's (n_1 and n_2) the values which F will exceed 5 percent, 2.5 percent, 1 percent, and 0.5 percent of the time when s^2_1 and s^2_2 are randomly drawn from normal populations having the same σ^2. Each set of four values corresponding to these probability *points* has been computed from the sampling distribution of F for a particular combination of values of n_1 and n_2. It is convenient to denote a particular F-ratio by subscripts as F_{n_1,n_2}, where the first subscript is the df for the numerator and the second is the df for the denominator.

In testing a hypothetical value of σ^2 the df corresponding to that population value is taken as ∞. Thus, if the sample s^2 is larger than the hypothetical value of σ^2, we compute

$$F_{n_1,\infty} = \frac{s^2_1}{\sigma^2_{hyp}}$$

and H_0 is $\sigma^2 \leq \sigma^2_{hyp}$

If s^2 is smaller than the hypothesis

$$F_{\infty,n_2} = \frac{\sigma^2_{hyp}}{s^2_2}$$

and H_0 is $\sigma^2 \geq \sigma^2_{hyp}$

The values in Table H are probability points for one-tailed tests, but since our object is to test the significance of a difference between a variance estimate and the hypothesis *regardless of direction,* a two-tailed test is required. This can be accomplished simply by doubling the probabilities of Table H. For example, the value of F required for significance at the .025 *point* (a one-tailed test) is the same as that required for significance at the .05 *level* (a two-tailed test).

To test a difference between two sample standard deviations we compute s^2 for each sample, denote the larger value as s^2_1 and compute F. Here it must be remembered that the choice of s^2_1 is based on sample data and was not stipulated before the result of the experiment was known. For this reason the correct statement of α must include both tails of the F-distribution. Table H considers only the upper tail because the most common application of F, which will be discussed in Chapter XIII, requires a one-tailed test.

The F-ratio assumes that both samples are randomly and independently drawn from normal populations and that the variances of these populations are equal. Nothing is assumed concerning the population means. The ratio will exceed the critical values of the table more often than would be expected according to chance if either of the two assumptions is not true. Thus, in order to reject the null hypothesis (the second assumption) at a known level of significance we must be willing to accept the assumption of normality. Moderate departure from normality does not seriously affect this test, but it does tend to increase the frequency with which significant ratios occur.

It is usually convenient to compute variance estimates directly from raw data. The necessary computational formula for the sum of squares is easily derived.

$$\Sigma(X - \bar{X})^2 = \Sigma X^2 - 2\Sigma X\bar{X} + N\bar{X}^2$$
$$= \Sigma X^2 - 2\frac{(\Sigma X)^2}{N} + \frac{(\Sigma X)^2}{N}$$
$$\Sigma(X - \bar{X})^2 = \Sigma X^2 - \frac{(\Sigma X)^2}{N} \tag{75}$$

If the data have been classified into a frequency distribution the formula becomes

$$\Sigma(X - \bar{X})^2 = i^2 \left[\Sigma f d^2_i - \frac{(\Sigma f d_i)^2}{N} \right] \tag{75a}$$

Examples:

1. The standard deviation of freshman scores throughout the U.S. on a certain college aptitude test is reported as 100. In one college it was found that s^2 for the entering class of 118 freshmen was 8010.6. Is the population represented by this class more homogeneous in college aptitude than the standardization population? Our H_0 is $\sigma^2 \geqq 10000$. Of course, this one-tailed H_0 must have been specified before the data were observed. $F = 1.249$. Table H does not show the required values for $F_{\infty,117}$. However, the 5 percent

point of significance for $F_{\infty,120}$ is found to be 1.25. We can reject H_0 if we are willing to run a risk of approximately $\alpha = .05$.

2. A manufacturer states that 50 percent of the axles produced by his plant are within a range of 1.250 $\pm$ .002 inches in diameter. A random sample of 20 axles yielded $s^2 = .000003$. Does the sample disprove the manufacturer's assertion?

$.002 = .6745\sigma_{\text{hyp}}$, since the middle 50 percent of a normal distribution lies within $\mu \pm .6745\sigma$

$\sigma_{\text{hyp}} = .00296$

$\sigma^2_{\text{hyp}} = .00000876$

Since $s^2 < \sigma^2_{\text{hyp}}$, $F_{19,\infty}$ is not computed. The sample does not exceed the range of variation implied in the manufacturer's claims. It is possible, on the other hand, that his claim is too modest. We should, therefore, compute $F_{\infty,19}$ in order to see whether the sample variation is significantly less than his assertion implies.

Since $F_{\infty,19}$ must be 2.49 to achieve the 1 percent point (or the 2 percent level) of significance, the sample s^2 is significantly smaller than the hypothetical σ^2. This might lead the manufacturer to claim even greater precision for his product.

3. An attitude scale to measure belief in a deity was administered to a random sample of thirty teachers in a city school system and to a sample of fifty adult women. The standard deviation for women school teachers was 1.08, and for adult women it was 0.79. Is there a difference in the degree of homogeneity of belief in deity within the two groups?

	S^2	NS^2 Sum of Squares	df	$\dfrac{\Sigma x^2}{N-1}$ s^2
Teachers	1.1664	34.992	29	1.207
Adult Women	.6241	31.205	49	.637

$$F_{29,49} = \frac{1.207}{.637} = 1.89$$

Since this is a two-tailed test, we decide to accept H_0. (What is the value of α?)

Confidence Intervals for σ^2

To find a confidence interval for σ^2 it is necessary to define the limits of the range of hypothetical population values of this parameter for which the sample s^2 would not lead to rejection of H_0. Table H can be used for this purpose.

The lower confidence limit for σ^2 is computed directly from the tabled probability point for $F_{n_1,\infty}$. This point is the value which $F_{n_1,\infty}$ has a specified probability of exceeding where s^2 is randomly drawn from a normal population. Knowing F and s^2, we can solve for σ^2_{hyp}

$$F_{n,\infty} = \frac{s^2_n}{\sigma^2_{hyp}}$$

thus, $\sigma^2_{hyp} = \dfrac{s^2_n}{F_{n,\infty}}$ (lower confidence limit)

The upper confidence limit is the value of σ^2_{hyp} *below* which the sample s^2 deviates to a specified probability point. To find this we must know the *lower* probability point for $F_{n,\infty}$ where $s^2_n < \sigma^2_{hyp}$. Since only the upper tail of the F-distribution is included in Table H, the required probability point cannot be read directly from the table. It can easily be secured, however, by making use of the following relationship.

$$F_{n_1,n_2} = \frac{s^2_1}{s^2_2} = \frac{1}{\dfrac{s^2_2}{s^2_1}} = \frac{1}{F_{n_2,n_1}}$$

Since a *lower* probability point for $F_{n_1,\infty}$ is simply the reciprocal of the *upper* probability point for F_{∞,n_2} the upper confidence limit for σ^2_{hyp} is computed as follows.

1. Find from Table H the required probability point for $F_{\infty,n}$.
2. Compute the reciprocal $\dfrac{1}{F_{\infty,n}}$. This is the *lower* probability point for $F_{n,\infty}$.
3. Find the upper confidence limit for σ^2_{hyp}.

$$\sigma^2_{hyp} = \frac{S^2_n}{\dfrac{1}{F_{\infty,n}}} \text{ (upper confidence limit)}$$

This, of course, reduces more simply to

$$\sigma^2_{hyp} = s^2_n F_{\infty,n}$$

FIGURE 46

$\sigma^2{}_{hyp}$ _____ $\sigma^2{}_{hyp}$

$$\uparrow$$
$$s^2{}_n$$

$$F_{n,\infty} = \frac{s^2{}_n}{\sigma^2{}_{hyp}} \qquad\qquad F_{n,\infty} = \frac{1}{\dfrac{\sigma^2{}_{hyp}}{s^2{}_n}}$$

Lower Limit: $\qquad\qquad\qquad$ Upper Limit:

$$\sigma^2{}_{hyp} = \frac{s^2{}_n}{F_{n,\infty}} \qquad\qquad \sigma^2{}_{hyp} = s^2{}_n F_{\infty,n}$$

Example:

$N = 25$, $s^2 = 34.7$. What is the 99 percent confidence interval for the population variance?

lower limit: $\quad \sigma^2{}_{hyp} = \dfrac{s^2{}_n}{F_{n,\infty}} = \dfrac{34.7}{1.90} = 18.3$

upper limit: $\quad \sigma^2{}_{hyp} = s^2{}_n F_{\infty,n} = 34.7(2.43) = 84.3$

Thus, the desired interval is $18.3 < \sigma^2 < 84.3$.

If the 99 percent confidence interval for the population standard deviation is desired, we simply find the square roots of the limits for σ^2.

Testing Differences between r's

Sometimes it is necessary to test the hypothesis that two coefficients of correlation differ from each other only by chance. This can be done by transforming the r's to z_r's by Table F and computing a C.R. for the difference between the z_r's. If these are significantly different, it follows that the null hypothesis concerning the difference between the r's can be rejected at the same level of significance. The standard error of the difference between z_r's corresponding to uncorrelated r's is given by

$$\sigma_{z_{r_1} - z_{r_2}} = \sqrt{\sigma^2{}_{z_{r_1}} + \sigma^2{}_{z_{r_2}}} = \sqrt{\frac{1}{N_1 - 3} + \frac{1}{N_2 - 3}} \tag{76}$$

Note that this formula does not require the use of estimates since σ_{z_r} depends only on degrees of freedom. Dividing the difference between the z_r's by this standard error provides a ratio which can be interpreted as a z of the normal distribution.

Formula (76) is limited to independent samples because the correct term for the correlation between sample z_r's is unknown. A common situation which requires a test of the difference between correlated r's is the case where three measures, X_1, X_2, and X_3, have been obtained from the same group of subjects and we wish to decide if r_{12} is significantly different from r_{13}. For instance, we might have administered two tests of college aptitude to the same freshman class in an experiment designed to discover which test is a better predictor of grades. This problem can be satisfactorily handled by

$$t = \frac{(r_{12} - r_{13})\sqrt{(N - 3)(1 + r_{23})}}{\sqrt{2(1 - r^2_{12} - r^2_{13} - r^2_{23} + 2r_{12}r_{13}r_{23})}} \qquad (77)$$

This test is evaluated by the t-distribution for $N - 3$ degrees of freedom.

EXERCISES

1. If $N = 25$ and $s^2 = 10.24$, what are the 95 percent confidence limits for σ^2?

2. Is there a significant difference in variability between the two groups in Exercise 6, page 228?

3. Given: the following information concerning the scores made by a hypothetical group of sixty-five college freshmen.

	College Aptitude Test X	Mathematics Test Y	French Test Z
M	74.2	48.7	54.1
S	8.1	10.3	9.5
	$r_{xy} = .53$	$r_{xz} = .41$	$r_{yz} = .46$

 a) Assuming that these are standard scores with reference to a large group of college freshmen, is this group significantly better in French than they are in mathematics?

 b) Which test is more closely related to college aptitude score, mathematics or French?

4. Using the data of Exercise 4, page 228, decide for each group whether there is a significant change in dispersion from the second to the final trial.

5. Apply the F-ratio to Exercise 2, page 188 and compare the result with that of the less precise method using formula (55).

6. The standard deviation of Part I of a test is 14 and the S of Part II is 28. The correlation between the two parts is $r = .71$. What is the standard deviation of total scores on the test made up of the sum of scores on the two parts? Hint: Go back and follow the development of formula (66), but start with *sums* instead of *differences*.

7. A personality inventory is administered in a small class to ten boys whose behavior has been exemplary and to eight who have been involved in various sorts of discipline problems. The scores are shown below.

Group 1	Group 2
111	117
112	115
110	112
97	103
102	116
95	109
88	100
102	119
99	
100	

Do you consider the difference between the group means to be significant? What is the 95 percent confidence interval for the difference between μ_1 and μ_2?

CHAPTER XII

Frequency Comparisons

Most of our discussion thus far has dealt with methods which are appropriate for treating data obtained from interval scales of measurement. In some instances we have considered methods, such as the sign test, which can be used with ordinal data. Many experiments, however, produce data which cannot be treated by these methods because the observations are on a nominal scale, having no meaningful numerical values, but belonging only to one or another category of classification. The degree of separation of the categories on an ordinal scale is either unknown or unused in the statistical analysis of such data, and in some cases even the ordinal position of the categories is not known. Sometimes the nature of the categories is such that they could be assigned numerical values on an interval scale of measurement. But even if the original data are numerical measurements we might decide to group them into non-numerical categories to avoid restrictive assumptions about sampling distributions. Of course, measurements are categorized when they are tabulated into the class intervals of a frequency distribution, but these categories retain numerical values on the original scale of measurement.

If data fall into two categories, such as "pass-fail," "yes-no," "increase-decrease," or "above-below," hypotheses about frequencies can be tested by methods discussed in earlier chapters. With more categories of classification different methods of analysis are required; but before considering methods applicable to more than two categories, let us first illustrate some further applications of more familiar tests.

TESTING DIFFERENCES BETWEEN INDEPENDENT PROPORTIONS

H_0 sometimes requires a test of significance for the difference between the proportions of two samples falling in a certain category. For instance, suppose the proportions of last year's graduates of two high schools who enrolled in college were .23 for school A and .38 for school B. Is this merely a chance difference? Such a question can be decided by computing a critical ratio and testing the null hypothesis. The standard deviation of the sampling distribution of differences between *independent* proportions is given by the generalized formula (66).

$$\sigma_{p_1-p_2} = \sqrt{\sigma^2_{p_1} + \sigma^2_{p_2}} = \sqrt{\frac{P_1 Q_1}{N_1} + \frac{P_2 Q_2}{N_2}}$$

Since our purpose is to evaluate the null hypothesis that $P_1 = P_2$, we can restate this formula by using a single value of P and thus assuming the null hypothesis to be true.

$$\sigma_{p_1-p_2} = \sqrt{PQ\left(\frac{1}{N_1} + \frac{1}{N_2}\right)}$$

The parameter P is unknown, but a satisfactory estimate can be made by combining the relative frequencies from the two samples. Thus, the standard error of a difference between independent proportions is estimated by

$$\sigma_{p_1-p_2} = \sqrt{P'Q'\left(\frac{1}{N_1} + \frac{1}{N_2}\right)}, \quad \text{where} \quad P' = \frac{f_1 + f_2}{N_1 + N_2}, \tag{78}$$

f_1 and f_2 being the frequencies of the observed characteristic in the two samples.

We will illustrate this method with the results of a questionnaire administered to a group of college students. The following table shows responses of men and women to the question, "Do you think there should be rules concerning proper dress for dinner in the college commons?" Is there a significant sex difference?

RESPONSES TO ITEM No. 12

	Yes	No	Total
Men	79	200	279
Women	92	35	127
Total	171	235	406

Of the total group, 57.9 percent answered "no." This differs significantly from the hypothesis that opinion is evenly divided. (C.R. = 3.18, and $p < .002$.) Our present interest, however, is in the question of whether men and women respond differently to the item. Using formula (78) and taking the proportion of "no" answers in the entire sample as the best available estimate of P, we find the following result.

Proportion of men answering "no": $p_1 = .717$
Proportion of women " " : $p_2 = .276$

$$H_0: \quad P_1 - P_2 = .00$$

$$\sigma_{p_1 - p_2} = \sqrt{(.579)(.421)\left(\frac{1}{279} + \frac{1}{127}\right)} = .053$$

$$\text{C.R.} = \frac{.717 - .276}{.053} = 8.32$$

The decision is to reject H_0, and we conclude that women are more favorable than men toward rules concerning proper dress.

Certain precautions must be observed in using this method. The sampling distribution of p is a symmetrical discrete binomial distribution when $P = .50$. As N increases it approaches the normal curve. It becomes increasingly skewed, however, as P approaches 0.00 or 1.00, and as N decreases when $P \neq .50$. When the distribution of p_1 or p_2 is skewed, that of $(p_1 - p_2)$ is also skewed, but less so. Thus, the question of whether the normal approximation can be used depends on both P and N. In general, if the product obtained by multiplying P' (or Q', whichever is smaller) by the N of the smaller sample is greater than five, formula (78) and the normal approximation can be used. If this product is between five and ten we should correct for the fact that the continuous normal curve is used to approximate a discrete sampling distribution. The required correction for continuity is most easily performed by reducing the observed difference $(p_1 - p_2)$ by the quantity

$$\frac{1}{2}\left(\frac{1}{N_1} + \frac{1}{N_2}\right)$$

Even with this correction it is wise to require a higher level of significance for rejecting H_0 when N is small or P' differs greatly from .50.

DIFFERENCES BETWEEN CORRELATED PROPORTIONS

Formula (78) assumes that the difference to be tested is between *independent* samples. Often situations arise in psychology and education where it is necessary to test a difference between correlated proportions. We may wish to know if two test items differ in difficulty for the same group of subjects, or if certain classroom experiences produce a significant change in the proportion of students expressing a favorable attitude towards a minority group. In general, this type of problem arises in comparing two tests of the same individuals, or in tests of matched groups under different experimental conditions. To illustrate the proper method for correlated proportions let us suppose that two test items provide the following data.

FREQUENCY OF PASSES AND FAILURES

Item No. 1

		Fail	Pass	Totals
Item No. 2	Pass	A 29	B 39	68
	Fail	C 22	D 10	32
	Totals	51	49	100

The tabulation is similar to a 2 x 2 scatter diagram in which each individual is classified according to two measures. Because frequencies in cells B and C represent individuals whose performance on the two items was not different, these cells provide no evidence which might disprove the null hypothesis. The combined frequencies in A and D, however, represent individuals who performed differently on the two items, thus providing evidence relevant to a test of the hypothesis of equal difficulty.

H_0 implies that 50 percent of those who performed differently on the items passed No. 1 and failed No. 2, and that the remainder failed No. 1 and passed No. 2. Thus we need only to test by means of a C.R. the hypothesis that the observed proportion, $D/(A + D)$, was drawn randomly from a sampling distribution having a mean of .50. The computation is as follows.

Number who differ on No. 1 and No. 2: $A + D = 39$

Proportion who pass No. 1 and fail No. 2: $p = \dfrac{D}{A + D} = .2564$

$$H_0: \quad P = .50$$

$$\sigma_p = \sqrt{\frac{(.5)(.5)}{A + D}} = \sqrt{\frac{.25}{39}} = .08$$

$$\text{C.R.} = \frac{.2564 - .50}{.08} = -3.04$$

The decision is to reject H_0 and we conclude that Item 1 is more difficult than Item 2.

By reformulating this type of problem in terms of *frequencies* instead of proportions we can easily obtain a simplified computational formula. We will express the observed frequency D as a deviation from the expected frequency $(A + D)/2$ and divide by σ_f.

$$\text{C.R.} = \frac{D - \dfrac{A + D}{2}}{\sigma_f} = \frac{D - \dfrac{A + D}{2}}{\sqrt{(A + D)(\tfrac{1}{2})(\tfrac{1}{2})}}$$

$$= \frac{D - \dfrac{A + D}{2}}{\tfrac{1}{2}\sqrt{A + D}} \qquad \frac{2D - (A + D)}{\sqrt{A + D}}$$

$$\text{C.R.} = \frac{D - A}{\sqrt{A + D}} \tag{79}$$

This method, known as McNemar's test, is similar to the sign test described in Chapter XI. The only difference is that in using the sign test we usually start with numerical rather than categorical data. In the sign test the data are reduced to categories as an expedient device for avoiding unjustifiable assumptions regarding the sampling distribution. The computation for the above example is the same as it would be for the sign test where there are 29 +'s and 10 −'s, with 61 ties which are ignored. In interpreting the McNemar test, as well as the sign test, we must not forget the number of ties in which no change is observed. It may well be that change is statistically significant in one direction even though it occurs so rarely as to be unimportant. The assumption of normality in McNemar's test concerns only the sampling distribution of $(f - F_{\text{hyp}})$. Consequently it is possible to use this method for testing related samples when the assumption of a normal population of original measurements is untenable.

THE CHI SQUARE TEST

A general method for testing hypotheses about frequencies classified into any number of categories is provided by the statistic χ^2 (chi square). With k categories of classification and N observations of such nature that each must fall into one and only one category, differences between observed frequencies and those expected according to some hypothesis can be evaluated by

$$\chi^2 = \sum_{i=1}^{k} \frac{(f_i - e_i)^2}{e_i}, \quad \text{where} \quad \begin{array}{l} f_i = \text{observed frequency} \\ e_i = \text{expected frequency} \end{array} \quad (80)$$

The expected frequencies are any set of values which are logically consistent with the hypothesis to be tested. However, they must in all cases satisfy the requirement that

$$\sum_{i=1}^{k} e_i = \sum_{i=1}^{k} f_i = N$$

The theoretical probability distribution of χ^2 takes different forms depending on the number of degrees of freedom, or the number of *independent* discrepancies $(f_i - e_i)$, from which it is computed. If only the one restriction is imposed that $\sum_{i=1}^{k} e_i = N$, χ^2 has $(k - 1)$ degrees of freedom. As we shall see, there are many applications of χ^2 where $df \neq (k - 1)$, but a general rule to follow in deciding the correct df for a table is to ascertain by inspection the smallest number of entries which must be known in order to fill in the table completely without changing the marginal totals.

Table I shows for various degrees of freedom the values of chi square which have specified probabilities of being exceeded by chance. For example, if χ^2 with 2 df is 5.99, the hypothesis that the observed discrepancies $(f_i - e_i)$ are due to chance can be rejected at the 5 percent level of significance. It should be noted that this is a two-tailed test because a deviation of f_i from e_i in *either* direction increases the magnitude of chi square. If a one-tailed test is required, the data should be inspected to see if the discrepancies are in the *predicted* direction. If so, the probability of a type 1 error can be taken as one-half of the value shown in the table. When chi square is based on more than 30 degrees of freedom its significance can be evaluated by the quantity $\sqrt{2\chi^2} - \sqrt{2df - 1}$, which has a sampling distribution very similar to the z of the normal curve. Note that large chi squares and large values of this expression reflect large $(f_i - e_i)$ discrepancies in *either* direction. Thus, although positive values for this expression are taken as z's in the upper tail of the normal distribution, the one-tailed normal curve areas so obtained are two-tailed probabilities for incorrectly rejecting the null hypothesis. If a one-tailed test is appropriate these probabilities should be halved.

Although only the upper tail of the chi square distribution is used in deciding to accept or reject H_0, we cannot ignore the lower end of the distribution. If a correctly computed value of chi square is so small that $p \leq .95$, the *agreement* between observed and expected frequencies is so close that we should critically examine the experimental procedures used in gathering the data. Significantly small values can be produced by conditions which restrict normal chance variations. Similarly, if $\sqrt{2\chi^2} - \sqrt{2df - 1}$ deviates in the negative direction farther than -1.64, that result should be viewed with suspicion.

Let us now apply chi square to the results of the question about rules concerning proper dress for dinner. We will first test the hypothesis that opinion is evenly divided on this question.

FREQUENCIES OF RESPONSE TO
ITEM NO. 12

Yes	No	Total
171	235	406

According to H_0 the expected frequency of response in each category is 203.

$$\chi^2 = \frac{(171 - 203)^2}{203} + \frac{(235 - 203)^2}{203} = 10.09$$

Table *I* shows that χ^2 with 1 *df* must be at least 6.64 to reach the .01 level of significance for a two-tailed test. The obtained χ^2 is slightly less than 10.83, which is the required value for $p = .001$. Thus, we decide to reject the null hypothesis. The C.R. for testing this same set of data was found earlier to be 3.18 ($p < .002$), which is approximately the square root of the computed chi square (p. 238). Actually, were it not for slight rounding error, χ^2 with 1 *df* is equal to C.R.^{2} this is easily demonstrated for cases like the present example, where we wish to test the hypothesis that a population is evenly divided into two categories. In proving this equality we will develop a useful chi square formula for tests of this type.

We have already seen that the C.R. utilized in McNemar's test for the significance of change reduces to

$$\text{C.R.} = \frac{(D - A)}{\sqrt{A + D}}, \quad \text{where } A \text{ and } D \text{ are the fre-} \qquad (79)$$
quencies of change in either
direction

Now let A and D denote the observed frequencies in any two categories where χ^2 is used to test the hypothesis of equal distribution.

$$e_i = \frac{A + D}{2} \quad \text{for each category}$$

$$\chi^2 = \sum_{i=1}^{2} \frac{(f_i - e_i{}^2)}{e_i} = \frac{\left(A - \dfrac{A + D}{2}\right)^2}{\dfrac{A + D}{2}} + \frac{\left(D - \dfrac{A + D}{2}\right)^2}{\dfrac{A + D}{2}}$$

$$\chi^2 = \frac{A^2 - 2AD + D^2}{A + D} = \frac{(A - D)^2}{A + D}$$

$$\chi^2 = \frac{(D - A)^2}{A + D} \qquad (81)$$

Formula (81) is a convenient method for the sign test, the McNemar test, or any other situation where data are classified into two categories and we wish to test the hypothesis of equal distribution in the population. The following examples illustrate its application to three problems which we have already treated by other methods.

1. Memorization Scores under Muscle
Tension and Control Conditions

Subject	Tension	Control	Sign
A	78	68	+
B	38	30	+
C	81	57	+
D	61	46	+
E	55	38	+
F	61	39	+
G	82	65	+
H	51	53	−
I	55	37	+
J	69	44	+
K	55	41	+
L	59	76	−

$$A = 10 \quad \text{(number of +'s)}$$
$$D = 2 \quad \text{(number of −'s)}$$
$$\chi^2 = \frac{(10 - 2)^2}{10 + 2} = \frac{64}{12} = 5.33$$
$$.05 > p > .02$$

2. Frequency of Passes and Failures on
Two Test Items

Item No. 1

		Fail	Pass
		A	B
Pass		29	39
Item No. 2			
		C	D
Fail		22	10

$A = 29$ (changes fail—pass)
$D = 10$ (changes pass—fail)

$$\chi^2 = \frac{(29 - 10)^2}{29 + 10} = 9.26$$

$$.01 > p > .001$$

3. Responses to Item No. 12

Yes	*No*	*Total*
171	235	406

$A = 171$ (frequency "yes")
$D = 235$ (frequency "no")

$$\chi^2 = \frac{(171 - 235)^2}{171 + 235} = 10.09$$

$$.01 > p > .001$$

Assumptions

Although the mathematical model of the chi square test is considerably beyond the scope of this book, we must note two important assumptions in its derivation since they define situations in which chi square can legitimately be used. The first assumption is that the observed frequencies are independent of one another as far as their inclusion in the sample is concerned. To illustrate the restriction imposed by this assumption let us suppose that a playground supervisor is studying aggressive behavior in young children. A particular group is observed over a period of a week and every instance of aggressive behavior is classified according to the kind of situation in which it occurred. The data are to be analyzed to see if aggression occurs significantly more often in some situations than in others. Now, if some children contribute more than one instance of aggression to the total N this assumption of independence is violated and chi square can not be properly used. On the other hand, if each child can be characterized according to the kind of situation in which he usually aggresses, even though there are different numbers of aggressive incidents for different children, χ^2 can be used. Here, each categorized item corresponds to a different child and is thus independent of the others. Furthermore, if a large number of observations of the behavior of one child have been classified, χ^2 can be used to test hypotheses about the universe of that child's behavior. The important requirement is that each categorized observation be *independently* drawn from whatever universe is being sampled.

The second assumption pertains to the theoretical sampling distribution of observed frequencies. It is assumed that within each category of classification f_i is normally distributed with $\mu = e_i$. Since frequencies are discrete this assumption is never completely met in practice. For this reason it is necessary to apply a *correction for continuity* when chi square is based on only 1 *df* as in the examples we have considered. The correction consists merely in subtracting .5 from each of the absolute values of $(f_i - e_i)$, thus treating f_i as the mid-point of a continuous interval extending one-half of a frequency unit on either side. If there are more than one independent observation of $(f_i - e_i)$, the possible values of the total chi square become more numerous and differ less from one another. Thus, with more than 1 *df* the correction for continuity is not ordinarily used.

A second implication of the assumption of normality imposes an important restriction. Since an observed frequency cannot be less than zero, the sampling distribution of $(f_i - e_i)$ is skewed when e_i is close to zero. For this reason it is generally agreed that χ^2 should not be used when any *expected* frequency is less than 5. (Some statisticians recommend the more conservative rule that none be less than 10.) This is an arbitrary rule-of-thumb which may on occasion be violated. For instance, if χ^2 is based on a number of comparisons of $(f_i - e_i)$ and e_i is too small in only one or two of these, the error is not likely to lead to an incorrect decision. We might thus apply χ^2 and exercise more than usual caution in deciding how to interpret the result.

If $N \leqq 10$, dichotomous classifications must be tested by computing exact probabilities from the binomial distribution (Chapter VIII).

Further Applications of Chi Square

In general, χ^2 can be used to test the null hypothesis that observed frequencies do not differ significantly from any specified theoretical distribution. The following example illustrates this type of problem.

The recommended distribution of grades over a period of years in freshman and sophomore courses at a certain college is

> A—10 percent
> B—30 percent
> C—40 percent
> D and F—20 percent

The distribution of grades actually assigned in a required freshman course during a three year period was

> A— 18
> B— 95
> C—182
> D— 60
> F— 26
> Incompletes and Withdrawals—19

Can we conclude that the instructor in this course was not following the recommended grade distribution? Omitting the incompletes and withdrawals, we find that a total of 381 grades were assigned. Distributing the 381 assigned grades according to the recommended percentages, we obtain e_i's and compute $\chi^2 = 19.2$. Here there are three degrees of freedom since there are four observations of $(f_i - e_i)$ with the single requirement that $\sum_{i=1}^{4} e_i = 381$. From Table I we find that the probability of $\chi^2 \geq 16.27$ with 3 df is .001. H_0 is rejected, and we conclude that this instructor has not graded according to the recommended standards.

	GRADES				
	A	B	C	D and F	Total
f_i	18	95	182	86	381
e_i	38.1	114.3	152.4	76.2	381.0
$\dfrac{(f_i - e_i)^2}{e_i}$	10.6	3.3	4.0	1.3	

$$\chi^2 = 19.2$$

It appears that he has given too many C's, too few A's, and too few B's. The D's and F's agree fairly well with the recommended distribution since the component of χ^2 for that category is small. The discrepancy for each grade can be tested by constructing four new tables and computing χ^2 for each.

	A	Other Grades	Total
f_i	18	363	381
e_i	38.1	342.9	381
$\dfrac{(f_i - e_i)^2}{e_i}$	10.6	1.2	

$$\chi^2 = 11.8,\ 1\ df \qquad p < .001$$

	B	Other Grades	Total
f_i	95	286	381
e_i	114.3	266.7	381
$\dfrac{(f_i - e_i)^2}{e_i}$	3.3	1.4	

$$\chi^2 = 4.7,\ 1\ df \qquad .02 < p < .05$$

	C	Other Grades	Total
f_i	182	199	381
e_i	152.4	228.6	381
$\dfrac{(f_i - e_i)^2}{e_i}$	4.0	3.8	

$$\chi^2 = 7.8,\ 1\ df \qquad p < .01$$

	D and F	Other Grades	Total
f_i	86	295	381
e_i	76.2	304.8	381
$\dfrac{(f_i - e_i)^2}{e_i}$	1.26	.32	

$$\chi^2 = 1.58,\ 1\ df \qquad .20 < p < .30$$

From this analysis we can conclude that the instructor assigned too few A's and B's, too many C's, and a reasonable number of D's and F's.

Chi square can be used in this way to test the agreement of a sample with expected frequencies derived from any a priori distribution. This type of problem is often encountered in genetics, where the observed distribution of some characteristic is compared with one predicted from genetic theory.

Another application of χ^2 is in testing *goodness of fit*. In this type of test expected frequencies are derived from the mathematical function which defines the theoretical distribution. Chi square is computed in the same manner as before but the degrees of freedom are less than $(k - 1)$ because of restrictions imposed on the e_i's by the particular mathematical formula used in computing them. This technique can be used to test the hypothesis that a sample was drawn from a normal population.

Suppose a sample of test scores yielded the frequency distribution shown on the next page.

Class Interval	Frequency	
70–71	4	
68–69	10	
66–67	14	
64–65	19	
62–63	32	
60–61	31	
58–59	40	$\bar{X} = 58.1$
56–57	28	$S = 5.84$
54–55	29	$N = 266$
52–53	21	
50–51	18	
48–49	10	
46–47	6	
44–45	1	
42–43	3	

We assume as a null hypothesis that this is a random sample drawn from a normal population with $\mu = 58.1$ and $\sigma = 5.84$, the values obtained from the sample. Using these as parameters, we computed

FITTING A NORMAL CURVE, WHERE $\bar{X} = 58.1$, $S = 5.84$, AND $N = 266$

Class Intervals	Limits	z	Area from μ to z	Area in Interval	e_i	Rounded e_i
70–71				.0256*	6.8	7
	69.5	+1.95	.4744			
68–69				.0281	7.5	7
	67.5	+1.61	.4463			
66–67				.0483	12.8	13
	65.5	+1.27	.3980			
64–65				.0768	20.4	20
	63.5	+.92	.3212			
62–63				.1022	27.2	27
	61.5	+.58	.2190			
60–61				.1242	33.0	33
	59.5	+.24	.0948			
58–59				.1346	35.8	36
	57.5	−.10	.0398			
56–57				.1338	35.6	36
	55.5	−.45	.1736			
54–55				.1116	29.7	30
	53.5	−.79	.2852			
52–53				.0866	23.0	23
	51.5	−1.13	.3718			
50–51				.0547	15.3	15
	49.5	−1.47	.4292			
48–49				.0364	9.7	10
	47.5	−1.82	.4656			
46–47				.0190	5.1	
	45.5	−2.16	.4846			
44–45				.0092	2.4	9
	43.5	−2.50	.4938			
42–43				.0062†	1.6	

Total Area = 1.0000 $\Sigma e_i = 266$

*Area above lower limit of interval.
†Area below upper limit of interval.

expected frequencies in class intervals by the method described in Chapter VIII (p. 145).

In computing the e_i's it is necessary to convert the exact limits of the class interval to z-values for the normal distribution. Using these, we find the area within each interval from Table C. This area, when multiplied by N, gives the e_i for the interval.

Three intervals at the lower end of the distribution are combined to meet the requirement that no e_i is less than 5. Also, the computed e_i of 7.5 for the interval 68–69 is rounded down to 7 instead of upward, as is conventional when the preceding digit is odd. The rule is violated in this case because otherwise the sum of expected frequencies would not be equal to the sum of observed frequencies. Chi square is now computed in the usual manner, and we decide to accept H_0.

Interval	f_i	e_i	$\dfrac{(f_i - e_i)^2}{e_i}$
above 69	4	7	1.16
68–69	10	7	1.16
66–67	14	13	.08
64–65	19	20	.05
62–63	32	27	.93
60–61	31	33	.12
58–59	40	36	.44
56–57	28	36	1.78
54–55	29	30	.33
52–53	21	23	.17
50–51	18	15	.60
48–49	10	10	.00
below 49	10	9	.11

$$\chi^2 = 6.93,\ 10\ df$$
$$.70 < p < .80$$

Although there are thirteen observations of $(f_i - e_i)$ in this table, $df = 10$ because three separate restrictions are imposed on the distribution of expected frequencies—$N = 266$, $\sigma = 5.84$, and $\mu = 58.1$. Here again, as in other tests of the null hypothesis, we have not proved that the population is normal; we have merely shown that this sample is consistent with the hypothesis of a normal population.

It should be noted here that different results may be obtained from this test depending on the number of categories used in computing χ^2. Consider, for instance, the limiting case in which only two categories are used—above and below $\bar{X}$. Would this test be appropriate for a decision concerning normality of the population from which the sample was drawn? Obviously the answer is "no." As a general rule-of-thumb the chi square test of normality should be computed with at least ten categories.

Although a significantly large value of χ^2 provides adequate evidence for rejecting H_0 at a specified value of α, the chi square test of normality is inferior to a more modern method known as the Kolmogorov-Smirnov (K-S) test. The K-S test, which is described in more advanced texts and in treatments dealing specifically with nonparametric or distribution-free methods, has two advantages over chi square as a test of normality. It can be used with smaller samples, and it is a more powerful test. In situations where we are interested in justifying the decision to assume that the sample was drawn from a normal population the K-S test is less likely to result in a type 2 error.*

The other major application of chi square is in *contingency tests*. In this type of problem H_0 states that the distribution of observations in one set of categories is independent of some other dimension of classification, and expected frequencies are derived directly from this hypothesis. To illustrate this use of chi square we will test the hypothesis that performance on two test items is uncorrelated. This set of data was used above to illustrate McNemar's test of a difference between correlated proportions. Now our interest is in the question of deciding whether or not the items are correlated and although chi square is again used the computation is not the same because we are testing a different H_0.

		Item No. 1 Fail	Item No. 1 Pass	Totals
Item No. 2	Pass	A 29	B 39	68
	Fail	C 22	D 10	32
	Totals	51	49	100

The marginal totals show that 49 percent of the subjects passed item No. 1. According to the null hypothesis that the two items are unrelated this same percentage of passes on No. 1 is expected among those who passed No. 2, and among those who failed No. 2.

---

* S. Siegel, *Nonparametric Statistics* (New York: McGraw-Hill Book Co., 1956).

In other words, if the items are independent the proportion of passes on item No. 1 should be the same for two sub-groups selected according to their performance on item No. 2. This line of reasoning leads to e_i values in agreement with the null hypothesis concerning contingency. The computations are shown below in parentheses.

EXPECTED FREQUENCIES

| | | Item No. 1 | | Observed |
		Fail	Pass	Totals
Item No. 2	Pass	$A \left(\dfrac{51}{100} \times 68 \right)$ 34.7	$B \left(\dfrac{49}{100} \times 68 \right)$ 33.3	68
	Fail	$C \left(\dfrac{51}{100} \times 32 \right)$ 16.3	$D \left(\dfrac{49}{100} \times 32 \right)$ 15.7	32
	Observed Totals	51	49	100

For ease in computation it should be noted that the e_i for each cell is equal to the product of the marginal totals divided by the grand total.

Chi square, computed by formula (80) and including a correction for continuity, is 4.97. Since there is one degree of freedom we decide to reject the null hypothesis, concluding that the two items are correlated. It is important to remember that chi square is not a direct measure of the *degree* of relationship. We have merely tested, and rejected, the null hypothesis that the items are not related.

$$A: \quad \frac{(|29 - 34.7| - .5)^2}{34.7} = .78$$

$$B: \quad \frac{(|39 - 33.3| - .5)^2}{33.3} = .81$$

$$C: \quad \frac{(|22 - 16.3| - .5)^2}{16.3} = 1.66$$

$$D: \quad \frac{(|10 - 15.7| - .5)^2}{15.7} = 1.72$$

$$\chi^2 = 4.97, 1 \ df \quad .05 > p > .02$$

You may have noticed that $(f_i - e_i)^2$ is the same value for each cell. This is always true for 2×2 contingency tables, since there is only one degree of freedom. Because of this the following formula, which includes a correction for continuity, will give the same result as the method illustrated above.

$$\chi^2 = \frac{N\left(|AD - BC| - \dfrac{N}{2}\right)^2}{(A + B)(C + D)(A + C)(B + D)} \tag{82}$$

At the beginning of the present chapter we used a C.R. to test the H_0 that men and women do not differ in their response to the question, "Do you think there should be rules concerning proper dress for dinner in the college commons?" The critical ratio was found to be 8.32. When formulated in other words, "The answer to the question is not related to the sex of the respondent," this is seen to be a contingency hypothesis. Observed and expected frequencies (in parentheses) are shown below for the same data. $\chi^2 = 69.7$, which, except for a small rounding error, is equal to $(8.32)^2$. Here again is an illustration that χ^2 for 1 df is the same as C.R.^{2}, a fact which we have proved algebraically for the particular H_0 that a population is evenly divided into two categories. The general proof for contingency tables, and for any hypothetical P, while somewhat more complicated than the one we have given, involves only simple algebraic manipulation.

f_i'S AND e_i'S FOR ITEM No. 12

	Yes	No	Totals
Men	79 (117.5)	200 (161.5)	279
Women	92 (53.5)	35 (73.5)	127
Totals	171	235	406

$$\chi^2 = 69.7 , \quad 1 \; df$$

The chi square test of contingency can be applied to frequency tables containing any number of columns and rows. In a contingency table of k columns and r rows, the degrees of freedom will be equal to the product $(k - 1)(r - 1)$. This is because the sum of expected frequencies for each column and for each row must equal the marginal total. To illustrate this we will analyze some data from a study of admission procedures at a small college. High school grades and college aptitude scores of one entering class were studied in relation to college grades during the freshman year. It was found that within each of three levels of college aptitude, freshman grades were very different for students who were above or below the median of their college class with respect to high school grades. This led to the formulation of an index of relative achievement, based on aptitude, but heavily weighting the extent to which a student's high school grades had been relatively higher or lower than his college aptitude score. Of course this index was closely related to college grades for this sample because it was adjusted by trial and error to obtain maximum agreement. Thus there was a real possibility that the index was nothing more than a description of *chance* coincidences in a single sample and that it would not show a similar relationship with a different freshman class. To test this possibility, data were obtained for 8 entering classes from previous years and χ^2 was used to test the contingency H_0 of no relationship between freshman grades and the index. This procedure, in which a generalization empirically derived from the data of one sample is tested independently with a different sample, is called *cross validation.*

The results of the χ^2 contingency test are shown below. The null hypothesis was rejected, and the index is now used as a standard for admission to the college. A coefficient of correlation between the index and grades was not computed here because the purpose was to discriminate good and poor applicants for admission, and not to describe the relationship by a regression equation.

FRESHMAN GRADES

Index	Unsatisfactory	Satisfactory	Superior	Totals
70 and Above	53 (113)	133 (178)	268 (163)	454
40 to 69	150 (132)	235 (209)	147 (191)	532
Below 40	111 (69)	129 (110)	38 (99)	278
Totals	314	497	453	1264

$$\chi^2 = \frac{(60)^2}{113} + \frac{(18)^2}{132} + \frac{(42)^2}{69} + \frac{(45)^2}{178} + \frac{(26)^2}{209} + \frac{(19)^2}{110} + \frac{(105)^2}{163} + \frac{(44)^2}{191} + \frac{(61)^2}{99}$$

$$\chi^2 = 193.1, \quad 4\ df$$

As a further check on the value of this index, the three freshman classes which had entered college five, six, and seven years earlier were studied with respect to their persistence through the four years of college. Again χ^2 was applied, leading to the conclusion that the index of relative achievement is useful in selecting applicants who are likely to remain enrolled throughout the full four years.

INDEX	STUDENTS LEAVING COLLEGE				
	Before Sophomore Year	Before Junior Year	Before Senior Year	Enrolled in Senior Year	Totals
90–100	9 (13)	6 (14)	8 (9)	37 (24)	60
80–89	6 (10)	7 (12)	12 (8)	24 (19)	49
70–79	18 (20)	30 (22)	4 (15)	41 (36)	93
60–69	19 (18)	16 (20)	22 (13)	28 (34)	85
50–59	31 (22)	25 (25)	11 (16)	37 (41)	104
40–49	20 (20)	22 (22)	16 (14)	34 (36)	92
30–39	11 (13)	17 (14)	14 (10)	19 (24)	61
10–29	10 (8)	16 (10)	4 (6)	9 (15)	39

$$\chi^2 = 57.26 , \quad 21 \ df$$
$$p < .001$$

The Median Test

Chi square is a nonparametric test since no restrictive assumptions are made concerning the form of the population distribution from which the sample of original observations was drawn. The only requirements pertaining to the original observations are that they be independent of one another and that they be in a form that permits classification into categories. Because of this, chi square provides a simple method for testing differences between groups in situations which do not meet the requirements of the C.R. or the t-ratio for differences between means. This application of chi square is known as the median test. The first step in applying this test is to find the *approximate* median for the combined experimental and control groups. This should be a point which divides the entire set of combined data as nearly as possible into two equal portions. It also should be a point which falls between possible scores so that every observation can be clearly classified as either above or below that point.

Suppose we have the following measures for an experimental and a control group of subjects.

Experimental X_1	Control X_2
6	5
8	3
5	7
6	3
10	5
4	4
9	3
5	2
7	8
9	9
10	3
6	7
8	6
6	
11	
7	

We first tabulate a frequency distribution for the combined groups and locate the approximate median.

X	f	
11	1	
10	2	
9	3	
8	3	$N = 29$
7	4	approx. Mdn = 6.5
6	5	
5	4	
4	2	
3	4	
2	1	

Chi square is then used to test the hypothesis that the proportion of cases above and below the approximate median is not significantly different for the control and experimental groups. The correction for continuity is used because $df = 1$.

	Experimental	Control	Totals
Above 6.5	A 9	B 4	13
Below 6.5	C 7	D 9	16
Totals	16	13	29

From formula (82), $\quad \chi^2 = \dfrac{29\left(|(9)(9) - (4)(7)| - \dfrac{29}{2}\right)^2}{(9+4)(7+9)(9+7)(4+9)} = .36$

Since $.70 > p > .50$ for $\chi^2 = .36$ with 1 df, the null hypothesis cannot be rejected.

This same procedure can be used as a distribution free test of the null hypothesis that any number of groups do not differ significantly from each other. However, it is not as powerful a test as the analysis of variance, which will be considered in the next chapter.

Exact Probabilities

In testing hypotheses about proportions, the continuous normal distribution, or the χ^2 distribution with 1 df, can usually be used as an approximation of a discrete sampling distribution. We have seen, however, that some problems of this type require computation of exact probabilities from the binomial distribution. The sampling distribution of the possible arrangements of frequencies in a 2×2 contingency table is also discrete, and if N is less than 30 and the expected frequency for any cell less than 5, the χ^2 approximation can lead to serious error. (The smallest e_i can easily be found by dividing the product of the two smallest marginal totals by N.) In cases such as this, and also wherever $N < 20$, it is necessary to use R. A. Fisher's exact probabilities test. The following formula gives the probability of any specified set of observed frequencies in a 2×2 contingency table.

$$*p = \frac{(A + B)!(C + D)!(A + C)!(B + D)!}{N!A!B!C!D!} \tag{83}$$

The exact probability of the twenty-nine observations in the preceding example being distributed as they were, is

$$p = \frac{(9 + 4)!(7 + 9)!(9 + 7)!(4 + 9)!}{29!9!4!7!9!} = .121$$

This is the probability of the observed distribution if the null hypothesis is correct. But there are four other possible distributions with these marginal totals which deviate in the observed direction from the null hypothesis even farther than this one.

A	B		A	B		A	B		A	B	
10	3	13	11	2	13	12	1	13	13	0	13
C	D		C	D		C	D		C	D	
6	10	16	5	11	16	4	11	16	3	12	16
16	13	29	16	13	29	16	13	29	16	13	29

* The computation of this test can be greatly simplified by using a table of logarithms of factorials.

To obtain the probability of a deviation *this large or larger in the observed direction* we must find the sum of the separate probabilities for all five distributions.

$$p_1 = \frac{13!16!16!13!}{29!9!4!7!9!} = .121$$

$$p_2 = \frac{13!16!16!13!}{29!10!3!6!10!} = .034$$

$$p_3 = \frac{13!16!16!13!}{29!11!2!5!11!} = .005$$

$$p_4 = \frac{13!16!16!13!}{29!12!1!4!12!} = .0004$$

$$p_5 = \frac{13!16!16!13!}{29!13!0!3!13!} = \frac{.000008}{p = .160408}$$

This is the probability of a deviation *in one direction* as great as, or greater than, the one observed. Thus, if our experimental hypothesis had predicted the direction of deviation, and if the data had agreed with that prediction, this would be the correct probability for a one-tailed test. If a two-tailed test is appropriate, the probability figure obtained in this way must be doubled. In the present example the two-tailed probability is $p = .32$, which is more accurate than the result of the χ^2 approximation applied to the same example. In this example the decision is the same for both tests, but in many cases the incorrect use of chi square with small samples can lead to serious error.

SUGGESTED READINGS

1. McNemar, Q. *Psychological Statistics,* chap. xiii. 2d ed. New York: John Wiley & Sons, 1955.
2. Walker, H. M., and Lev, J. *Statistical Inference,* chap. iv and pp. 119–23. New York: Henry Holt and Co., 1953.

EXERCISES

1. A single die was rolled 200 times, producing the following frequency distribution. What is your interpretation?

Spots	Frequency
1	25
2	32
3	51
4	30
5	33
6	29

2. Does Figure 9 (p. 28) show a significant variation in the number of accidents at the ten most dangerous intersections? Evaluate the claim that E. Burnside, 12th Ave., and Sandy Blvd., should be given special consideration because it is by far the most dangerous intersection.

3. Five years after they had entered college the application forms of 156 freshmen were studied. When these students were divided into two groups according to whether or not they had stated an academic objective when applying for admission, the following results were obtained. Would you recommend that the statement of an academic objective be used as one of the criteria for admission?

College Work Completed	Number Stating Objective	Number Not Stating Objective
Less than One Year	27	9
One Year	21	2
Two Years	24	5
Three Years	18	1
Four Years (Graduated)	40	0

4. The following results were obtained for two items in an objective test. (a) Is there a correlation between the items? (b) Do the items differ in difficulty?

		Item No. 21	
		Pass	Fail
Item No. 8	Pass	43	26
	Fail	35	30

5. Would you be willing to conclude that the following distribution of scores on a personality inventory is a random sample from a normal population?

Score	f
92–95	1
88–81	8
84–87	8
80–83	4
76–79	36
72–75	23
68–71	39
64–67	32
60–63	20
56–59	7
52–55	3
48–51	0
44–47	2

6. Three years after entering college the graduates of four high schools were studied to discover whether the high schools differed in the quality of their preparation for college work. One of the results is summarized in the following table. What can be concluded from this?

| | High School | | | |
	A	B	C	D
Number Majoring in Natural Science........161		82	20	32
Number from Class Who Are Still in College....366		116	52	54
Number in Freshman Class................451		135	98	57

7. The following scores were obtained from two groups of subjects in a learning experiment. Is there a significant difference between the groups?

Score	Control Group f	Experimental Group f
20..............10		0
19.............. 7		1
18.............. 2		5
17.............. 1		4
16.............. 3		8
15.............. 2		3
14.............. 5		2
13.............. 1		1
12.............. 0		4
11.............. 0		0
10.............. 0		1

8. Show the missing steps in the algebraic derivation of formula (81) on page 244.

9. Fifty-eight boys in advanced shop were randomly assigned to three different methods of training to operate a lathe. Effectiveness of the training methods was measured by the length of time required to turn a tapered shaft within specified limits of accuracy. Students in the three classes were classified as above or below the median time required for the entire group of fifty-eight as follows.

| | Method | | |
	A	B	C
Above Mdn	7	14	8
Below Mdn	10	8	11

Test at the .05 level the hypothesis that the methods do not differ with respect to the time required to reach the criterion.

10. A study of reading preferences of children in Grades 6 through 8 is summarized in the following table. What can be concluded concerning sex differences in reading interests?

First Choice	Boys	Girls
Adventure	73	12
Fiction	60	56
Science	39	10
Current Events	22	25
Art	15	80
Miscellaneous	15	17

11. The following table represents a percentage distribution of a group of people into four categories.

	A	B	C	D
Percent	12	37	46	5

In order to test the hypothesis of equal distribution in these categories we must know the total N, because chi square cannot be computed from percentages alone. Compute chi square, assuming N to be 100, 200, 400, and 600. Now, although it is incorrect, compute chi square directly from the percentages. What can you conclude from a comparison of these five values of chi square?

CHAPTER XIII

Introduction to the Analysis of Variance

Although the simple comparison of an experimental and control group is adequate for many research problems, it is often desirable to compare several means, each having been obtained under a different experimental condition or under a different value of the independent variable. Where there are a number of experimental groups a t-ratio can be computed for every possible combination of two. It is difficult and confusing to attempt to draw from a number of comparisons a single statement of probability which can be used in evaluating a general H_0 appropriate to the experiment as a whole. Furthermore, the use of a number of t-ratios in a problem of this sort can lead to a serious error in interpretation. To illustrate this, suppose that we have obtained data under seven experimental conditions and have computed t for each of the twenty-one possible comparisons of two means. Finding that one ratio reaches the .05 level for a two-tailed test, we decide to reject H_0 for that particular comparison, and we state that $p < .05$. This is incorrect because $p < .05$ refers to *the probability that a random sample of one* t-*ratio will produce a value this large or larger if* H_0 *is actually true.* Our sample contains twenty-one t-ratios, which are not independent, and the fact that one of them exceeds the critical value for the .05 level of significance cannot be taken as evidence that the overall H_0 concerning the group means is false. To evaluate the result of this experiment we must know the probability that one or more t-ratios in a sample such as this one would reach the specified critical value if H_0 were true.

The probability of obtaining a t-ratio, or any other statistical test, within the critical region for rejecting H_0 is inflated if a single sample produces a number of such tests. Because of this, it is incorrect to select from a number of comparisons a few which exceed some critical value *and to attach to those the value of* α *which is appropriate for a single test.*

Sometimes in constructing psychological tests a large number of items will be administered to two criterion groups of subjects selected to represent extremes of what the test is intended to measure. A statistic, such as chi square, t, or z is then computed from the difference between the groups for each item and the final test is composed of items for which this statistic exceeds some arbitrary value. This procedure is a legitimate method for selecting test items because the statistical test is used here simply as a numerical measurement of the discriminative ability of the items and no attempt is made to estimate the probability of an erroneous decision about any single item.

SIMPLE ANALYSIS OF VARIANCE FOR TWO GROUPS

The analysis of variance is a convenient method for evaluating by a single test the overall differences among the means of several experimental groups. Not only is it convenient, but it provides a means of avoiding errors of interpretation due to the inflation of probabilities when a number of means are to be compared.

Let us first apply this method to the problem of testing a single difference between means in order to illustrate the principles upon which it is based. Suppose we have a total of N observations of a dependent variable X. Of the total, n_1 observations are of X_1, and n_2 are of X_2. The subscripts, 1 and 2, refer to two levels of the *independent* variable which is being experimentally tested. Our statistical test requires no special symbol for this variable because it is used only to define experimental operations and is not part of the data to be tested. We will find it convenient to specify the limits of summation and to identify the groups by subscripts.

$$\text{For the combined groups} \quad \bar{X}_T = \frac{\sum\limits^{N} X}{N}$$

$$\text{For Group 1} \quad \bar{X}_1 = \frac{\sum\limits^{n_1} X_1}{n_1}$$

$$\text{For Group 2} \quad \bar{X}_2 = \frac{\sum\limits^{n_2} X_2}{n_2}$$

Analysis of the Total Sum of Squares

If both groups are combined, the total sum of squares about $\bar{X}_T$ is given by formula (75).

$$\sum^N (X - \bar{X}_T)^2 = \sum^N X^2 - \frac{\left(\sum^N X\right)^2}{N} \tag{75}$$

(Definition)   (Computation)

Note that the left hand expression is a *definition* of the total sum of squares, while the right side of the equation describes a convenient method of computation. In the discussion which follows you will find it helpful to distinguish clearly between definition and computation formulas.

Our problem is to divide the total sum of squares into two independent portions. Let us start by considering the deviations $(X - \bar{X}_T)$ which enter into the total sum of squares. Each deviation can be thought of as the sum of two identifiable components: (1) the deviation of an X from the mean of its group and (2) the deviation of the group mean from $\bar{X}_T$. Thus, the deviation from $\bar{X}_T$ of an observation in Group 1 can be expressed as

$$X_1 - \bar{X}_T = (X_1 - \bar{X}_1) + (\bar{X}_1 - \bar{X}_T)$$

Let us next express the sum of squared deviations from $\bar{X}_T$ for all of the X_1's in terms of these two components.

$$\sum^{n_1}(X_1 - \bar{X}_T)^2 = \sum^{n_1}[(X_1 - \bar{X}_1) + (\bar{X}_1 - \bar{X}_T)]^2$$
$$= \sum^{n_1}(X_1 - \bar{X}_1)^2 + 2(\bar{X}_1 - \bar{X}_T)\sum^{n_1}(X_1 - \bar{X}_1) + n_1(\bar{X}_1 - \bar{X}_T)^2$$

Since

$$\sum^{n_1}(X_1 - \bar{X}_1) = 0$$

the middle term disappears, and

$$\sum^{n_1}(X_1 - X_T)^2 = \sum^{n_1}(X_1 - \bar{X}_1)^2 + n_1(\bar{X}_1 - \bar{X}_T)^2$$

Similarly,

$$\sum^{n_2}(X_2 - \bar{X}_T)^2 = \sum^{n_2}(X_2 - \bar{X}_2)^2 + n_2(\bar{X}_2 - \bar{X}_T)^2$$

By adding these sums of squares for the two groups and letting the subscript g signify either group, we can define the components of the total sum of squares by

$$\sum^N (X - \bar{X}_T)^2 = \sum_{g=1}^{2}\sum_{1}^{n_g}(X_g - \bar{X}_g)^2 + \sum_{g=1}^{2} n_g(\bar{X}_g - \bar{X}_T)^2$$

(Total)   (Within Groups)   (Between Groups)

Computational formulas are easily obtained from this statement.

Within groups sum of squares:

$$\sum_{g=1}^{2}\sum_{1}^{n_g}(X_g - \bar{X}_g)^2 = \sum_{g=1}^{2}\sum_{1}^{n_g}(X^2_g - 2X_g\bar{X}_g + \bar{X}^2_g)$$

(Definition)

$$= \sum_{g=1}^{2}\left[\sum_{1}^{n_g}X^2_g - \frac{2\left(\sum_{1}^{n_g}X_g\right)^2}{n_g} + n_g\bar{X}^2_g\right]$$

$$= \sum_{g=1}^{2}\left[\sum_{1}^{n_g}X^2_g - \frac{\left(\sum_{1}^{n_g}X_g\right)^2}{n_g}\right] \tag{84a}$$

(Computation)

Between groups sum of squares:

$$\sum_{g=1}^{2}n_g(\bar{X}_g - \bar{X}_T)^2 = \sum_{g=1}^{2}n_g(\bar{X}^2_g - 2\bar{X}_g\bar{X}_T + \bar{X}^2_T)$$

(Definition)

$$= \sum_{g=1}^{2}\left[\frac{\left(\sum_{1}^{n_g}X_g\right)^2}{n_g}\right] - 2\sum_{g=1}^{2}\left[\sum_{1}^{n_g}X_g \frac{\sum^N X}{N}\right]$$

$$+ \sum_{g=1}^{2}\left[n_g\frac{\left(\sum^N X\right)^2}{N^2}\right]$$

$$= \sum_{g=1}^{2} \left[\frac{\left(\sum_{1}^{n_g} X_g \right)^2}{n_g} \right] - 2 \frac{\left(\sum^{N} X \right)^2}{N} + \frac{\left(\sum^{N} X \right)^2}{N}$$

$$= \sum_{g=1}^{2} \frac{\left(\sum_{1}^{n_g} X_g \right)^2}{n_g} - \frac{\left(\sum^{N} X \right)^2}{N} \qquad (84b)$$

(Computation)

Example (from p. 226):

A group of six subjects is tested under condition A and another group of eight under condition B. Is there a significant difference between the means?

	A		B
X_1	$X^2{}_1$	X_2	$X^2{}_2$
8	64	20	400
15	225	12	144
12	144	25	625
8	64	18	324
7	49	19	361
9	81	16	256
		23	529
		10	100
$\Sigma X_1 = \overline{59}$	$\Sigma X^2{}_1 = \overline{627}$	$\Sigma X_2 = \overline{143}$	$\Sigma X^2{}_2 = \overline{2739}$

$$\sum^{N} X = 202$$

$$\sum^{N} X^2 = 3366$$

Total sum of squares:

$$\sum^{N}(X - \bar{X}_T)^2 = 3366 - \frac{(202)^2}{14} = 451.54 \qquad (75)$$

Within groups sum of squares:

$$\sum_{g=1}^{2} \sum_{1}^{n_g} (X_g - \bar{X}_g)^2 = \left[627 - \frac{(59)^2}{6} \right] + \left[2739 - \frac{(143)^2}{8} \right] = 229.70 \quad (84a)$$

Between groups sum squares:

$$\sum_{g=1}^{2} n_g (\bar{X}_g - \bar{X}_T)^2 = \frac{(59)^2}{6} + \frac{(143)^2}{8} - \frac{(202)^2}{14} = 221.84 \qquad (84b)$$

The total sum of squares for the fourteen observations has $(N - 1) = 13$ degrees of freedom because of the requirement that $\sum\limits^{N}(X - \bar{X}) = 0$. Within each group, $\sum\limits^{n_g}(X_g - \bar{X}_g)$ must equal zero. For this reason the combined within groups sum of squares has $(n_1 - 1) + (n_2 - 1) = 12$ degrees of freedom. The between groups sum of squares is computed from two observations of $(\bar{X}_g - \bar{X}_T)$, but there is only one degree of freedom since these two quantities, when weighted according to the n for each group, must add to zero.

Having obtained two independent sums of squares from the data, and knowing the degrees of freedom for each, we can compute two independent estimates of σ^2. The variance estimate computed from the between groups sum of squares is s^2_b, and the estimate obtained from the within groups sum of squares is s^2_w. In the present problem, s^2_w is easily obtained by dividing the within groups sum of squares by the degrees of freedom $(n_1 + n_2 - 2)$. This gives $s^2_w = 19.14$, which is the same as s^2 for testing the same data by means of a t-ratio (p. 226). In both tests we use an unbiased estimate of σ^2 computed from a within groups sum of squares. The meaning of s^2_b is not so obvious, but it is easily demonstrated. Let us refer back to formula (47) for the standard deviation of a sampling distribution of means.

$$\sigma_{\bar{x}} = \frac{\sigma}{\sqrt{N}} \tag{47}$$

From this it follows that

$$\sigma = \sqrt{N}\sigma_{\bar{x}}$$
$$\text{and} \quad \sigma^2 = N\sigma^2_{\bar{x}}$$

Substituting unbiased estimates for variances, we have

$$s^2_x = Ns^2_{\bar{x}}$$

$s^2_{\bar{x}}$, like any other variance estimate, is obtained by dividing the sum of squares for a sample of individual measures of $\bar{X}$ by the degrees of freedom. In the analysis of variance the between groups sum of squares measures the sampling variation in a set of group means. Let us specify that fact by restating the above expression.

$$s^2_b = n_g \frac{\sum\limits_{g=1}^{k}(\bar{X}_g - \bar{X}_T)^2}{k - 1},$$

where k is the number of samples and n_g is the number of individual observations in each sample

When n_g is not constant for all groups it is placed after the summation sign, and the formula for S^2_b becomes

$$s^2_b = \frac{\sum\limits^{k} n_g (\bar{X}_g - \bar{X}_T)^2}{k - 1}$$

In the present example there are only two groups and one df, so $S^2_b = 221.84$.

If s^2_b and s^2_w are randomly drawn from normal populations of the same variance, the ratio S^2_b / S^2_w follows the F-distribution. But, if our experimental variable has produced greater differences among the group means than would be expected to occur through random sampling, this ratio will be larger than the critical values of the F table more often than chance would indicate. Thus, in the analysis of variance the F-ratio can be used to test the significance of the differences among the means of experimental groups.

In our present problem s^2_w was found to be 19.14, so

$$F = \frac{221.84}{19.14} = 11.59$$

which, except for a small rounding error, is equal to the square of t computed from the same data (p. 226). This illustrates the fact that $t^2 = F$ in the limited case where the s^2 in the numerator of F has one degree of freedom.

ANALYSIS OF VARIANCE FOR SEVERAL INDEPENDENT GROUPS

The total sum of squares and its two components for any number of groups can be summarized by the following formulas, where k is the number of groups.

Sum of Squares	Definition	Computation	
Total	$\sum\limits^{N} (X - \bar{X}_T)^2 =$	$\sum\limits^{N} X^2 - \dfrac{\left(\sum\limits^{N} X\right)^2}{N}$	(75)
Within Groups	$\sum\limits^{k} \sum\limits^{n_g} (X_g - \bar{X}_g)^2 =$	$\sum\limits^{k} \left[\sum\limits^{n_g} X^2_g - \dfrac{\left(\sum\limits^{n_g} X_g\right)^2}{n_g} \right]$	(85a)
Between Groups	$\sum\limits^{k} n_g (\bar{X}_g - \bar{X}_T)^2 =$	$\sum\limits^{k} \dfrac{\left(\sum\limits^{n_g} X_g\right)^2}{n_g} - \dfrac{\left(\sum\limits^{N} X\right)^2}{N}$	(85b)

The total sum of squares is equal to the sum of the two components, shown by adding the two computation formulas.

$$\sum_{}^{N}(X - \bar{X}_T)^2 = \sum_{}^{k}\left[\sum_{}^{n_g}X^2_g - \frac{\left(\sum^{n_g}X_g\right)^2}{n_g}\right]$$

$$+ \left[\sum_{}^{k}\frac{\left(\sum^{n_g}X_g\right)^2}{n_g} - \frac{\left(\sum^{N}X\right)^2}{N}\right]$$

$$= \sum_{}^{k}\sum_{}^{n_g}X^2_g - \sum_{}^{k}\frac{\left(\sum^{n_g}X_g\right)^2}{n_g}$$

$$+ \sum_{}^{k}\frac{\left(\sum^{n_g}X_g\right)^2}{n_g} - \frac{\left(\sum^{N}X\right)^2}{N}$$

$$\sum_{}^{N}(X - \bar{X}_T)^2 = \sum_{}^{N}X^2 - \frac{\left(\sum^{N}X\right)^2}{N}$$

The within groups sum of squares is seldom computed directly.
Common practice is to find the total and the between groups sums
and obtain the within groups component by subtraction. However,
the within groups sum can be computed by using formula (75) to
obtain a separate sum of squares within each group. These sums can
then be combined to obtain the overall within group sum of squares
as in formula (85a).

Degrees of Freedom

The total sum of squares has $N - 1$ degrees of freedom because
$\Sigma(X - \bar{X}) = 0$. This can be divided into two portions corresponding to the two components of the total sum of squares. Within
each group there are $(n_g - 1)$ independent measures of variation
and the sum of these for k groups gives the within group degrees of
freedom as $(N - k)$. There are k values of $(\bar{X}_g - \bar{X}_T)^2$ contained
in the between group sum of squares, which thus has $(k - 1)$
degrees of freedom.

The degrees of freedom for the total sum of squares must equal
the sum of the component degrees of freedom.

$$N - 1 = (N - k) + (k - 1)$$

The Variance Estimates

Two independent unbiased estimates of σ^2 are computed as in the example where we tested the difference between two means. Here, however, $S^2{}_b$ has $(k-1)$ degrees of freedom and $F \neq t^2$. The two variance estimates for any number of groups are defined by the following formulas.

$$s^2{}_b = \frac{\sum_{}^{k} n_g (\bar{X}_g - \bar{X}_T)^2}{k-1} \tag{86}$$

$$s^2{}_w = \frac{\sum_{}^{k}\sum_{}^{n_g} (X_g - \bar{X}_g)^2}{n-k} \tag{87}$$

According to the null hypothesis that the various group means are randomly drawn from the same population, the ratio obtained by dividing $s^2{}_b$ by $s^2{}_w$ will follow the F-distribution. On the other hand, if the experimental groups are from different populations, variation among their means will be greater than among means of random sample and $s^2{}_b$ will then be greater than $s^2{}_w$, the unbiased estimate of σ^2, by an amount determined by the differences among the group means. Thus, if F is larger than the tabled values we can reject H_0, asserting that the differences among group means are significantly greater than expected differences among sample means drawn from the same population.

Assumptions

Here, as in other statistical tests, the mathematical model involves other assumptions than the H_0 being tested. The additional critical assumptions are (1) that the measures in each group have been randomly drawn from a normal population and (2) that the populations represented by the various groups have the same variance. The second is the assumption of homogeneity of variance, which was discussed earlier in connection with the t-ratio. Homogeneity of variance is required by the fact that sums of squares within the groups are combined, as in the t-ratio, to obtain the best estimate of σ^2.

Normality can be tested for each group by means of chi square or the K-S test. Homogeneity of variance can be roughly checked by computing an s^2 from the sum of squares within each group and comparing the largest and the smallest s^2 by means of the F-ratio. If this F, evaluated as a two-tailed test, is not significant, we can safely assume that the requirement of homogeneity of variance is adequately met. If F is significant, the interpretation is not always clear because in selecting the two extreme values of s^2 we have increased the probability of obtaining a large value of F. A more adequate method—Bartlett's test—is described in advanced texts.

It is fortunate that the distribution of F is not greatly distorted by moderate departures from normality and homogeneity of variance. Furthermore, the distortion has been identified as a slight increase in the probability that F will exceed the values of Table H. Thus, when there is reason to question the assumption of normality or of homogeneity we might well require a higher level of significance for rejecting H_0.

The following example, consisting of artificial data, illustrates the computations required for testing differences among several means.

	Group 1		Group 2		Group 3		Group 4	
	X_1	X^2_1	X_2	X^2_2	X_3	X^2_3	X_4	X^2_4
	5	25	4	16	10	100	11	121
	5	25	8	64	8	64	10	100
	2	4	7	49	10	100	12	144
	4	16	5	25	9	81	14	196
	3	9	6	36	8	64	11	121
			8	64	8	64		
			7	49				
n_g	5		7		6		5	
$\overset{n}{\Sigma}X_g$	19		45		53		58	
$(\overset{n}{\Sigma}X_g)^2$	361		2025		2809		3364	
$\overset{n}{\Sigma}X^2_g$		79		303		473		682

$$N = \sum^{k} n_g = 23$$

$$\sum^{N} X = \sum^{k} \sum^{n_g} X_g = 175$$

$$\sum^{N} X^2 = \sum^{k} \sum^{n_g} X^2_g = 1537$$

Total sum of squares:

$$\sum_{}^{N} X^2 - \frac{\left(\sum_{}^{N} X\right)^2}{N} = 1537 - \frac{(175)^2}{23} = 205.48$$

Between groups sum of squares:

$$\sum_{}^{k} \frac{\left(\sum_{}^{n_g} X_g\right)^2}{n_g} - \frac{\left(\sum_{}^{N} X\right)^2}{N}$$

$$= \frac{361}{5} + \frac{2025}{7} + \frac{2809}{6} + \frac{3364}{5} - \frac{(175)^2}{23} = 170.94$$

Within groups sum of squares:

$$\text{Within} = \text{Total} - \text{Between} = 205.48 - 170.94 = 34.54$$

Between groups variance estimate:

$$s^2_b = \frac{\text{Between groups sum of squares}}{k-1} = \frac{170.94}{3} = 56.98$$

Within groups variance estimate:

$$s^2_w = \frac{\text{Within groups sum of squares}}{N-k} = \frac{34.54}{19} = 1.82$$

$$F_{3,19} = \frac{s^2_b}{s^2_w} = \frac{56.98}{1.82} = 31.31$$
$$p < .001$$

We decide to reject H_0, concluding that differences among the means are significantly greater than zero.

It is customary and convenient to present the results in the form of an analysis of variance table, such as the following.

ANALYSIS OF VARIANCE

Source of Variation	df	Sum of Squares	s^2*	F	p
Total..............	22	205.48			
Between Groups......	3	170.94	56.98	31.31	<.001
Within Groups.......	19	34.54	1.82		

* In the analysis of variance s^2 is sometimes referred to as the "mean square" and is so designated in the summary table.

The analysis of variance is not only more convenient than the t-ratio for problems of this type, but it helps to avoid a common error of interpretation in comparing the means of several groups. To illustrate this error let us suppose that at noon on each of thirty successive days we toss ten pennies onto a table and count the number of heads. At the end of the month, trials are selected which deviate $\pm 1.96\sigma$ or more from the expected number of five heads. We then assert that the particular days of the month when these deviations occurred are especially favorable or unfavorable, as the case may be, for the appearance of heads. Of course this is preposterous, since one in twenty trials is expected to deviate this far, or farther, by chance. But it is no more preposterous than computing t-ratios for all of the possible comparisons among a group of means and attaching special significance to those which exceed a certain value. This fallacy can be avoided if we first apply the analysis of variance when several groups are to be compared. Only if the overall F turns out to be significant is it legitimate to single out large differences for special attention. The only exception to this rule occurs in situations where theoretical considerations have led the experimenter to predict *before the data have been observed* that certain differences will be found. If such predictions have been made, it is proper to attach significance to differences in the predicted direction even though the overall F is not significant. But when this is done *all* predicted differences must be tested and considered in evaluating the results—the unverified predictions as well as those which are supported by the data.

In *exploratory experiments,* without predictions derived from theory, it is permissible to test particular differences by a t-ratio if, and only if, the overall F has turned out to be significant. Here it is good practice to use the s^2_w from the analysis of variance in computing the t-ratio because this estimate is based on more degrees of freedom than one computed from the data of only two groups and is thus a better estimate of σ^2. To test the difference between the means of Groups 1 and 2 in our illustrative example we would proceed as follows, substituting s^2_w in formula (70).

$$t = \frac{\bar{X}_1 - \bar{X}_2}{\sqrt{\dfrac{s^2_w}{n_1} + \dfrac{s^2_w}{n_2}}} = \frac{\dfrac{19}{5} - \dfrac{45}{7}}{\sqrt{\dfrac{1.82}{5} + \dfrac{1.82}{7}}} = -3.33$$

$$df = 19 \qquad p < .01$$

Note that the t table is entered with the df from which s^2_w was obtained in the analysis of variance. This procedure is correct regardless of the number of observations in the groups being compared.

If only the data from groups 1 and 2 were available for estimating σ^2 the computation would be

$$s^2 = \frac{\Sigma(X_1 - \bar{X}_1)^2 + \Sigma(X_2 - \bar{X}_2)^2}{n_1 + n_2 - 2} = \frac{4.8 + 13.7}{5 + 7 - 2} = 1.85$$

$$t = \frac{\dfrac{19}{5} - \dfrac{45}{7}}{\sqrt{\dfrac{1.85}{5} + \dfrac{1.85}{7}}} = -3.30$$

$$df = 10 \qquad p < .01$$

Although α is different, the improved estimate of σ^2 does not in this case lead to a different decision.

In our illustrative problem all of the differences between means turned out to be significant, and H_0 regarding particular differences can be rejected. However, when isolated and *unexpected* differences are found in a number of possible comparisons, it is best to regard them as merely suggestions for further research even though the overall F is significant. On the other hand, if the experimenter has identified certain meaningful comparisons and has *planned them before obtaining his data,* it is quite legitimate to test these differences between means, using F or t, even though the overall F is not significant. Such a priori planned comparisons are always justified regardless of the outcome of the rest of the experiment. A posteriori post-mortem comparisons must always be viewed with caution. Methods which can be used for post-mortem data snooping are described in advanced textbooks.*

THE MEDIAN TEST

A distribution-free method applicable to several groups is the median test, which was described in Chapter XII. The first step is to find the approximate median of the entire set of data, ignoring

---

* B. J. Winer, *Statistical Principles in Experimental Design* (New York: McGraw-Hill Book Co., 1962), chap. iii.

the group classification. A $2 \times k$ contingency table is then constructed to test by χ^2 the null hypothesis that the groups do not differ with respect to the frequency of scores falling above and below the approximate median. It must be remembered, however, that this test, like other non-parametric methods, is less powerful than the analysis of variance in detecting departures from the null hypothesis.

EXERCISES

1. Prove the following.

$$\sum_{}^{N}(X - X)^2 = \sum_{}^{N}X^2 - \frac{(\Sigma X)^2}{N}$$

2. This is an easy example for practice. Compute the following sums of squares: (a) total, (b) between groups, (c) within groups by formula (75). Does $(a) - (b) = (c)$?

Group A	Group B
26	22
45	19
43	35
30	40
29	36

3. A scale to measure attitude towards smoking was administered to the freshmen in a boys' high school. High scores signify favorable attitude. When scores were grouped according to students' reports of their smoking behavior the following results were obtained.

Smoking Behavior	N	ΣX	ΣX^2
Have never smoked........	90	4508	240278
Have experimented, but have never smoked regularly .	165	9298	553172
Used to smoke regularly, but quit....................	70	4514	306548
Now regularly smoke once a week or more.............	89	6939	557309

What can you conclude concerning the relationship between attitude toward smoking and smoking behavior?

4. The following data represent measurements of an experimental and a control group.

    a) Apply the analysis of variance and compute the F-ratio.

    b) Apply the t-ratio. Now find the value of t^2 and compare it with F.

Control	Experi- mental
10	11
7	9
9	10
12	14
10	12
8	15
5	13
8	12
11	13
9	10
	12
	8

5. Forty subjects were randomly assigned to four experimental groups of ten subjects. Each group was then randomly assigned to one of four experimental conditions, *A, B, C,* or *D*.

    a) Compute the total sum of squares, and the between groups and within groups separately. Do the two components add up to the total?

    b) Use the analysis of variance to test the hypothesis that the group means do not differ significantly from one another.

    c) Code the scores by subtracting 50 from each and again apply the analysis of variance. Does the coding change the values of the various sums of squares? Is the F-ratio the same? Explain your results.

Group A	Group B	Group C	Group D
55	54	54	51
58	59	53	55
56	58	57	51
57	54	56	56
58	53	51	50
59	56	53	54
60	57	53	54
58	56	55	56
60	56	54	52
57	55	52	53

6. The distributions of scores on the Verbal section of the College Board Scholastic Aptitude Test are given below for three entering classes of college freshmen. Is there a significant overall difference among the three means? Here you must apply computational techniques used earlier for grouped data. What would be the result if the entire computation, including F, were carried through with d_i values—class interval deviations from an arbitrary origin?

DISTRIBUTIONS OF COLLEGE BOARD VERBAL SCORES

CLASS INTERVALS	FREQUENCIES		
	1952	1953	1954
750–799	0	3	1
700–749	6	15	14
650–699	22	33	42
600–649	28	47	49
550–599	21	39	39
500–549	20	39	28
450–499	21	22	20
400–449	17	15	10
350–399	4	2	1
300–349	1	0	2

7. The following data represent the numbers of puzzle problems solved by three groups of subjects working under different instructions. Group *A* was given broad hints about the method of solution. No suggestions were given the subjects in Group *B;* and Group *C* was given misleading suggestions, which could not possibly lead to a solution. The scores are the numbers of correct solutions in five minutes. Apply the median test to these data. What reservations would you have regarding the use of the analysis of variance here?

Number of Correct Solutions

Group A				*Group B*				*Group C*			
10	10	10	10	9	5	6	4	3	5	0	1
8	9	10	9	8	6	7	6	1	4	2	5
9	8	10	10	3	7	6	7	0	3	0	2
8	7	10	9	5	9	4	6	1	0	1	3

TESTING DIFFERENCES BETWEEN CORRELATED MEANS

The analysis of variance can be used to test differences among several correlated means where the same subjects have been observed under more than two experimental conditions or the various groups have been matched. This method is an extension to more than two groups of the *t*-ratio for correlated scores which was discussed in Chapter XI. In comparing two groups we found it possible to allow for correlation by computing s^2 from differences between paired observations. Since differences can be used only with *pairs* of matched scores we must now find a general method for handling more than two correlated samples. We shall first examine the sampling distribution of *sums,* because a sum can be obtained for any number of matched observations.

The Variance of a Sum

Suppose that pairs of scores are drawn from the populations of X_1 and X_2. The mean of the sums for pairs will be

$$M_{x_1 + x_2} = \frac{\Sigma(X_1 + X_2)}{N} = \bar{X}_1 + \bar{X}_2$$

The deviation of a single sum from $M_{(x_1 + x_2)}$ is

$$(X_1 + X_2) - (\bar{X}_1 + \bar{X}_2) = x_1 + x_2$$

The standard deviation of the distribution of sums* is

$$S_{(x_1 + x_2)} = \sqrt{\frac{\Sigma(x_1 + x_2)^2}{N}} = \sqrt{S^2_1 + S^2_2 + 2r_{12}S_1S_2} \qquad (88)$$

This statement and formula (66), p. 219, show that a positive correlation between samples *decreases* the standard deviation of differences but *increases* the standard deviation of sums. This is illustrated by the following example.

X_1	X_2	D $X_1 - X_2$	Σ $X_1 + X_2$	X_1	X_2	D $X_1 - X_2$	Σ $X_1 + X_2$	X_1	X_2	D $X_1 - X_2$	Σ $X_1 + X_2$
15	10	5	25	15	6	9	21	15	8	7	23
14	9	5	23	14	7	7	21	14	7	7	21
13	8	5	21	13	8	5	21	13	10	3	23
12	7	5	19	12	9	3	21	12	6	6	18
11	6	5	17	11	10	1	21	11	9	2	20

Even though the same values for X_1 and X_2 are used in each of the three arrangements, the D column and the Σ column are quite different depending on the pairing (the correlation) of X_1 and X_2. The sums, and therefore the means, vary maximally from each other when X_1 and X_2 are positively correlated. Thus, the sum of squares between groups of scores from matched sets of subjects is a measure of intercorrelation.

---

* See the development of formula (66), pp. 218–19.

The Difference between Two Correlated Means

To illustrate this method we will first apply it to the muscle tension data for which a t-ratio was computed in Chapter XI, p. 214.

The procedure is simply to compute a between groups sum of squares corresponding to subjects. This sum of squares represents the amount of variation associated with individual differences among subjects, or among matched sets. The sum obtained in this way is then subtracted from the total sum of squares, leaving a remainder which can be further analyzed into two portions—that due to differences between experimental conditions and a residual which is taken as a measure of sampling errors, since its source cannot be identified.

Subject	X_1 Tension	X_2 Control	$(X_1 + X_2)$	$(X_1 + X_2)^2$
A	78	68	146	21316
B	38	30	68	4624
C	81	57	138	19044
D	61	46	107	11449
E	55	38	93	8649
F	61	39	100	10000
G	82	65	147	21609
H	51	53	104	10816
I	55	37	92	8464
J	69	44	113	12769
K	55	41	96	9216
L	59	76	135	18225
Sums	745	594	1339	156181
$(\Sigma X_g)^2$	555025	352836		

$$\sum^{N} X^2 = 79823$$

Total sum of squares:

$$\sum^{N} X^2 - \frac{\left(\sum^{N} X\right)^2}{N} = 79823 - \frac{(1339)^2}{24} = 5117.96$$

Between subjects sum of squares:

$$\sum^{12} \frac{(X_1 + X_2)^2}{N_g} - \frac{\left(\sum^{N} X\right)^2}{N} = \frac{156181}{2} - \frac{(1339)^2}{24} = 3385.46$$

Between groups sum of squares:

$$\sum^2 \frac{\left(\sum^{n_g} X_g\right)^2}{n_g} - \frac{\left(\sum^N X\right)^2}{N} = \frac{555025 + 352836}{12} - \frac{(1339)^2}{24} = 950.04$$

Residual sum of squares:

$$(5117.96 - 3385.46) - 950.04 = 782.46$$

$$F_{1,11} = \frac{s^2_b}{s^2_r} = \frac{950.04}{71.13} = 13.36$$

The results of this treatment are summarized in the following analysis of variance table. For comparison note that the t-ratio for the same data was based on 11 df because the estimate of σ^2 was obtained from 12 observations of the difference $(X_1 - X_2)$.

ANALYSIS OF VARIANCE

Source of Variation	df	Sum of Squares	s^2	F	p
Total................	23	5117.96			
Between Subjects.....	11	3385.46			
Between Groups......	1	950.04	950.04	13.36	<.005
Residual............	11	782.46	71.13		

Here, as in any analysis of variance, the total df is the sum of the component df's, and the total sum of squares is the sum of the three component sums of squares.

$F_{1,11} = 13.36$, which, except for a small rounding error, is the square of the t-ratio computed from the same data. Although either method is applicable, the t-ratio is usually easier to compute when comparing only two groups.

Differences among Several Correlated Means

To illustrate this procedure we will describe an experiment designed to study the influence of different exposure intervals on nonsense syllable learning. The data are artificial and serve merely to illustrate this application of the analysis of variance.

Suppose that before the actual experiment begins a number of subjects have had preliminary practice in learning three lists of nonsense syllables. On the basis of their scores for the third list, four matched groups of ten subjects are selected. These forty subjects will now memorize another list to a criterion of two successive correct trials, but for each group the exposure interval for separate syllables will be different. Assume that the following data have been obtained.

TRIALS REQUIRED TO REACH CRITERION

Matched Sets of Subjects	Group				ΣX_r	$\bar{X}_r$
	I	II	III	IV		
A	6	8	8	10	32	8.00
B	10	10	11	9	39	9.75
C	4	5	7	8	24	6.00
D	6	6	8	10	30	7.50
E	3	5	4	7	19	4.75
F	9	8	10	12	39	9.75
G	5	7	6	8	26	6.50
H	5	5	6	5	21	5.25
I	8	8	9	11	36	9.00
J	7	9	10	10	36	9.00
ΣX_c	63	71	79	90		
$\bar{X}_c$	6.3	7.1	7.9	9.0		

Every score can be classified according to two dimensions with respect to the two experimental conditions: (1) the exposure interval and (2) the matched sets of four subjects. Differences among the means of the columns, $\bar{X}_c$, suggest that the length of exposure interval influences learning, but we must apply a statistical test before deciding whether or not to reject H_0.

Differences between the means of rows provide a measure of individual differences between matched sets of subjects and by computing a between row sum of squares, in addition to the between groups and within groups sums, we can apply the method used in the preceding example where there were only two groups. In the following table R stands for the number of rows and C for the number of columns. Thus, $N = RC$. The subscripts r and c designate particular rows and columns. They can take any value from one to R or C. For example, the summation over the ten rows of the X's in Column II would be specified as $\sum\limits^{R} X_2$. The procedure for obtaining a between groups sum of squares is simplified by using the common denominator when n_g's are equal.

Matched Sets of Subjects	X_1	$X^2{}_1$	X_2	$X^2{}_2$	X_3	$X^2{}_3$	X_4	$X^2{}_4$	$\overset{C}{\Sigma X_r}$
A	6	36	8	64	8	64	10	100	32
B	10	100	10	100	11	121	9	81	40
C	4	16	5	25	7	49	8	64	24
D	6	36	6	36	8	64	10	100	30
E	3	9	5	25	4	16	7	49	19
F	9	81	8	64	10	100	12	144	39
G	5	25	7	49	6	36	8	64	26
H	5	25	5	25	6	36	5	25	21
I	8	64	8	64	9	81	11	121	36
J	7	49	9	81	10	100	10	100	36
$\overset{R}{\Sigma X_c}$	63		71		79		90		$\overset{C\ R}{\Sigma\Sigma X_c} = 303$
$\overset{R}{\Sigma X^2{}_c}$		441		533		667		848	$\overset{C\ R}{\Sigma\Sigma X^2{}_c} = 2489$

Total sum of squares:

$$2489 - \frac{(303)^2}{40} = 193.78$$

Between groups sum of squares (matched subjects):

$$\frac{(32)^2 + (40)^2 + (24)^2 + (30)^2 + (19)^2 + (39)^2 + (26)^2 + (21)^2 + (36)^2 + (36)^2}{4} - \frac{(303)^2}{40} = 127.53$$

Total sum of squares with correlation component removed:

$$193.78 - 127.53 = 66.25$$

Between groups sum of squares (exposure interval):

$$\frac{(63)^2 + (71)^2 + (79)^2 + (90)^2}{10} - \frac{(303)^2}{40} = 39.88$$

Residual sum of squares:

$$(193.78 - 127.53) - 39.88 = 26.37$$

Since the entire table contains forty items, there are a total of thirty-nine degrees of freedom. The four column sums have 3 df, and the ten rows have 9 df. Subtracting these from the total, we find that there are 27 df for the residual sum of squares. Another way of looking at this is to consider the $R \times C$ table with its marginal totals and find the number of entries we can arbitrarily place in the cells with no restriction as to their magnitude. In this case nine rows can each be assigned three entries without restriction. When the twenty-seven entries have been assigned in this manner the remaining thirteen cells must be given values which agree with the marginal totals.

The results of the analysis are summarized in the following table. Only two s^2's are computed because the only test of interest in this experiment is concerned with differences among the four experimental conditions. The $F_{3,27}$ obtained by dividing the s^2 for columns by the s^2 computed from the residual sum of squares leads us to reject the null hypothesis.

ANALYSIS OF VARIANCE FOR MEMORIZATION WITH DIFFERENT EXPOSURE INTERVALS

Source of Variation	df	Sum of Squares	s^2	F	p
Total.	39	193.78			
Matched Sets of Subjects.	9	107.78			
Exposure Intervals	3	39.88	13.29	7.77	<.005
Residual.	27	46.12	1.71		

Here, as before, if any two means for exposure intervals are to be compared, the best value of s for the t-ratio is obtained from the residual s^2.

THE RESIDUAL SUM OF SQUARES

To illustrate further the meaning of the residual sum of squares, let us consider a smaller problem of the same type. Suppose each of five subjects were presented with four levels of an independent variable and that the following scores were obtained for the dependent variable.

| Subjects | Levels of Independent Variable | | | | $\overset{c}{\Sigma}X_r$ | $\bar{X}_r$ | $(\bar{X}_r - \bar{X}_T)$ |
	I	II	III	IV			
A	1	3	3	5	12	3.0	−1.8
B	3	3	5	7	18	4.5	−0.3
C	2	4	6	6	18	4.5	−0.3
D	5	6	8	7	26	6.5	+1.7
E	3	4	6	9	22	5.5	+0.7
$\overset{R}{\Sigma}X_c$	14	20	28	34	$\overset{N}{\Sigma}X = 96$		
$\bar{X}_c$	2.8	4.0	5.6	6.8	$\bar{X}_T = 4.8$		
$(\bar{X}_c - \bar{X}_T)$	−2.0	−0.8	+0.8	+2.0			

Differences among subjects are shown by deviations of row means from $\bar{X}_T$. Differences among conditions are shown by deviations of column means from $\bar{X}_T$. Now if the separate scores were entirely consistent with the means of the columns and rows, the deviation of any individual score from $\bar{X}_T$ should equal the sum of the deviations of its column and row means from $\bar{X}_T$. For example, the score for subject C under the third level of the independent variable, $\bar{X}_{CIII}$, would be expected to deviate $+0.5$ because the deviations of its column and row means are, respectively, $+0.8$ and -0.3. In this manner expected deviations can be computed for each cell.

$$\text{Expected}\quad (X_{rc} - \bar{X}_T) = (\bar{X}_r - \bar{X}_T) + (\bar{X}_c - \bar{X}_T)$$

The following table shows expected deviations in parentheses, together with actual deviations of the observed X's.

EXPECTED AND OBSERVED DEVIATIONS FROM $\bar{X}_T$

Subjects	Levels of Independent Variable			
	I	II	III	IV
A	-3.8 (-3.8)	-1.8 (-2.6)	-1.8 (-1.0)	$+0.2$ $(+0.2)$
B	-1.8 (-2.3)	-1.8 (-1.1)	$+0.2$ $(+0.5)$	$+2.2$ $(+1.7)$
C	-2.8 (-2.3)	-0.8 (-1.1)	$+1.2$ $(+0.5)$	$+1.2$ $(+1.7)$
D	$+0.2$ (-0.3)	$+1.2$ $(+0.9)$	$+3.2$ $(+2.5)$	$+2.2$ $(+3.7)$
E	-1.8 (-1.3)	-0.8 (-0.1)	$+1.2$ $(+1.5)$	$+4.2$ $(+2.7)$

Each observed deviation from $\bar{X}_T$ can be broken down into two portions: (1) an amount which is consistent with the column and row means and thus has an identifiable source and (2) a remainder which has no identifiable source in the design of the experiment. This variation over and above the identifiable components is the residual variation. The residual sum of squares is actually the sum of squared discrepancies between *identifiable* and *observed* variations from $\bar{X}_T$. Since such discrepancies are unidentified and unpredicted, they are used as a measure of error for evaluating the results of the experiment.

From the above table we can compute the residual sum of squares as

$$\sum_{}^{N} \left\{ (X_{rc} - \bar{X}_T) - \left[(\bar{X}_r - \bar{X}_T) + (\bar{X}_c - \bar{X}_T) \right] \right\}^2 = 9.6$$

The regular method of computation gives the same result.

Total:

$$\sum^{N} (X - \bar{X}_T)^2 = 544 - \frac{(96)^2}{20} = 83.2$$

Columns:

$$\sum^{C} R(\bar{X}_c - \bar{X}_T)^2 = \frac{(14)^2 + (20)^2 + (28)^2 + (34)^2}{5} - \frac{(96)^2}{20} = 46.4$$

Rows:

$$\sum^{R} C(X_r - \bar{X}_T)^2 = \frac{(12)^2 + (18)^2 + (18)^2 + (26)^2 + (22)^2}{4} - \frac{(96)^2}{20} = 27.2$$

Residual: $83.2 - 46.4 - 27.2 = 9.6$

EXERCISES

1. Three groups of ninth-grade pupils were matched on the basis of IQ and first-semester grades. The pupils of each set of three were randomly assigned to three classes. The classes were then randomly assigned to three teachers. During the second semester they studied the same topics in algebra, using the same textbook. At the end of the year the following scores were obtained on an algebra achievement test. What can you conclude concerning possible differences in effectiveness among the three teachers?

Matched Sets of Pupils	Class A	Class B	Class C
A	15	14	13
B	7	5	4
C	9	8	7
D	14	15	10
E	3	5	4
F	5	6	3
G	9	9	8
H	9	6	7
I	12	10	9
J	8	7	6
K	10	10	9
L	5	5	4
M	10	8	10
N	9	7	6

Would your conclusions be different if you had not allowed in the analysis of variance for the fact that the pupils in the three classes were matched? Compute F and compare it with the correct value.

2. Test the difference between the means of class A and class C by using (a) the t-ratio and (b) the analysis of variance. In both tests use the

method appropriate for correlated groups. Do both give the same probability of a type 1 error? What are the numerical values of t^2 and F for this problem?

3. The following data are memorization scores obtained from the same group of subjects under four levels of muscular tension. Test the significance of the influence of tension on memorization.

Subject	Control (No Tension) 0	Levels of Tension Induced by Squeezing a Hand Dynamometer		
		I	II	III
1	68	78	71	71
2	30	38	48	35
3	46	61	57	61
4	38	55	51	28
5	39	61	35	52
6	65	82	56	54
7	37	55	48	37
8	44	69	65	63
9	37	31	32	40
10	32	57	63	36
11	46	58	34	36
12	63	57	68	37
13	59	76	74	88
14	39	58	49	41
15	47	53	56	20
16	50	60	56	50
17	63	76	74	74
18	68	70	102	60
19	52	72	43	73
20	75	89	94	73

The computation can be made easier by subtracting a constant, say 40, from each score. What effect will such coding have on the obtained sums of squares?

4. Show the steps in the derivation of formula (88), p. 278.

5. Can you express r as a function of the variance of the sums of paired scores? (See formula (67), p. 219.)

FACTORIAL DESIGNS

The analysis of variance can be used to test the effect of more than one independent variable in a single experiment. Such experiments follow the principles of factorial design and the results can be evaluated by the analysis of variance. Factorial designs systematically combine the various levels of two or more independent variables in such a manner that the analysis of variance can be used to test the influence of separate variables as well as the effect produced by their interaction in various combinations.

To illustrate this use of the analysis of variance we shall design an experiment to test the effect of three degrees of spaced practice on retention of verbal material over four intervals of time. Our subjects will learn a list of twelve nonsense syllables to a criterion of one errorless trial. After an interval of time, retention will be measured by the number of syllables correctly anticipated in a test trial. We shall use three levels of distribution—nine seconds, sixty seconds, and five minutes between practice trials. Recall will be tested after twelve hours, twenty-four hours, three days, and seven days. The factorial design will systematically combine each level of the first variable with each level of the second. Thus, there will be twelve different combinations of experimental conditions. The plan of the experiment is illustrated by the following table.

A 3 × 4 FACTORIAL DESIGN

B: Time Following Original Learning

		(1) 12 hrs.	(2) 24 hrs.	(3) 3 days	(4) 7 days
A: Interval between Trials	(1) 9 secs.	A_1B_1	A_1B_2	A_1B_3	A_1B_4
	(2) 60 secs.	A_2B_1	A_2B_2	A_2B_3	A_2B_4
	(3) 5 mins.	A_3B_1	A_3B_2	A_3B_3	A_3B_4

Each cell contains a different combination of the levels of the two independent variables. Thus, A_2B_3 represents retention after three days where sixty-second intervals separated the trials in original learning. Suppose four subjects have been randomly assigned to each cell of the table. The following artificial data represent a possible outcome of the experiment.

The first step in the analysis is to compute the total, the between groups, and the within groups sums of squares by the usual method.

RECALL SCORES

Time Following Original Learning

		12 hrs.	24 hrs.	3 days	7 days	$\overset{c}{\Sigma X_r}$
	9 secs.	12 9 10 9	4 6 5 5	3 4 2 3	2 3 5 3	85
	$\overset{4}{\underset{1}{\Sigma X_{1c}}}$	40	20	12	13	
	60 secs.	8 10 11 10	7 5 6 5	5 4 3 4	3 2 4 2	89
Interval between Trials	$\overset{4}{\underset{1}{\Sigma X_{2c}}}$	39	23	16	11	
	5 mins.	10 12 10 9	8 9 9 10	8 8 7 9	7 6 8 6	136
	$\overset{4}{\underset{1}{\Sigma X_{3c}}}$	41	36	32	27	
	$\overset{R}{\Sigma X_c}$	120	79	60	51	$\overset{N}{\Sigma X} = 310$

Total sum of squares [formula (75)]:

$$2406 - \frac{(310)^2}{48} = 403.92$$

Between groups sum of squares [formula (85b)]:

$$\frac{(40)^2 + (20)^2 + (12)^2 + (13)^2 + (39)^2 + (23)^2 + (16)^2 + (11)^2 + (41)^2 + (36)^2 + (32)^2 + (27)^2}{4}$$
$$- \frac{(310)^2}{48} = 365.42$$

Within groups sum of squares:

$$403.92 - 365.42 = 38.50$$

Although F could be computed from s^2_b and s^2_w, there is nothing to be gained from such a test because clear interpretation would be impossible. If F were significantly large H_0 could be rejected, but there would be no way of identifying the experimental variables responsible for the differences. Significant differences might have been produced by distribution of practice, time following original learning, or interaction between these factors.

It is possible to identify the factors responsible for variation between the groups in a factorial experiment by proceeding farther with the analysis of variance. The next step is to compute two more between groups sums of squares corresponding to the two independent variables. This is done by successively applying formula (85*b*) to the columns and the rows.

Between columns sum of squares (time following original learning):

$$\frac{(120)^2 + (79)^2 + (60)^2 + (51)^2}{12} - \frac{(310)^2}{48} = 234.75$$

Between rows sum of squares (interval between trials):

$$\frac{(85)^2 + (89)^2 + (136)^2}{16} - \frac{(310)^2}{48} = 100.54$$

By subtracting these experimentally identified components from the between groups sum of squares for the twelve groups we find that the variation of the separate cells around $\bar{X}_T$ is greater than the variation of rows and columns around $\bar{X}_T$. This means that the twelve groups differ from each other by a residual amount which is not associated with, or predictable from, differences between columns and between rows.

Between groups sum of squares:	365.42
Between columns sum of squares:	⎧234.75
	⎨
Between rows sum of squares:	⎩100.54
Residual:	30.13

This residual sum of squares may be nothing more than unpredictable variation, or it may represent *identifiable interaction* between the two independent variables. If the residual consists only of sampling variation among cell means, s^2 computed from this component should not be significantly greater than s^2_w. A significant F is evidence that the particular *combinations of row and column treatments* produced an effect over and above that which can be identified when rows and columns are considered separately. The variance estimate computed from the residual between groups classification is denoted as $s^2_{R \times C}$, or the interaction variance estimate. It is possible to identify interaction only when each cell contains more than one observation because there is no within group sum of squares to provide a test for possible interaction effects if each cell contains only one score.

Let us now summarize the results of this analysis. Note that the total sum of squares is first divided into a between groups and a within groups component. The between groups sum of squares is then separated into three components corresponding to columns, rows, and interaction. The df for interaction is the remainder when the df's for columns and for rows are subtracted from the between groups df. This remainder must equal the product of the column and row df's.

Source of Variation	df	Sum of Squares	s^2	F	p
Total...................	47	445.92			
Between Groups*........	11	365.42			
Between Columns........	3	234.75	78.25	73.13	<.001
Between Rows...........	2	100.54	50.27	46.98	<.001
Rows × Columns........	6	30.13	5.02	4.69	<.01
Within Groups...........	36	38.50	1.07		

* Since this is made up of three identifiable components and does not lead to a meaningful test of significance, it is ordinarily not shown in the summary table.

The significant F for rows permits us to conclude that the amount retained increases with increasing intervals between trials within the range of intervals used in this experiment. The significant column effect shows that there is a decrease in retention over the seven days.

The significant interaction, however, requires that statements concerning the row and column effects be qualified. Thus, although retention decreases with the passage of time, the relationship between these two variables is different depending upon the rest interval between learning trials. This can be represented by the following graph which shows three retention curves, one for each rest interval (Figure 47).

The relative average heights of the curves correspond to the significant differences between rest intervals. If there were no interaction these curves would be roughly parallel throughout their length since the relative levels of retention would be the same for all three intervals between trials.

By utilizing the principles of factorial design and the analysis of variance we can study the separate effects of more than one

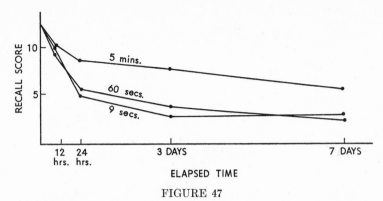

FIGURE 47

RETENTION FOLLOWING LEARNING WITH DIFFERENT INTERVALS BETWEEN
TRIALS

independent variable and the effect of interaction between them. In
factorial designs the data are classified according to experimental
variables which have been systematically manipulated so that the
various levels occur together in all possible combinations. Factorial
designs are not restricted to laboratory variables such as time,
intensity of stimulation, amount of practice, etc., which can be
intentionally modified by the experimenter. They can also be used
with variables such as sex, socio-economic group, diagnostic category, and level of intelligence, for which the desired levels can be
obtained only through careful selection of cases which fit the
various categories of classification. The levels may be defined by
numerical measurements or by any other discriminable attribute.
Although our introductory discussion is limited to experiments
involving double classification, factorial designs can be used with
any number of independent variables. These, and other complex
experimental designs associated with the analysis of variance, are
discussed in advanced texts.

SUGGESTED READINGS

1. Lindquist, E. F. *Design and Analysis of Experiments in Psychology
   and Education.* New York: Houghton Mifflin Co., 1953.

2. McNemar, Q. *Psychological Statistics*, chaps. xiv, xv, and xvi. 3d ed.
   New York: John Wiley & Sons, 1962.

3. Ray, W. S. *An Introduction to Experimental Design*, chaps. ix, x,
   xi, xii, and xv. New York: The Macmillan Co., 1960.

4. Snedecor, G. W. *Statistical Methods,* chaps. x and xi. 4th ed. Ames, Iowa: The Iowa State College Press, 1946.

EXERCISES

1. Suppose that at the beginning of the year students in a required course were asked to rate their interest in the subject matter of the course on a linear scale extending from "low" to "high." The twenty-four students with the lowest interest rating were identified, as were the twenty-four with the highest ratings. Twelve students from each of the identified groups of twenty-four were then randomly selected to form a high interest and a low interest class. These two classes were taught by the discussion method, while the remaining two groups of twelve were assigned to a large class which was taught by the lecture method. The same course material was covered by all three classes, and they were taught by the same instructor. At the end of the term the following scores were made on the final examination.

High Interest		Low Interest	
Discussion	Lecture	Discussion	Lecture
73	94	90	58
102	79	76	82
118	98	94	69
114	95	65	71
92	101	86	86
100	103	67	81
87	91	90	70
117	75	102	90
105	83	73	85
105	87	80	98
90	100	82	100
97	92	71	95

Apply the analysis of variance and interpret the results of this experiment.

2. An experiment was performed to study the influence of muscular effort on the amplitude of the knee-jerk. Ten responses were recorded under each of 3 levels of effort induced by having the subject maintain his grip on a hand dynamometer at 0, 5, or 15 kg. Each of 6 subjects was randomly assigned one of the 6 possible orders of the levels of effort. The following table shows the mean amplitude of response for each subject under each of the 3 levels of effort and there is no indication of the orders of presentation used for the various subjects.

SUBJECT	MUSCULAR EFFORT		
	0 kg.	5 kg.	15 kg.
1	1.4	12.5	33.3
2	21.7	34.7	40.7
3	43.9	52.1	56.4
4	5.7	7.6	10.5
5	17.6	19.6	23.9
6	12.0	14.2	17.0

a) What conclusions can be drawn from the analysis of variance of these results?

b) In what way do possible interaction effects enter into the analysis?

c) Would you interpret these results differently if you knew the values of the ten individual responses in each cell of the table?

d) It is known that the amplitude of the knee-jerk decreases over a series of thirty consecutive responses. How is this source of variation taken into account in the design of the experiment? Where does such variation appear in the breakdown of the total sum of squares?

3. Describe how you would perform an experiment involving two independent variables, one varied over three levels and the other over four. Design the experiment so that individual differences are randomly sampled and so that there are ten measurements in each cell. Construct a summary table showing the sources of variation and the *df* for each. Indicate which of the possible s^2's and F's you would compute and explain how they would be interpreted.

4. Find an application of a double classification factorial design in a psychological journal and describe the results of the experiment in your own words.

5. Apply the analysis of variance to the following table. Is it reasonable for significant interaction to occur although neither variable alone has a significant effect?

Variable 2	Variable 1			
	I	II	III	IV
A	5	10	16	5
	8	15	12	5
	6	9	11	9
	9	11	13	6
B	10	6	9	12
	15	4	7	14
	9	2	5	12
	17	8	4	10

CHAPTER XIV

The Analysis of Variance and Correlation

In using the coefficient of correlation it is sometimes difficult to justify the assumption of linearity. The only satisfactory test of this assumption makes use of the analysis of variance. This test is closely related to one of the important interpretations of r discussed in Chapter VII, where it was shown that the descriptive variance of the dependent variable Y can be separated into two portions.

$$S^2_y \quad = \quad S^2_{y'} \quad + \quad S^2_{y \cdot x} \qquad (37)$$

total   predicted   unpredicted

variance   variance   variance

Before developing the test of linearity we will first consider a test of the hypothesis that $\rho = 0.00$. Substituting the definition formulas in (37), we obtain the following equality between sums of squares, since the common denominator N disappears.

$$\sum_{}^{N} (Y - \bar{Y})^2 = \sum_{}^{N} (Y' - \bar{Y})^2 + \sum_{}^{N} (Y - Y')^2$$

This shows that the total sum of squares for Y can be broken down into two parts—a component predicted by the regression equation of Y' on X and a residual portion which is not predictable from X.

Imagine a scatter diagram containing k groups defined according to class intervals on X. From the regression equation a value of Y' can be computed for each group. Using these predicted values of Y' and the observed values of Y, we can express the two components of a correlational analysis in a form similar to the between groups and within groups sums of squares in a simple analysis of variance.

However, the between groups sum of squares in a correlational analysis measures variation between column values of Y', and not differences among means of columns. Similarly, the within groups sum of squares in this treatment measures variation around predicted values of Y' instead of deviations around group means.

$$\sum_{}^{N} (Y - \bar{Y})^2 = \sum_{}^{k} n_g(Y'_g - \bar{Y}_T)^2 + \sum_{}^{k}\sum_{}^{n_g} (Y - Y'_g)^2 \quad (89)$$

| total sum of squares | predicted between groups sum of squares | unpredictable within groups sum of squares |

Since r^2 is the proportion of variance in Y which can be predicted from X, the component sums of squares in a correlational analysis can be expressed in terms of r and the total sum of squares.

$$\sum_{}^{N} (Y - \bar{Y}_T)^2 = r^2 \sum_{}^{N} (Y - \bar{Y}_T)^2 + (1 - r^2) \sum_{}^{N} (Y - \bar{Y}_T)^2$$

| total sum | predicted component | unpredictable component |

Because sample r's rarely turn out to be exactly zero, the total sum of squares can be broken down in this way even when $\rho = 0.00$, and the relative magnitude of the two components will vary with the sample value of r. Each component divided by its df provides an unbiased estimate of σ^2_y. These will be denoted as $s^2_{y'}$, and $s^2_{y \cdot x}$.

$s^2_{y'}$ has one df because all of the deviations from which this estimate is obtained are determined by a single sample value of r. If one value of Y' is known, all the rest are determined because the line $Y' = BX + A$ must pass through this point and through the intersection of $\bar{X}$ and $\bar{Y}$. Subtracting this one df from the total $(N - 1)$, we find that $s^2_{y \cdot x}$ has $(N - 2)$ df. Thus, the two estimates of σ^2_y are defined by the following formulas.

$$s^2_{y'} = \frac{r^2 \sum_{}^{N} (Y - \bar{Y}_T)^2}{1} \quad (90)$$

$$s^2_{y \cdot x} = \frac{(1 - r^2) \sum_{}^{N} (Y - \bar{Y}_T)^2}{N - 2} \quad (91)$$

Substituting these in the F-ratio, we obtain a simple computational formula which requires only N and r.

$$F = \frac{r^2 \displaystyle\sum_{1}^{N} (Y - \bar{Y})^2}{\dfrac{(1 - r^2) \displaystyle\sum^{N} (Y - \bar{Y})^2}{N - 2}}$$

$$F_{1,(N-2)} = \frac{r^2}{\dfrac{1 - r^2}{N - 2}} \tag{92}$$

If coefficients of correlation are computed for random samples from a population in which $\rho = 0.00$, this ratio follows the F distribution. Thus, it can be used to test the H_0 that $\rho = 0.00$.

The t-ratio described earlier for testing the significance of r becomes more meaningful now, because again we find that $F_{1,n_2} = t^2$.

$$t = \frac{r}{\sqrt{\dfrac{1 - r^2}{N - 2}}} \tag{65}$$

TESTING LINEARITY OF REGRESSION

Because of sampling errors the column means of a scatter diagram will not fall exactly on a straight line, even though the population relationship is actually linear. Sample deviations of column means from linear regression provide an unbiased estimate of σ^2_y which is used to test the assumption of linearity.

A single deviation of Y from $\bar{Y}_T$ can be considered as the sum of three separate deviations.

$$Y - \bar{Y}_T = (Y'_g - \bar{Y}_T) + (\bar{Y}_g - Y'_g) + (Y - \bar{Y}_g)$$

If this expression is squared and summed, all three sums of cross-products equal zero and the total sum of squares is broken down into three parts.

$$\sum^{N} (Y - \bar{Y}_T)^2 = \sum^{k} n_g(Y'_g - \bar{Y}_T)^2 + \sum^{k} n_g(\bar{Y}_g - Y'_g)^2 +$$

total sum   regression   deviations from
of squares   sum of squares   regression

$$+ \sum^{k} \sum^{n_g} (Y - \bar{Y}_g)^2$$

within groups
sum of squares

Comparing this with the simple analysis of a total sum of squares into a between groups and a within groups component, we see that this treatment actually divides the *between groups* sum of squares into two parts.

Total = regression + deviations from regression + within groups
Total = between groups + within groups

$$\sum^{k} n_g(\bar{Y}_g - \bar{Y}_T)^2 = \sum^{k} n_g(Y' - \bar{Y}_T)^2 + \sum^{k} n_g(\bar{Y}_g - Y'_g)^2$$

| between groups sum of squares | regression sum of squares | deviations from regression |

Thus it is possible to compute the sum of squares for deviations from regression by the following formula, remembering that r^2 is the predictable proportion of the total sum of squares.

$$\sum^{k} n_g(\bar{Y}_g - Y'_g)^2 = \sum^{k} n_g(\bar{Y}_g - \bar{Y}_T)^2 - r^2 \left(\sum^{N} (Y - \bar{Y})^2 \right)$$

| deviations from regression | between groups sum of squares | regression sum of squares |

The deviation from regression sum of squares is based on $(k - 2)$ degrees of freedom because the between groups sum of squares has a total of $(k - 1)$ df, and one of these is associated with the regression line. An unbiased estimate of σ^2_y can now be obtained from

$$s^2_{\bar{Y}_g - Y'_g} = \frac{\sum^{k} n_g(\bar{Y}_g - \bar{Y}_T)^2 - r^2 \sum^{N} (Y - \bar{Y}_T)^2}{k - 2} \tag{93}$$

If this is significantly larger than s^2_w the assumption of linearity must be rejected, and r should not be used to describe the relationship. Since $s^2_{\bar{Y}_g - Y'_g}$ and s^2_w are unbiased and independent estimates of σ^2_y the test is easily applied by computing F.

We have developed two important uses of the analysis of variance in problems of linear correlation.

1. The F-ratio can be used to test the hypothesis that $\rho = 0.00$.

$$F_{1,(N-2)} = \frac{r^2}{\dfrac{1 - r^2}{N - 2}} \tag{92}$$

2. F provides a test of the assumption of linearity required by r.

$$F_{(k-2),\ (N-k)} = \frac{s^2_{\bar{Y}_g - Y'_g}}{s^2_w} = \frac{\dfrac{\displaystyle\sum_{}^{k} n_g(\bar{Y}_g - \bar{Y}_T)^2 - r^2 \displaystyle\sum_{}^{N} (Y - \bar{Y}_T)^2}{k - 2}}{\dfrac{\displaystyle\sum_{}^{k} \displaystyle\sum_{}^{n_g} (Y_g - \bar{Y}_g)^2}{N - k}} \qquad (94)^*$$

Before illustrating the application of these to a correlation problem, let us briefly consider another measure of correlation.

THE CORRELATION RATIO

Sometimes it is useful to measure the degree of correlation between X and Y without defining the form of the relationship. This is done by the correlation ratio, η (eta), which is defined by the following formula.

$$\eta_{yx} = \sqrt{\frac{\displaystyle\sum_{}^{k} n_g(\bar{Y}_g - Y_T)^2}{\displaystyle\sum_{}^{N} (Y - \bar{Y}_T)^2}} \qquad (95)$$

Eta is a descriptive statistic which measures the extent to which variation in Y can be accounted for by variation between the column means of a scatter diagram. If column means do not differ from one another, $\eta = 0.00$. If the column means differ and there is no variation within columns, $\eta = 1.00$. Whereas r can be positive or negative, depending on the slope of the best-fit straight line, eta is always positive because it specifies nothing concerning the form of the relationship.

Formula (95) shows that η^2 is the proportion of the between groups sum to the total sum of squares in a simple analysis of variance applied to a scatter diagram. A similar statement of the product moment coefficient of correlation is easily obtained.

$$r^2 = \frac{S^2_{y'}}{S_y} \quad \text{(pp. 116-20)}$$

---

* In the next section we will develop a simplified formula for this test (94a).

$$= \frac{\dfrac{\displaystyle\sum_{}^{k} n_g (Y'_g - \bar{Y}_T)^2}{N}}{\dfrac{\displaystyle\sum_{}^{N} (Y - \bar{Y}_T)^2}{N}}$$

$$r^2 = \frac{\displaystyle\sum_{}^{k} n_g (Y'_g - \bar{Y}_T)^2}{\displaystyle\sum_{}^{N} (Y - \bar{Y}_T)^2} \tag{96}$$

Thus, r^2 is the proportion of the regression sum of squares to the total sum of squares.

Since r^2 and η^2 are both proportions of the total sum of squares, the statement of the sum of squares required for testing linearity can be simplified. The proportion of the total sum of squares which is associated with deviations from linearity is simply $(\eta^2 - r^2)$. Thus, $s^2_{\bar{Y}_g - Y'_g}$, formula (93), can be restated.

$$s^2_{Y_g - Y'_g} = \frac{(\eta^2 - r^2) \displaystyle\sum_{}^{N} (Y - \bar{Y}_T)^2}{k - 2} \tag{93a}$$

Similarly, the statement of s^2_w can be simplified because $(1 - \eta^2)$ is the proportion of the within groups to the total sum of squares.

$$s^2_w = \frac{(1 - \eta^2) \displaystyle\sum_{}^{N} (Y - \bar{Y}_T)^2}{N - k} \tag{87a}$$

Substituting these expressions in the formula for F, we obtain a simplified formula for testing the assumption of linearity.

$$F_{(k-2),\,(N-k)} = \frac{s^2_{\bar{Y}_g - Y'_g}}{s^2_w} \tag{94}$$

$$= \frac{\dfrac{(\eta^2 - r^2) \displaystyle\sum_{}^{N} (Y - \bar{Y}_T)^2}{k - 2}}{\dfrac{(1 - \eta^2) \displaystyle\sum_{}^{N} (Y - \bar{Y}_T)^2}{N - k}}$$

$$F_{(k-2),\,(N-k)} = \frac{\dfrac{\eta^2 - r^2}{k - 2}}{\dfrac{1 - \eta^2}{N - k}} \tag{94a}$$

Example:

The difference between r and η is illustrated by the methods used in computing these coefficients. To obtain r we must find cross-products for paired deviations on X and Y, whereas in computing η, X is used only as a dimension of classification for grouping the observations and does not enter into the computation. Although η could be obtained from sums of squares of the sort used in the analysis of variance, the actual mechanics of computation are somewhat different because the correlation ratio is usually computed directly from a scatter diagram, whereas the simple analysis of variance is usually applied to ungrouped raw measurements. The following example, consisting of artificial data, illustrates a convenient method. The entire computation can be carried out in class interval units because the size of the interval enters equally into the numerator and denominator of both measures of correlation.

Total sum of squares (in class interval units):

$$930 - \frac{(-102)^2}{130} = 849.97$$

$X \longrightarrow$

Y

	30-39	40-49	50-59	60-69	70-79	80-89	90-99	100-109	110-119	120-129	d_y	f_y	f_yd_y	$f_yd^2_y$
42-44	2										+6	2	+12	72
39-41	4	1									+5	5	+25	125
36-38	1	4	1								+4	6	+24	96
33-35	1	3	2								+3	6	+18	54
30-32		1	0	1							+2	2	+4	8
27-29			5	3	1	1					+1	10	+10	10
24-26			6	7	2	0	3	2	1		0	21	0	0
21-23			1	3	6	2	1	1	0	1	-1	15	-15	15
18-20				2	5	7	7	0	2	0	-2	23	-46	92
15-17					1	4	5	5	6	5	-3	26	-78	234
12-14						2	3	1	4	4	-4	14	-56	224
$f_x = n_y$	8	9	15	16	15	16	19	9	13	10		$\Sigma f d_y = -102$		
R $\Sigma f_x d_y$	39	32	14	-2	-18	-35	-42	-20	-38	-32		$\Sigma f d^2_y = 930$		
d_x	-5	-4	-3	-2	-1	0	+1	+2	+3	+4				
$f_x d_x$	-40	-36	-45	-32	-15	0	19	18	39	40		$\Sigma f d_x = -52$		
$f_x d^2_x$	200	144	135	64	15		19	36	117	160		$\Sigma f d^2_x = 890$		
R $d_x \Sigma f_x d_y$	-195	-128	-42	+4	+18		-42	-40	-114	-128		$\Sigma f d_x d_y = -667$		

Between groups sum of squares (in class interval units):

$$\frac{(39)^2}{8} + \frac{(32)^2}{9} + \frac{(14)^2}{15} + \frac{(-2)^2}{16} + \frac{(-18)^2}{15} + \frac{(-35)^2}{16} + \frac{(-42)^2}{19}$$

$$+ \frac{(-20)^2}{9} + \frac{(-38)^2}{13} + \frac{(-32)^2}{10} - \frac{(-102)^2}{130} = 685.75$$

$$\eta^2_{yx} = \frac{685.75}{849.97} = .8068$$

$$\eta_{xy} = .898$$

$$r_{xy} = \frac{130(-667) - (-52)(-102)}{\sqrt{130(890) - (52)^2} \sqrt{130(930) - (-102)^2}} = -.729$$

The H_0 that $\tilde{\eta} = 0.00^*$ is easily tested by computing an F-ratio from s^2_b and s^2_w. This is the same as testing the H_0 that column means are equal.

$$s^2_b = \frac{685.75}{9} = 76.19$$

$$s^2_w = \frac{164.22}{120} = 1.37$$

$$F_{9,\,120} = \frac{76.19}{1.37} = 55.61 \qquad p < .001$$

The significance of r is tested by comparing s^2_y and $s^2_{y \cdot x}$. F is computed from the simplified formula (65).

$$F_{1,\,128} = \frac{(-.729)^2}{\dfrac{1 - (-.729)^2}{130 - 2}} = 145.2 \qquad p < .001$$

The test of linearity is obtained from formula (94a).

$$F_{8,\,120} = \frac{\dfrac{(.898)^2 - (-.729)^2}{10 - 2}}{\dfrac{1 - (.898)^2}{130 - 10}} = 24.85 \qquad p < .001$$

Since all three F's are well above the critical values required for $p = .001$, we conclude that although there is a significant linear correlation, the relationship between X and Y is not appropriately described by r. In reporting data such as this the investigator should plot a graph to show the relationship of the column means to the X-variable, or, even better, he should present the bivariate frequency distribution. Neither η nor r would be adequate to describe the data.

In itself, the correlation ratio is not a particularly useful statistic,

---

* Here, we use $\tilde{\eta}$ to designate the population parameter, since the correlation ratio obtained from a sample is conventionally denoted by η.

because it simply measures the degree of correlation without specifying the type of relationship. Moreover, η can produce misleading results if care is not exercised in choosing the number of class intervals for X. As the number of classes increases, the within group sum of squares decreases and η becomes larger. The limiting case would be where X is grouped in such fine units that no class contains more than one observation. The between groups sum of squares for any set of data would then equal the total sum and eta would be 1.00. Because of this, η should be used only where the number of classes for the independent variable does not exceed 12 and $N \geqq 100$. If η and r are used to test linearity both coefficients must be computed from the same class intervals.

In this chapter we have shown how the analysis of variance can be applied to problems of correlation. F-ratios can be used to test three separate hypotheses concerning correlation: (1) $\rho = 0.00$, (2) $\bar{\eta} = 0.00$, and (3) $\bar{\eta} - \rho = 0.00$. The third is a test of the hypothesis that the relationship of X and Y in the population from which the sample was drawn is linear.

EXERCISES

1. Would you expect η_{yx} to equal η_{xy}? Explain.

2. Explain why $\eta \geqq r$.

3. The following table is for practice. Compute r and η, and test for linearity.

	20–29	30–39	40–49	50–59	60–69	70–79
40–44	1					
35–39	2	2				
30–34		1				
25–29	1	1	3			1
20–24		1	2	1	1	1
15–19				4	3	2
10–14			1	2	1	
5–9				1		

4. Test the regression of weight on height for linearity using the data for female students in data B, p. 31.

CHAPTER XV

Special Correlation Methods

The product moment coefficient of correlation is limited to linear relationships between graduated measurements of two variables. The degree of non-linear association between graduated variables can be measured by the correlation ratio. It often happens, however, that psychological and educational data do not permit the use of r or η because measurements of one or both variables are in the form of rank-orders or categories of classification. Because of this a variety of methods have been devised for estimating the degree of association in special situations. Since a detailed treatment of all of these is far beyond the scope of an introductory course, our discussion will be limited to several of the more common and generally useful methods.

CORRELATING RANKS

Spearman's Rank-Difference Correlation

One measure of correlation between two sets of ranks is given by the rank-difference coefficient of correlation, which we will denote by r_s.* This measure is defined by the following formula.

$$r_s = 1 - \frac{6\Sigma D^2}{N(N^2 - 1)} \tag{97}$$

D is the difference between two paired ranks, and N is the number of pairs. Formula (97) can be derived directly from the product moment formula by letting X and Y stand for ranks instead of graduated measurements. Like r, Spearman's rank-difference coefficient can vary from -1.00 to $+1.00$ depending on the degree and direction of association between the two sets of ranks. Although it is possible under certain restrictive conditions to interpret r_s as a

---

* Although this coefficient is denoted by ρ in the older literature, and even by some contemporary writers, we will use r_s in order to reserve ρ for the population value of r.

close approximation of r, the required assumptions are seldom justified in practice. For this reason r_s is usually taken simply as an index of relationship without requirements concerning the population distributions of the ranked variables and with no assumption of linearity. Thus, r_s provides a distribution-free measure of correlation.

The original data need not be in the form of ranks. By transforming measurements to ranks we can apply this method to data measured on a scale of unequal units, or to problems in which measurements on an interval scale are to be correlated with ordinal data.

The following example consists of data obtained from a small undergraduate class in statistics. Near the end of the semester the students were ranked by their instructor according to the quality of their participation in class discussions. They were then given an objective test over the semester's work.

Note that the sum of the D's must equal zero. This provides a check on the ranking and the computation to this point. When ties occur, each of the tied scores is assigned the average of the ranks which would have been used if they were not tied.

Student	Rank in Discussion	Test Score	Rank on Test	D	D^2
F.B.	8	7	9.5	-1.5	2.25
J.C.	1	15	3	-2	4
C.F.	7	7	9.5	-2.5	6.25
J.F.	3	17	1	$+2$	4
W.G.	10	15	3	$+7$	49
L.H.	11	10	6.5	$+4.5$	20.25
R.H.	4	14	5	-1	1
N.L.	9	4	12	-3	9
G.S.	5	10	6.5	-1.5	2.25
V.S.	2	15	3	-1	1
K.W.	12	9	8	$+4$	16
P.W.	6	6	11	-5	25

$$\Sigma D = 0.0 \quad \Sigma D^2 = 140.0$$

$$r_s = 1 - \frac{6(140)}{12(144 - 1)} = +.51$$

If $N \geq 10$, the H_0 that $\rho_s = 0.00$ can be tested by a t-ratio with $df = (N - 2)$.

$$t = r_s \sqrt{\frac{N - 2}{1 - r_s^2}} \qquad (98)$$

For this example

$$t = .51 \sqrt{\frac{12 - 2}{1 - (51)^2}} = 1.88$$

If we had set out to test a one-tailed hypothesis, this H_0 could be rejected and $p < .05$. However, we cannot ignore the possibility that a two-tailed test is more appropriate because proficiency in discussion may be impaired by an abundance of factual information, the instructor may be a poor judge of quality of participation, or the objective test may be an inadequate sample of knowledge about statistics.

Kendall's Coefficient of Concordance

Sometimes it is useful to measure the agreement among a number of rank-orders assigned to the same set of objects. For example we may wish to study the extent of agreement among art experts in ranking a group of esthetic objects, consistency in psychotherapists' ratings of a group of patients, or agreement between the various readers of a group of essays. This kind of problem is conveniently handled by Kendall's coefficient of concordance, W, which is a measure of the degree of association among k sets of ranks assigned to n objects. To illustrate the use of this statistic we will suppose that four teachers (k) have independently ranked a group of eight pupils (n) with respect to originality. In the following table $\overset{k}{\Sigma} R_n$ is the sum of the ranks assigned to each pupil by k teachers.

Pupil

Teacher	a	b	c	d	e	f	g	h
X	2	8	5	1	4	7	3	6
Y	3	5	7	1	2	4	6	8
Z	2	6	8	4	1	5	3	7
$\overset{k}{\Sigma} R_n$	7	19	20	6	7	16	12	21

If the teachers were in perfect agreement, $\overset{k}{\Sigma} R_n$ would have the values 3, 6, 9, 12, 15, 18, 21, 24, and the mean ranks assigned to the n pupils would be the series of the whole numbers from 1 to 8 because $k = 3$ for each column. If there were no agreement, the mean ranks of the pupils would be approximately equal. As agreement increases, the sum of squares of the mean ranks increases from zero to a maximum value which is the sum of squares for the series 1, 2, 3, . . . , $(n - 1)$, n. The coefficient of concordance, W, is simply the ratio obtained by dividing the observed sum of squares between mean ranks by the maximum value, which could occur only if agreement were perfect.

A computational scheme for W is easily obtained. Let us first consider the sum of squares for mean ranks where there is perfect agreement. This is simply the sum of squared deviations of the first n whole number from their mean, which is known from the algebra of sequences and series to be $(n^3 - n)/12$. Using this in the denominator, we can define W by the following formula.

$$W = \frac{\sum\limits^{n} (M_{R_n} - M_{R_T})^2}{\dfrac{n^3 - n}{12}} \tag{99}$$

Substituting the usual computational formula (75) for a sum of squares, we obtain

$$W = \frac{\sum\limits^{n} M^2{}_{R_n} - \dfrac{\left(\sum\limits^{n} M_R\right)^2}{n}}{\dfrac{n^3 - n}{12}}$$

Computation can be simplified by observing that the sum of the first n whole numbers is equal to $n(n + 1)/2$.

$$W = \frac{\dfrac{\sum\limits^{n}\left(\sum\limits^{k} R_n\right)^2}{k^2} - \dfrac{n(n + 1)^2}{4}}{\dfrac{n^3 - n}{12}} \tag{99a}$$

For our illustrative problem the following computations are required to find W.

$$\sum_{n}^{k} R_n \qquad \left(\sum_{n}^{k} R_n\right)^2$$

$\sum_{n}^{k} R_n$	$\left(\sum_{n}^{k} R_n\right)^2$
7	49
19	361
20	400
6	36
7	49
16	256
12	144
21	441

$$\sum_{n}^{n} \left(\sum_{n}^{k} R_n\right)^2 = 1736$$

$$W = \frac{\dfrac{1736}{9} - \dfrac{8(9)^2}{4}}{\dfrac{(8)^3 - 8}{12}} = \frac{30.89}{42} = .735$$

If $n > 7$ the significance of W can be tested by computing χ^2 with $df = n - 1$.

$$\chi^2 = k(n - 1)W \tag{100}$$

In the present example H_0 is rejected.

$$\chi^2 = 3(8 - 1).735 = 15.435$$
$$.02 < p < .05$$

W, unlike r_s, cannot be negative, because a perfect inverse relationship would be impossible if there were more than two sets of ranks. Thus, the range of W is from 0.00 to $+1.00$. The interpretation of W is simplified by the fact that it is directly related to the average value of r_s computed for all possible pairs of observed rank-orders. The average r_s can be obtained from the following formula, which is much easier than finding the separate values of r_s and averaging them.

$$r_{s_{\text{av.}}} = \frac{kW - 1}{k - 1} \tag{101}$$

This average can assume any value from -1.00 to $+1.00$.

For our illustrative problem the three values of r_s are $r_{s_{xy}} = +.524$, $r_{s_{xz}} = +.571$, $r_{s_{yz}} = +.714$. The average of these is $+.60$. From formula (101) the same result is obtained.

$$r_{s_{\text{av.}}} = \frac{3(.735) - 1}{3 - 1} = +.60$$

In applying W or $r_{s_{av.}}$ to ranks assigned by a group of judges we must remember that these coefficients measure nothing more than *consistency* or *agreement* among the judges. Such agreement may be either correct or incorrect with respect to the alleged basis for the ranking. The validity of teachers' rankings for originality could be established only by correlating these ranks with some objective criterion of originality.

Both W and r_s are distribution-free measures of correlation since they assume nothing beyond the requirement that each set of observations can be arranged in an ordered series of ranks.

CORRELATION OF ATTRIBUTES

The Contingency Coefficient

This measure of correlation, denoted by C, is an extremely versatile statistic because it assumes nothing about the variables beyond the requirement that each observation can be classified according to two sets of categories. There can be any number of classes as long as two or more categories can be discriminated for each variable. The variables can be discrete or continuous, ordered or unordered, and their population distributions can be of any form.

This measure of correlation is obtained directly from χ^2.

$$C = \sqrt{\frac{\chi^2}{N + \chi^2}} \tag{102}$$

In an earlier section (p. 254), we computed χ^2 to test the H_0 that freshman grades and an index of relative achievement are unrelated. With $df = 4$ the chi square of 193.1 led to the rejection of H_0, but this treatment implied nothing about the *degree* of relationship beyond the statement that it is greater than zero. We will now compute the coefficient of contingency for the same data as a measure of the degree of association.

FRESHMAN GRADES

Index	*Unsatisfactory*	*Satisfactory*	*Superior*
70 and Above	53	133	268
40–69	150	235	147
Below 40	111	129	38

$$N = 1264$$
$$\chi^2 = 193.1$$

$$C = \sqrt{\frac{193.1}{1264 + 193.1}} = .36$$

This result must be interpreted with caution because C does not behave like other measures of correlation. The exact meaning of a coefficient of contingency is difficult to ascertain because its upper limit, the value which indicates perfect agreement between two variables, is different depending on the number of cells used in computing chi square. In general, the upper limit for a square table containing k rows and k columns is given by $\sqrt{(k-1)/k}$. For a 3×3 table, such as this, C cannot exceed $\sqrt{2/3} = .816$. As the number of cells increases, the upper limit of C approaches, but never reaches, $+1.00$. For example, the upper limit for a 10×10 table is $+.949$. The lower limit is always zero, because negative values are impossible. Although upper limits are not precisely known for rectangular tables of k columns and r rows, the limits for such tables increase with increases in the number of cells.

In spite of this major disadvantage, C is a very useful statistic because it can be applied to any contingency table which permits the use of χ^2. Moreover, the significance of a coefficient of contingency is easily tested by evaluating the observed chi square from which it was computed. Furthermore, a number of values of C derived from similar contingency tables can be compared as an indication of different degrees of relationship.

2 × 2 TABLES

Tetrachoric Correlation

If both variables are measured on a two-point scale and if we can assume that both are continuous and normally distributed, the product moment coefficient of correlation can be estimated by r_t, the tetrachoric correlation coefficient. Although the derivation of r_t is complex, the basic idea behind this coefficient can be understood without a detailed mathematical treatment.

Let us begin by imagining large samples of X and Y, each randomly drawn from a normal population. Observations of X will be paired with observations of Y, producing a *bivariate distribution* in which each pair is defined according to the two variables.

Suppose that we now represent the bivariate distribution by stacking poker chips on a checker board where columns and rows correspond to class intervals for X and Y, and the number of chips in each stack represents frequency. By carefully fitting a sheet of flexible material over the stacks of chips we can form a surface to represent the bivariate distribution. The distribution of the volume under this surface represents the distribution of frequencies. This is analogous to representing the frequency distribution of a single variable by the distribution of area under a frequency polygon. As in the case of a frequency polygon, the bivariate surface becomes smooth as N becomes very large and class intervals become very small.

The shape of such a smooth surface depends on the population distribution of X and Y, and on the correlation between them. If X and Y are normally distributed and $\rho = 0.00$, the surface obtained by plotting both variables in standard units is perfectly symmetrical. Horizontal cross-sections at any distance above the base are perfect circles and the proportions of total volume under the surface in the four portions produced by cutting vertically at μ_x and μ_y are equal. If the correlation between X and Y is linear, and if dispersion about both regression lines is normal and homoscedastic, cross-sections at different heights are concentric ellipses which become narrower as ρ approaches ± 1.00. The following diagram is an example of a normal correlation surface.

If this surface is cut vertically at any two points defined by proportional dichotomies on X and Y, the proportion of the total volume contained in each quadrant, which corresponds to a proportion of N, can be obtained from the equation which defines the shape of the surface for any given value of ρ. Because of this, it is

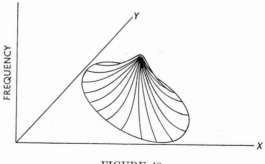

FIGURE 48

possible to work backwards from the observed proportions in the cells of a 2×2 table to an inference of what the value of ρ would be *if X and Y were normally distributed, the relation between them linear, and dispersion about both regression lines normal and homoscedastic.* In other words, we find the value of ρ for which the observed fourfold distribution would be most likely. This inference is r_t.

Obviously the use of the tetrachoric correlation coefficient requires a number of restrictive assumptions. Two of these are critical: (1) that the dichotomized observations refer to continuous normally distributed variables, and (2) that the relationship is linear.

Computation of r_t would require an approximation based on the solution of a quartic equation were it not for the fact that diagrams and tables are available which make the process rapid and simple.[*] We will not illustrate the computation of r_t here because clear instructions accompany the diagrams.

The standard error of r_t requires a rather unwieldly formula which shows that even in the most favorable case σ_{r_t} is over 50 percent larger than σ_r. The hypothesis of zero correlation is easily tested by chi square.

The Phi Coefficient

If both dichotomies are discrete point distributions, the degree of association can be described by the *phi* coefficient, denoted by ϕ and sometimes called the fourfold point correlation coefficient. The value of r computed from a scatter diagram containing two columns and two rows is actually the same as the value of ϕ for the same table. However, ϕ must not be taken as an estimate of ρ; it is simply an index of the relationship between two dichotomized discrete measures. It has many important practical applications to problems involving the intercorrelations among test items. Several formulas are available for computing phi, but we will give only the one which shows its relationship to chi square.

$$\phi = \sqrt{\frac{\chi^2}{N}} \tag{102}$$

---

* L. Chesire, M. Saffir, and L. L. Thurstone, *Computing Diagrams for the Tetrachoric Correlation Coefficient* (Chicago: University of Chicago Bookstore, 1933). M. D. Davidoff and H. W. Goheen, "A table for the rapid determination of the tetrachoric correlation coefficient," *Psychometrika,* Vol. 18, pp. 115–21.

The null hypothesis of zero relationship is easily tested by chi square.

BISERIAL CORRELATION

If one variable is dichotomous while the other is measured on a graduated scale, the relationship between them is said to be biserial. In some biserial situations there is a genuine dichotomy, such as inoculated versus not inoculated, male versus female, etc. In other cases the dichotomy may refer to an underlying variable which is actually continuous. There are two measures of biserial correlation, each requiring a different assumption about the dichotomized variable.

The Point Biserial Coefficient of Correlation

If the categories of the dichotomy are assigned scores of 0 and 1 (or any other two numbers) and the graduated variable is grouped into a number of class intervals, we can compute r by the usual method. A product moment coefficient of correlation obtained in this way has the same value as the point biserial coefficient of correlation, denoted by r_{pb}. Although this is the basis of its derivation, r_{pb} is more conveniently found by either of the following formulas.

$$r_{pb} = \frac{\bar{Y}_2 - \bar{Y}_1}{S_y} \sqrt{p_1 p_2} \tag{103}$$

$$r_{pb} = \frac{\bar{Y}_2 - \bar{Y}_T}{S_y} \sqrt{\frac{N_2}{N_1}} \tag{103a}$$

where $\bar{Y}_1$ = mean of Y's in first category
$\bar{Y}_2$ = mean of Y's in second category
p_1 = proportion of N in first category
p_2 = proportion of N in second category
S_y = the standard deviation of all Y's

The significance of r_{pb} is conveniently evaluated by testing the H_0 that $\mu_2 - \mu_1 = 0$.

The sign of r_{pb} depends on which group is designated as Y_1. Since this is often arbitrary, r_{pb} should be accompanied by a clear statement of the direction of the relationship. In the following example it is necessary to state that boys are more favorable towards smoking than are girls, since higher scores signify more favorable attitude. A single r_{pb}, such as this, is difficult to interpret. However, if a number of attitude scales had been administered to the same group of students r_{pb} would facilitate comparison of the relative degrees of association between the various attitudes and sex.

Example:

A scale to measure attitude towards smoking was administered to all of the pupils in a small high school. An index of the relationship between this score and sex was obtained by computing r_{pb}.

Score	d_{iy}	Frequencies	
		Boys	Girls
105–109	17	1	
100–104	16	3	
95–99	15	9	1
90–94	14	9	4
85–89	13	12	7
80–84	12	22	8
75–79	11	20	18
70–74	10	22	18
65–69	9	40	21
60–64	8	27	16
55–59	7	16	39
50–54	6	20	26
45–49	5	17	28
40–44	4	14	21
35–39	3	18	17
30–34	2	6	25
25–29	1	3	7
20–24	0	3	2

(in class interval units)

$$\Sigma Y_1 = 2204 \qquad \Sigma Y_2 = 1714$$
$$\Sigma Y^2_1 = 23972 \qquad \Sigma Y^2_2 = 14190$$
$$N_1 = 262 \qquad N_2 = 258$$
$$p_1 = .500 \qquad p_2 = .500$$
$$\bar{Y}_1 = 8.41 \qquad \bar{Y}_2 = 6.64$$
$$S_y = 4.08$$

$$r_{pb} = \frac{6.64 - 8.41}{4.08} \sqrt{.25} = -.217$$

$t = 4.9$, and H_0 is rejected

The point biserial coefficient is best regarded merely as a useful index of the degree of association between two variables. It is not a direct estimate of ρ because even where such an estimate might be used, r_{pb} is systematically too small, just as r would be if computed from only two class intervals on X.

The Biserial Coefficient of Correlation

If the dichotomy refers to a continuous variable we can estimate the product moment coefficient of correlation between this variable and another for which graduated measurements are available. To do this we must assume the possibility of a normal distribution of the dichotomized variable and a linear relationship. The biserial coefficient of correlation, denoted by r_b, is this estimate. The derivation of r_b is based on the fact that the mean of a tail of the normal distribution can be computed if we know the proportion of the total area included in the tail and the ordinate at the cutting point. Thus, the distance in standard units between the group means of the dichotomized X-variable can be estimated. The separation between the two groups on the Y-scale is found directly from the data. Since the regression line, $z_{y'} = rz_x$, must pass through the points defined by these two pairs of means, its slope is easily obtained.

Because advanced mathematical treatment is required to derive the method used in estimating the means of the dichotomies we will not present a detailed derivation of r_b. It is easily seen, however, from

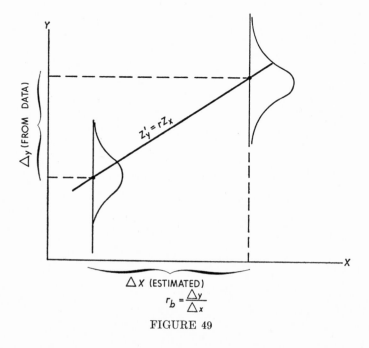

FIGURE 49

the above diagram that the biserial coefficient of correlation depends on crucial assumptions about the distribution which underlies the dichotomized variable. The diagram also shows that r_b is an estimate of the product moment correlation coefficient.

Either of the following formulas can be used for computing r_b.

$$r_b = \frac{(\bar{Y}_2 - \bar{Y}_1)(p_1 p_2)}{y S_y} \tag{104}$$

$$r_b = \frac{(\bar{Y}_2 - \bar{Y}_T)p_2}{y S_y} \tag{104a}$$

The only new symbol in these formulas is y, the ordinate of the unit normal curve at the cutting point. The value of y is found from Table D, which shows ordinates corresponding to various areas between μ and z. In using these formulas the subscript 2 is usually taken to designate the higher of the dichotomized groups in order to preserve the correct sign of r_b.

The following example illustrates the use of r_b to measure the correlation between performance on a single test item and the total grade on a final examination.

EXAMINATION GRADE	ITEM A		COMBINED FREQUENCIES
	Fail (1)	Pass (2)	
100–109		5	5
90–99		8	8
80–89	1	22	23
70–79	6	30	36
60–69	9	33	42
50–59	14	25	39
40–49	16	10	26
30–39	9	3	12
20–29	6	1	7
10–19	2		2

$$N_1 = 63 \qquad N_2 = 137 \qquad N = 200$$

$$p_1 = .315 \qquad p_2 = .685$$
$$\bar{Y}_1 = 48.79 \qquad \bar{Y}_2 = 68.88$$

$$\bar{Y}_T = 62.55$$
$$S_y = 18.5$$
$$y = .3552 \text{ (from Table } D)$$

$$r_b = \frac{68.88 - 48.79}{.3552(18.5)}(.685)(.315) = +.66 \tag{104}$$

$$r_b = \frac{68.88 - 62.55}{.3552(18.5)}(.685) = +.66 \tag{104a}$$

The H_0 that $\rho = 0.00$ can be tested by testing the significance of the difference between $\bar{Y}_1$ and $\bar{Y}_2$ by means of the t-ratio. In general, r_b has a larger sampling error than comparable values of r obtained from the same number of observations. The sampling distribution of r_b is not known, but R. F. Tate has derived a transformation for r_b which, like Fisher's z_r, can be used for testing hypotheses and for estimating ρ.*

We have seen that r_b is an estimate of what the product moment correlation would be *if* the dichotomized variable were measured so as to be normally distributed and *if* the two variables were linearly related. It should be used only in situations for which these conditions are reasonable possibilities. Since measurements of a truly discrete variable cannot be normally distributed, r_b can be used *only if it is reasonable to view the dichotomized variable as really continuous.* The second requirement, that of linear relationship, sometimes presents difficulties because the two points provided by any set of biserial data fall exactly on a straight line regardless of what might be the relationship between graduated measurements of these same variables.

If the dichotomy appears actually to be a point distribution the point biserial correlation coefficient should be used. In fact, r_{pb} is sometimes used even though the data meet the more demanding requirements of r_b, as in correlating test items scored on a two-point scale with a graduated criterion. This is quite permissible if our purpose is simply to measure the relative degrees of association of the different test items with the criterion. On the other hand, if we wish to estimate the product moment correlation we must use r_b. In using r_{pb} where r_b is defensible we should note that $r_{pb} < r_b$ for the same data and that the difference between them increases with the difference between p_1 and p_2. The relationship between these two coefficients is given by

$$r_{pb} = \left(\frac{y}{\sqrt{p_1 p_2}}\right) r_b \qquad (105)$$

In this chapter we have briefly discussed some of the more common measurements of correlation which are used in psychology. The purpose has been merely to enable you to recognize these

---

* This method is described in H. M. Walker and J. Lev, *Statistical Inference* (New York: Henry Holt and Company, 1953), pp. 269–70.

coefficients when you encounter them and to be aware of their major uses and limitations. More complete treatments of these methods are to be found in the following references.

SUGGESTED READINGS

1. Guilford, J. P. *Fundamental Statistics in Psychology and Education,* chap. xiii. New York: McGraw-Hill Book Co., 1950.
2. McNemar, Q. *Psychological Statistics,* chap. xii. 3d ed. New York: John Wiley & Sons, 1962.
3. Siegel, S. *Nonparametric Statistics for the Behavioral Sciences,* chap. ix. New York: McGraw-Hill Book Co., 1956.

EXERCISES

1. A group of college students were asked, "Did you usually attend church on Sunday before you came to college?" Their replies are shown in the following table. Compute a measure of correlation which can be used with this type of data and defend your choice of method.

	Yes	*No*
Men	198	96
Women	101	26

2. Nine seniors were ranked by three instructors in their major department with respect to their probable success in graduate school. Compute two measures of agreement in the rankings.

	Instructor		
Student	*A*	*B*	*C*
V.S.	1	3	5
B.C.	3	4	2
A.W.	9	8	6
S.Y.	6	2	4
T.M.	8	9	7
D.B.	2	1	3
F.B.	7	7	9
A.N.	4	5	1
D.D.	5	6	8

3. Ratings of above average and below average were assigned to a group of 235 employees. There were 137 in the above average group, and 98 were rated below average. The mean score on an aptitude test administered to the entire group was 83.7, and S was 1.09. The 98 below average employees had a mean score of 74.3. What is the corre-

lation between test scores and ratings? State and justify the assumptions of the method you choose.

4. Compute r_s and r for Exercise 2, p. 95, and compare them. Which do you consider more appropriate for this set of data?

5. How would you measure the correlation between the experimental and control groups in Exercise 7, p. 260? Justify your choice of method.

6. Compute an appropriate measure of the correlation between muscle tension and memorization for the data shown on page 213. What considerations enter into the choice of method?

Appendix

TABLE A. SQUARES AND SQUARE ROOTS*

N	N²	√N	√10N	N	N²	√N	√10N
1.00	1.0000	1.00000	3.16228	**1.40**	1.9600	1.18322	3.74166
1.01	1.0201	1.00499	3.17805	1.41	1.9881	1.18743	3.75500
1.02	1.0404	1.00995	3.19374	1.42	2.0164	1.19164	3.76829
1.03	1.0609	1.01489	3.20936	1.43	2.0449	1.19583	3.78153
1.04	1.0816	1.01980	3.22490	1.44	2.0736	1.20000	3.79473
1.05	1.1025	1.02470	3.24037	1.45	2.1025	1.20416	3.80789
1.06	1.1236	1.02956	3.25576	1.46	2.1316	1.20830	3.82099
1.07	1.1449	1.03441	3.27109	1.47	2.1609	1.21244	3.83406
1.08	1.1664	1.03923	3.28634	1.48	2.1904	1.21655	3.84708
1.09	1.1881	1.04403	3.30151	1.49	2.2201	1.22066	3.86005
1.10	1.2100	1.04881	3.31662	**1.50**	2.2500	1.22474	3.87298
1.11	1.2321	1.05357	3.33167	1.51	2.2801	1.22882	3.88587
1.12	1.2544	1.05830	3.34664	1.52	2.3104	1.23288	3.89872
1.13	1.2769	1.06301	3.36155	1.53	2.3409	1.23693	3.91152
1.14	1.2996	1.06771	3.37639	1.54	2.3716	1.24097	3.92428
1.15	1.3225	1.07238	3.39116	1.55	2.4025	1.24499	3.93700
1.16	1.3456	1.07703	3.40588	1.56	2.4336	1.24900	3.94968
1.17	1.3689	1.08167	3.42053	1.57	2.4649	1.25300	3.96232
1.18	1.3924	1.08628	3.43511	1.58	2.4964	1.25698	3.97492
1.19	1.4161	1.09087	3.44964	1.59	2.5281	1.26095	3.98748
1.20	1.4400	1.09545	3.46410	**1.60**	2.5600	1.26491	4.00000
1.21	1.4641	1.10000	3.47851	1.61	2.5921	1.26886	4.01248
1.22	1.4884	1.10454	3.49285	1.62	2.6244	1.27279	4.02492
1.23	1.5129	1.10905	3.50714	1.63	2.6569	1.27671	4.03733
1.24	1.5376	1.11355	3.52136	1.64	2.6896	1.28062	4.04969
1.25	1.5625	1.11803	3.53553	1.65	2.7225	1.28452	4.06202
1.26	1.5876	1.12250	3.54965	1.66	2.7556	1.28841	4.07431
1.27	1.6129	1.12694	3.56371	1.67	2.7889	1.29228	4.08656
1.28	1.6384	1.13137	3.57771	1.68	2.8224	1.29615	4.09878
1.29	1.6641	1.13578	3.59166	1.69	2.8561	1.30000	4.11096
1.30	1.6900	1.14018	3.60555	**1.70**	2.8900	1.30384	4.12311
1.31	1.7161	1.14455	3.61939	1.71	2.9241	1.30767	4.13521
1.32	1.7424	1.14891	3.63318	1.72	2.9584	1.31149	4.14729
1.33	1.7689	1.15326	3.64692	1.73	2.9929	1.31529	4.15933
1.34	1.7956	1.15758	3.66060	1.74	3.0276	1.31909	4.17133
1.35	1.8225	1.16190	3.67423	1.75	3.0625	1.32288	4.18330
1.36	1.8496	1.16619	3.68782	1.76	3.0976	1.32665	4.19524
1.37	1.8769	1.17047	3.70135	1.77	3.1329	1.33041	4.20714
1.38	1.9044	1.17473	3.71484	1.78	3.1684	1.33417	4.21900
1.39	1.9321	1.17898	3.72827	1.79	3.2041	1.33791	4.23084
1.40	1.9600	1.18322	3.74166	**1.80**	3.2400	1.34164	4.24264

* Table *A* is reprinted from Table *G* of Q. McNemar, *Psychological Statistics* (3d ed., New York: John Wiley & Sons, Inc.), by permission of the author and publishers.

TABLE A (Continued)

N	N²	$\sqrt{N}$	$\sqrt{10N}$	N	N²	$\sqrt{N}$	$\sqrt{10N}$
1.80	3.2400	1.34164	4.24264	2.20	4.8400	1.48324	4.69042
1.81	3.2761	1.34536	4.25441	2.21	4.8841	1.48661	4.70106
1.82	3.3124	1.34907	4.26615	2.22	4.9284	1.48997	4.71169
1.83	3.3489	1.35277	4.27785	2.23	4.9729	1.49332	4.72229
1.84	3.3856	1.35647	4.28952	2.24	5.0176	1.49666	4.73286
1.85	3.4225	1.36015	4.30116	2.25	5.0625	1.50000	4.74342
1.86	3.4596	1.36382	4.31277	2.26	5.1076	1.50333	4.75395
1.87	3.4969	1.36748	4.32435	2.27	5.1529	1.50665	4.76445
1.88	3.5344	1.37113	4.33590	2.28	5.1984	1.50997	4.77493
1.89	3.5721	1.37477	4.34741	2.29	5.2441	1.51327	4.78539
1.90	3.6100	1.37840	4.35890	2.30	5.2900	1.51658	4.79583
1.91	3.6481	1.38203	4.37035	2.31	5.3361	1.51987	4.80625
1.92	3.6864	1.38564	4.38178	2.32	5.3824	1.52315	4.81664
1.93	3.7249	1.38924	4.39318	2.33	5.4289	1.52643	4.82701
1.94	3.7636	1.39284	4.40454	2.34	5.4756	1.52971	4.83735
1.95	3.8025	1.39642	4.41588	2.35	5.5225	1.53297	4.84768
1.96	3.8416	1.40000	4.42719	2.36	5.5696	1.53623	4.85798
1.97	3.8809	1.40357	4.43847	2.37	5.6169	1.53948	4.86826
1.98	3.9204	1.40712	4.44972	2.38	5.6644	1.54272	4.87852
1.99	3.9601	1.41067	4.46094	2.39	5.7121	1.54596	4.88876
2.00	4.0000	1.41421	4.47214	2.40	5.7600	1.54919	4.89898
2.01	4.0401	1.41774	4.48330	2.41	5.8081	1.55242	4.90918
2.02	4.0804	1.42127	4.49444	2.42	5.8564	1.55563	4.91935
2.03	4.1209	1.42478	4.50555	2.43	5.9049	1.55885	4.92950
2.04	4.1616	1.42829	4.51664	2.44	5.9536	1.56205	4.93964
2.05	4.2025	1.43178	4.52769	2.45	6.0025	1.56525	4.94975
2.06	4.2436	1.43527	4.53872	2.46	6.0516	1.56844	4.95984
2.07	4.2849	1.43875	4.54973	2.47	6.1009	1.57162	4.96991
2.08	4.3264	1.44222	4.56070	2.48	6.1504	1.57480	4.97996
2.09	4.3681	1.44568	4.57165	2.49	6.2001	1.57797	4.98999
2.10	4.4100	1.44914	4.58258	2.50	6.2500	1.58114	5.00000
2.11	4.4521	1.45258	4.59347	2.51	6.3001	1.58430	5.00999
2.12	4.4944	1.45602	4.60435	2.52	6.3504	1.58745	5.01996
2.13	4.5369	1.45945	4.61519	2.53	6.4009	1.59060	5.02991
2.14	4.5796	1.46287	4.62601	2.54	6.4516	1.59374	5.03984
2.15	4.6225	1.46629	4.63681	2.55	6.5025	1.59687	5.04975
2.16	4.6656	1.46969	4.64758	2.56	6.5536	1.60000	5.05964
2.17	4.7089	1.47309	4.65833	2.57	6.6049	1.60312	5.06952
2.18	4.7524	1.47648	4.66905	2.58	6.6564	1.60624	5.07937
2.19	4.7961	1.47986	4.67974	2.59	6.7081	1.60935	5.08920
2.20	4.8400	1.48324	4.69042	2.60	6.7600	1.61245	5.09902

N	N²	√N	√10N	N	N²	√N	√10N
2.60	6.7600	1.61245	5.09902	**3.00**	9.0000	1.73205	5.47723
2.61	6.8121	1.61555	5.10882	3.01	9.0601	1.73494	5.48635
2.62	6.8644	1.61864	5.11859	3.02	9.1204	1.73781	5.49545
2.63	6.9169	1.62173	5.12835	3.03	9.1809	1.74069	5.50454
2.64	6.9696	1.62481	5.13809	3.04	9.2416	1.74356	5.51362
2.65	7.0225	1.62788	5.14782	3.05	9.3025	1.74642	5.52268
2.66	7.0756	1.63095	5.15752	3.06	9.3636	1.74929	5.53173
2.67	7.1289	1.63401	5.16720	3.07	9.4249	1.75214	5.54076
2.68	7.1824	1.63707	5.17687	3.08	9.4864	1.75499	5.54977
2.69	7.2361	1.64012	5.18652	3.09	9.5481	1.75784	5.55878
2.70	7.2900	1.64317	5.19615	**3.10**	9.6100	1.76068	5.56776
2.71	7.3441	1.64621	5.20577	3.11	9.6721	1.76352	5.57674
2.72	7.3984	1.64924	5.21536	3.12	9.7344	1.76635	5.58570
2.73	7.4529	1.65227	5.22494	3.13	9.7969	1.76918	5.59464
2.74	7.5076	1.65529	5.23450	3.14	9.8596	1.77200	5.60357
2.75	7.5625	1.65831	5.24404	3.15	9.9225	1.77482	5.61249
2.76	7.6176	1.66132	5.25357	3.16	9.9856	1.77764	5.62139
2.77	7.6729	1.66433	5.26308	3.17	10.0489	1.78045	5.63028
2.78	7.7284	1.66733	5.27257	3.18	10.1124	1.78326	5.63915
2.79	7.7841	1.67033	5.28205	3.19	10.1761	1.78606	5.64801
2.80	7.8400	1.67332	5.29150	**3.20**	10.2400	1.78885	5.65685
2.81	7.8961	1.67631	5.30094	3.21	10.3041	1.79165	5.66569
2.82	7.9524	1.67929	5.31037	3.22	10.3684	1.79444	5.67450
2.83	8.0089	1.68226	5.31977	3.23	10.4329	1.79722	5.68331
2.84	8.0656	1.68523	5.32917	3.24	10.4976	1.80000	5.69210
2.85	8.1225	1.68819	5.33854	3.25	10.5625	1.80278	5.70088
2.86	8.1796	1.69115	5.34790	3.26	10.6276	1.80555	5.70964
2.87	8.2369	1.69411	5.35724	3.27	10.6929	1.80831	5.71839
2.88	8.2944	1.69706	5.36656	3.28	10.7584	1.81108	5.72713
2.89	8.3521	1.70000	5.37587	3.29	10.8241	1.81384	5.73585
2.90	8.4100	1.70294	5.38516	**3.30**	10.8900	1.81659	5.74456
2.91	8.4681	1.70587	5.39444	3.31	10.9561	1.81934	5.75326
2.92	8.5264	1.70880	5.40370	3.32	11.0224	1.82209	5.76194
2.93	8.5849	1.71172	5.41295	3.33	11.0889	1.82483	5.77062
2.94	8.6436	1.71464	5.42218	3.34	11.1556	1.82757	5.77927
2.95	8.7025	1.71756	5.43139	3.35	11.2225	1.83030	5.78792
2.96	8.7616	1.72047	5.44059	3.36	11.2896	1.83303	5.79655
2.97	8.8209	1.72337	5.44977	3.37	11.3569	1.83576	5.80517
2.98	8.8804	1.72627	5.45894	3.38	11.4244	1.83848	5.81378
2.99	8.9401	1.72916	5.46809	3.39	11.4921	1.84120	5.82237
3.00	9.0000	1.73205	5.47723	**3.40**	11.5600	1.84391	5.83095

TABLE A (Continued)

N	N²	√N	√10N	N	N²	√N	√10N
3.40	11.5600	1.84391	5.83095	**3.80**	14.4400	1.94936	6.16441
3.41	11.6281	1.84662	5.83952	3.81	14.5161	1.95192	6.17252
3.42	11.6964	1.84932	5.84808	3.82	14.5924	1.95448	6.18061
3.43	11.7649	1.85203	5.85662	3.83	14.6689	1.95704	6.18870
3.44	11.8336	1.85472	5.86515	3.84	14.7456	1.95959	6.19677
3.45	11.9025	1.85742	5.87367	3.85	14.8225	1.96214	6.20484
3.46	11.9716	1.86011	5.88218	3.86	14.8996	1.96469	6.21289
3.47	12.0409	1.86279	5.89067	3.87	14.9769	1.96723	6.22093
3.48	12.1104	1.86548	5.89915	3.88	15.0544	1.96977	6.22896
3.49	12.1801	1.86815	5.90762	3.89	15.1321	1.97231	6.23699
3.50	12.2500	1.87083	5.91608	**3.90**	15.2100	1.97484	6.24500
3.51	12.3201	1.87350	5.92453	3.91	15.2881	1.97737	6.25300
3.52	12.3904	1.87617	5.93296	3.92	15.3664	1.97990	6.26099
3.53	12.4609	1.87883	5.94138	3.93	15.4449	1.98242	6.26897
3.54	12.5316	1.88149	5.94979	3.94	15.5236	1.98494	6.27694
3.55	12.6025	1.88414	5.95819	3.95	15.6025	1.98746	6.28490
3.56	12.6736	1.88680	5.96657	3.96	15.6816	1.98997	6.29285
3.57	12.7449	1.88944	5.97495	3.97	15.7609	1.99249	6.30079
3.58	12.8164	1.89209	5.98331	3.98	15.8404	1.99499	6.30872
3.59	12.8881	1.89473	5.99166	3.99	15.9201	1.99750	6.31664
3.60	12.9600	1.89737	6.00000	**4.00**	16.0000	2.00000	6.32456
3.61	13.0321	1.90000	6.00833	4.01	16.0801	2.00250	6.33246
3.62	13.1044	1.90263	6.01664	4.02	16.1604	2.00499	6.34035
3.63	13.1769	1.90526	6.02495	4.03	16.2409	2.00749	6.34823
3.64	13.2496	1.90788	6.03324	4.04	16.3216	2.00998	6.35610
3.65	13.3225	1.91050	6.04152	4.05	16.4025	2.01246	6.36396
3.66	13.3956	1.91311	6.04979	4.06	16.4836	2.01494	6.37181
3.67	13.4689	1.91572	6.05805	4.07	16.5649	2.01742	6.37966
3.68	13.5424	1.91833	6.06630	4.08	16.6464	2.01990	6.38749
3.69	13.6161	1.92094	6.07454	4.09	16.7281	2.02237	6.39531
3.70	13.6900	1.92354	6.08276	**4.10**	16.8100	2.02485	6.40312
3.71	13.7641	1.92614	6.09098	4.11	16.8921	2.02731	6.41093
3.72	13.8384	1.92873	6.09918	4.12	16.9744	2.02978	6.41872
3.73	13.9129	1.93132	6.10737	4.13	17.0569	2.03224	6.42651
3.74	13.9876	1.93391	6.11555	4.14	17.1396	2.03470	6.43428
3.75	14.0625	1.93649	6.12372	4.15	17.2225	2.03715	6.44205
3.76	14.1376	1.93907	6.13188	4.16	17.3056	2.03961	6.44981
3.77	14.2129	1.94165	6.14003	4.17	17.3889	2.04206	6.45755
3.78	14.2884	1.94422	6.14817	4.18	17.4724	2.04450	6.46529
3.79	14.3641	1.94679	6.15630	4.19	17.5561	2.04695	6.47302
3.80	14.4400	1.94936	6.16441	**4.20**	17.6400	2.04939	6.48074

N	N²	√N	√10N	N	N²	√N	√10N
4.20	17.6400	2.04939	6.48074	**4.60**	21.1600	2.14476	6.78233
4.21	17.7241	2.05183	6.48845	4.61	21.2521	2.14709	6.78970
4.22	17.8084	2.05426	6.49615	4.62	21.3444	2.14942	6.79706
4.23	17.8929	2.05670	6.50384	4.63	21.4369	2.15174	6.80441
4.24	17.9776	2.05913	6.51153	4.64	21.5296	2.15407	6.81175
4.25	18.0625	2.06155	6.51920	4.65	21.6225	2.15639	6.81909
4.26	18.1476	2.06398	6.52687	4.66	21.7156	2.15870	6.82642
4.27	18.2329	2.06640	6.53452	4.67	21.8089	2.16102	6.83374
4.28	18.3184	2.06882	6.54217	4.68	21.9024	2.16333	6.84105
4.29	18.4041	2.07123	6.54981	4.69	21.9961	2.16564	6.84836
4.30	18.4900	2.07364	6.55744	**4.70**	22.0900	2.16795	6.85565
4.31	18.5761	2.07605	6.56506	4.71	22.1841	2.17025	6.86294
4.32	18.6624	2.07846	6.57267	4.72	22.2784	2.17256	6.87023
4.33	18.7489	2.08087	6.58027	4.73	22.3729	2.17486	6.87750
4.34	18.8356	2.08327	6.58787	4.74	22.4676	2.17715	6.88477
4.35	18.9225	2.08567	6.59545	4.75	22.5625	2.17945	6.89202
4.36	19.0096	2.08806	6.60303	4.76	22.6576	2.18174	6.89928
4.37	19.0969	2.09045	6.61060	4.77	22.7529	2.18403	6.90652
4.38	19.1844	2.09284	6.61816	4.78	22.8484	2.18632	6.91375
4.39	19.2721	2.09523	6.62571	4.79	22.9441	2.18861	6.92098
4.40	19.3600	2.09762	6.63325	**4.80**	23.0400	2.19089	6.92820
4.41	19.4481	2.10000	6.64078	4.81	23.1361	2.19317	6.93542
4.42	19.5364	2.10238	6.64831	4.82	23.2324	2.19545	6.94262
4.43	19.6249	2.10476	6.65582	4.83	23.3289	2.19773	6.94982
4.44	19.7136	2.10713	6.66333	4.84	23.4256	2.20000	6.95701
4.45	19.8025	2.10950	6.67083	4.85	23.5225	2.20227	6.96419
4.46	19.8916	2.11187	6.67832	4.86	23.6196	2.20454	6.97137
4.47	19.9809	2.11424	6.68581	4.87	23.7169	2.20681	6.97854
4.48	20.0704	2.11660	6.69328	4.88	23.8144	2.20907	6.98570
4.49	20.1601	2.11896	6.70075	4.89	23.9121	2.21133	6.99285
4.50	20.2500	2.12132	6.70820	**4.90**	24.0100	2.21359	7.00000
4.51	20.3401	2.12368	6.71565	4.91	24.1081	2.21585	7.00714
4.52	20.4304	2.12603	6.72309	4.92	24.2064	2.21811	7.01427
4.53	20.5209	2.12838	6.73053	4.93	24.3049	2.22036	7.02140
4.54	20.6116	2.13073	6.73795	4.94	24.4036	2.22261	7.02851
4.55	20.7025	2.13307	6.74537	4.95	24.5025	2.22486	7.03562
4.56	20.7936	2.13542	6.75278	4.96	24.6016	2.22711	7.04273
4.57	20.8849	2.13776	6.76018	4.97	24.7009	2.22935	7.04982
4.58	20.9764	2.14009	6.76757	4.98	24.8004	2.23159	7.05691
4.59	21.0681	2.14243	6.77495	4.99	24.9001	2.23383	7.06399
4.60	21.1600	2.14476	6.78233	**5.00**	25.0000	2.23607	7.07107

N	N²	√N	√10N	N	N²	√N	√10N
5.00	25.0000	2.23607	7.07107	**5.40**	29.1600	2.32379	7.34847
5.01	25.1001	2.23830	7.07814	5.41	29.2681	2.32594	7.35527
5.02	25.2004	2.24054	7.08520	5.42	29.3764	2.32809	7.36206
5.03	25.3009	2.24277	7.09225	5.43	29.4849	2.33024	7.36885
5.04	25.4016	2.24499	7.09930	5.44	29.5936	2.33238	7.37564
5.05	25.5025	2.24722	7.10634	5.45	29.7025	2.33452	7.38241
5.06	25.6036	2.24944	7.11337	5.46	29.8116	2.33666	7.38918
5.07	25.7049	2.25167	7.12039	5.47	29.9209	2.33880	7.39594
5.08	25.8064	2.25389	7.12741	5.48	30.0304	2.34094	7.40270
5.09	25.9081	2.25610	7.13442	5.49	30.1401	2.34307	7.40945
5.10	26.0100	2.25832	7.14143	**5.50**	30.2500	2.34521	7.41620
5.11	26.1121	2.26053	7.14843	5.51	30.3601	2.34734	7.42294
5.12	26.2144	2.26274	7.15542	5.52	30.4704	2.34947	7.42967
5.13	26.3169	2.26495	7.16240	5.53	30.5809	2.35160	7.43640
5.14	26.4196	2.26716	7.16938	5.54	30.6916	2.35372	7.44312
5.15	26.5225	2.26936	7.17635	5.55	30.8025	2.35584	7.44983
5.16	26.6256	2.27156	7.18331	5.56	30.9136	2.35797	7.45654
5.17	26.7289	2.27376	7.19027	5.57	31.0249	2.36008	7.46324
5.18	26.8324	2.27596	7.19722	5.58	31.1364	2.36220	7.46994
5.19	26.9361	2.27816	7.20417	5.59	31.2481	2.36432	7.47663
5.20	27.0400	2.28035	7.21110	**5.60**	31.3600	2.36643	7.48331
5.21	27.1441	2.28254	7.21803	5.61	31.4721	2.36854	7.48999
5.22	27.2484	2.28473	7.22496	5.62	31.5844	2.37065	7.49667
5.23	27.3529	2.28692	7.23187	5.63	31.6969	2.37276	7.50333
5.24	27.4576	2.28910	7.23878	5.64	31.8096	2.37487	7.50999
5.25	27.5625	2.29129	7.24569	5.65	31.9225	2.37697	7.51665
5.26	27.6676	2.29347	7.25259	5.66	32.0356	2.37908	7.52330
5.27	27.7729	2.29565	7.25948	5.67	32.1489	2.38118	7.52994
5.28	27.8784	2.29783	7.26636	5.68	32.2624	2.38328	7.53658
5.29	27.9841	2.30000	7.27324	5.69	32.3761	2.38537	7.54321
5.30	28.0900	2.30217	7.28011	**5.70**	32.4900	2.38747	7.54983
5.31	28.1961	2.30434	7.28697	5.71	32.6041	2.38956	7.55645
5.32	28.3024	2.30651	7.29383	5.72	32.7184	2.39165	7.56307
5.33	28.4089	2.30868	7.30068	5.73	32.8329	2.39374	7.56968
5.34	28.5156	2.31084	7.30753	5.74	32.9476	2.39583	7.57628
5.35	28.6225	2.31301	7.31437	5.75	33.0625	2.39792	7.58288
5.36	28.7296	2.31517	7.32120	5.76	33.1776	2.40000	7.58947
5.37	28.8369	2.31733	7.32803	5.77	33.2929	2.40208	7.59605
5.38	28.9444	2.31948	7.33485	5.78	33.4084	2.40416	7.60263
5.39	29.0521	2.32164	7.34166	5.79	33.5241	2.40624	7.60920
5.40	29.1600	2.32379	7.34847	**5.80**	33.6400	2.40832	7.61577

TABLE A (Continued)

N	N²	√N	√10N	N	N²	√N	√10N
5.80	33.6400	2.40832	7.61577	**6.20**	38.4400	2.48998	7.87401
5.81	33.7561	2.41039	7.62234	6.21	38.5641	2.49199	7.88036
5.82	33.8724	2.41247	7.62889	6.22	38.6884	2.49399	7.88670
5.83	33.9889	2.41454	7.63544	6.23	38.8129	2.49600	7.89303
5.84	34.1056	2.41661	7.64199	6.24	38.9376	2.49800	7.89937
5.85	34.2225	2.41868	7.64853	6.25	39.0625	2.50000	7.90569
5.86	34.3396	2.42074	7.65506	6.26	39.1876	2.50200	7.91202
5.87	34.4569	2.42281	7.66159	6.27	39.3129	2.50400	7.91833
5.88	34.5744	2.42487	7.66812	6.28	39.4384	2.50599	7.92465
5.89	34.6921	2.42693	7.67463	6.29	39.5641	2.50799	7.93095
5.90	34.8100	2.42899	7.68115	**6.30**	39.6900	2.50998	7.93725
5.91	34.9281	2.43105	7.68765	6.31	39.8161	2.51197	7.94355
5.92	35.0464	2.43311	7.69415	6.32	39.9424	2.51396	7.94984
5.93	35.1649	2.43516	7.70065	6.33	40.0689	2.51595	7.95613
5.94	35.2836	2.43721	7.70714	6.34	40.1956	2.51794	7.96241
5.95	35.4025	2.43926	7.71362	6.35	40.3225	2.51992	7.96869
5.96	35.5216	2.44131	7.72010	6.36	40.4496	2.52190	7.97496
5.97	35.6409	2.44336	7.72658	6.37	40.5769	2.52389	7.98123
5.98	35.7604	2.44540	7.73305	6.38	40.7044	2.52587	7.98749
5.99	35.8801	2.44745	7.73951	6.39	40.8321	2.52784	7.99375
6.00	36.0000	2.44949	7.74597	**6.40**	40.9600	2.52982	8.00000
6.01	36.1201	2.45153	7.75242	6.41	41.0881	2.53180	8.00625
6.02	36.2404	2.45357	7.75887	6.42	41.2164	2.53377	8.01249
6.03	36.3609	2.45561	7.76531	6.43	41.3449	2.53574	8.01873
6.04	36.4816	2.45764	7.77174	6.44	41.4736	2.53772	8.02496
6.05	36.6025	2.45967	7.77817	6.45	41.6025	2.53969	8.03119
6.06	36.7236	2.46171	7.78460	6.46	41.7316	2.54165	8.03741
6.07	36.8449	2.46374	7.79102	6.47	41.8609	2.54362	8.04363
6.08	36.9664	2.46577	7.79744	6.48	41.9904	2.54558	8.04984
6.09	37.0881	2.46779	7.80385	6.49	42.1201	2.54755	8.05605
6.10	37.2100	2.46982	7.81025	**6.50**	42.2500	2.54951	8.06226
6.11	37.3321	2.47184	7.81665	6.51	42.3801	2.55147	8.06846
6.12	37.4544	2.47386	7.82304	6.52	42.5104	2.55343	8.07465
6.13	37.5769	2.47588	7.82943	6.53	42.6409	2.55539	8.08084
6.14	37.6996	2.47790	7.83582	6.54	42.7716	2.55734	8.08703
6.15	37.8225	2.47992	7.84219	6.55	42.9025	2.55930	8.09321
6.16	37.9456	2.48193	7.84857	6.56	43.0336	2.56125	8.09938
6.17	38.0689	2.48395	7.85493	6.57	43.1649	2.56320	8.10555
6.18	38.1924	2.48596	7.86130	6.58	43.2964	2.56515	8.11172
6.19	38.3161	2.48797	7.86766	6.59	43.4281	2.56710	8.11788
6.20	38.4400	2.48998	7.87401	**6.60**	43.5600	2.56905	8.12404

N	N²	√N	√10N	N	N²	√N	√10N
6.60	43.5600	2.56905	8.12404	**7.00**	49.0000	2.64575	8.36660
6.61	43.6921	2.57099	8.13019	7.01	49.1401	2.64764	8.37257
6.62	43.8244	2.57294	8.13634	7.02	49.2804	2.64953	8.37854
6.63	43.9569	2.57488	8.14248	7.03	49.4209	2.65141	8.38451
6.64	44.0896	2.57682	8.14862	7.04	49.5616	2.65330	8.39047
6.65	44.2225	2.57876	8.15475	7.05	49.7025	2.65518	8.39643
6.66	44.3556	2.58070	8.16088	7.06	49.8436	2.65707	8.40238
6.67	44.4889	2.58263	8.16701	7.07	49.9849	2.65895	8.40833
6.68	44.6224	2.58457	8.17313	7.08	50.1264	2.66083	8.41427
6.69	44.7561	2.58650	8.17924	7.09	50.2681	2.66271	8.42021
6.70	44.8900	2.58844	8.18535	**7.10**	50.4100	2.66458	8.42615
6.71	45.0241	2.59037	8.19146	7.11	50.5521	2.66646	8.43208
6.72	45.1584	2.59230	8.19756	7.12	50.6944	2.66833	8.43801
6.73	45.2929	2.59422	8.20366	7.13	50.8369	2.67021	8.44393
6.74	45.4276	2.59615	8.20975	7.14	50.9796	2.67208	8.44985
6.75	45.5625	2.59808	8.21584	7.15	51.1225	2.67395	8.45577
6.76	45.6976	2.60000	8.22192	7.16	51.2656	2.67582	8.46168
6.77	45.8329	2.60192	8.22800	7.17	51.4089	2.67769	8.46759
6.78	45.9684	2.60384	8.23408	7.18	51.5524	2.67955	8.47349
6.79	46.1041	2.60576	8.24015	7.19	51.6961	2.68142	8.47939
6.80	46.2400	2.60768	8.24621	**7.20**	51.8400	2.68328	8.48528
6.81	46.3761	2.60960	8.25227	7.21	51.9841	2.68514	8.49117
6.82	46.5124	2.61151	8.25833	7.22	52.1284	2.68701	8.49706
6.83	46.6489	2.61343	8.26438	7.23	52.2729	2.68887	8.50294
6.84	46.7856	2.61534	8.27043	7.24	52.4176	2.69072	8.50882
6.85	46.9225	2.61725	8.27647	7.25	52.5625	2.69258	8.51469
6.86	47.0596	2.61916	8.28251	7.26	52.7076	2.69444	8.52056
6.87	47.1969	2.62107	8.28855	7.27	52.8529	2.69629	8.52643
6.88	47.3344	2.62298	8.29458	7.28	52.9984	2.69815	8.53229
6.89	47.4721	2.62488	8.30060	7.29	53.1441	2.70000	8.53815
6.90	47.6100	2.62679	8.30662	**7.30**	53.2900	2.70185	8.54400
6.91	47.7481	2.62869	8.31264	7.31	53.4361	2.70370	8.54985
6.92	47.8864	2.63059	8.31865	7.32	53.5824	2.70555	8.55570
6.93	48.0249	2.63249	8.32466	7.33	53.7289	2.70740	8.56154
6.94	48.1636	2.63439	8.33067	7.34	53.8756	2.70924	8.56738
6.95	48.3025	2.63629	8.33667	7.35	54.0225	2.71109	8.57321
6.96	48.4416	2.63818	8.34266	7.36	54.1696	2.71293	8.57904
6.97	48.5809	2.64008	8.34865	7.37	54.3169	2.71477	8.58487
6.98	48.7204	2.64197	8.35464	7.38	54.4644	2.71662	8.59069
6.99	48.8601	2.64386	8.36062	7.39	54.6121	2.71846	8.59651
7.00	49.0000	2.64575	8.36660	**7.40**	54.7600	2.72029	8.60233

TABLE A (Continued)

N	N²	√N	√10N	N	N²	√N	√10N
7.40	54.7600	2.72029	8.60233	**7.80**	60.8400	2.79285	8.83176
7.41	54.9081	2.72213	8.60814	7.81	60.9961	2.79464	8.83742
7.42	55.0564	2.72397	8.61394	7.82	61.1524	2.79643	8.84308
7.43	55.2049	2.72580	8.61974	7.83	61.3089	2.79821	8.84873
7.44	55.3536	2.72764	8.62554	7.84	61.4656	2.80000	8.85438
7.45	55.5025	2.72947	8.63134	7.85	61.6225	2.80179	8.86002
7.46	55.6516	2.73130	8.63713	7.86	61.7796	2.80357	8.86566
7.47	55.8009	2.73313	8.64292	7.87	61.9369	2.80535	8.87130
7.48	55.9504	2.73496	8.64870	7.88	62.0944	2.80713	8.87694
7.49	56.1001	2.73679	8.65448	7.89	62.2521	2.80891	8.88257
7.50	56.2500	2.73861	8.66025	**7.90**	62.4100	2.81069	8.88819
7.51	56.4001	2.74044	8.66603	7.91	62.5681	2.81247	8.89382
7.52	56.5504	2.74226	8.67179	7.92	62.7264	2.81425	8.89944
7.53	56.7009	2.74408	8.67756	7.93	62.8849	2.81603	8.90505
7.54	56.8516	2.74591	8.68332	7.94	63.0436	2.81780	8.91067
7.55	57.0025	2.74773	8.68907	7.95	63.2025	2.81957	8.91628
7.56	57.1536	2.74955	8.69483	7.96	63.3616	2.82135	8.92188
7.57	57.3049	2.75136	8.70057	7.97	63.5209	2.82312	8.92749
7.58	57.4564	2.75318	8.70632	7.98	63.6804	2.82489	8.93308
7.59	57.6081	2.75500	8.71206	7.99	63.8401	2.82666	8.93868
7.60	57.7600	2.75681	8.71780	**8.00**	64.0000	2.82843	8.94427
7.61	57.9121	2.75862	8.72353	8.01	64.1601	2.83019	8.94986
7.62	58.0644	2.76043	8.72926	8.02	64.3204	2.83196	8.95545
7.63	58.2169	2.76225	8.73499	8.03	64.4809	2.83373	8.96103
7.64	58.3696	2.76405	8.74071	8.04	64.6416	2.83549	8.96660
7.65	58.5225	2.76586	8.74643	8.05	64.8025	2.83725	8.97218
7.66	58.6756	2.76767	8.75214	8.06	64.9636	2.83901	8.97775
7.67	58.8289	2.76948	8.75785	8.07	65.1249	2.84077	8.98332
7.68	58.9824	2.77128	8.76356	8.08	65.2864	2.84253	8.98888
7.69	59.1361	2.77308	8.76926	8.09	65.4481	2.84429	8.99444
7.70	59.2900	2.77489	8.77496	**8.10**	65.6100	2.84605	9.00000
7.71	59.4441	2.77669	8.78066	8.11	65.7721	2.84781	9.00555
7.72	59.5984	2.77849	8.78635	8.12	65.9344	2.84956	9.01110
7.73	59.7529	2.78029	8.79204	8.13	66.0969	2.85132	9.01665
7.74	59.9076	2.78209	8.79773	8.14	66.2596	2.85307	9.02219
7.75	60.0625	2.78388	8.80341	8.15	66.4225	2.85482	9.02774
7.76	60.2176	2.78568	8.80909	8.16	66.5856	2.85657	9.03327
7.77	60.3729	2.78747	8.81476	8.17	66.7489	2.85832	9.03881
7.78	60.5284	2.78927	8.82043	8.18	66.9124	2.86007	9.04434
7.79	60.6841	2.79106	8.82610	8.19	67.0761	2.86182	9.04986
7.80	60.8400	2.79285	8.83176	**8.20**	67.2400	2.86356	9.05539

N	N²	√N̄	√10N̄	N	N²	√N̄	√10N̄
8.20	67.2400	2.86356	9.05539	**8.60**	73.9600	2.93258	9.27362
8.21	67.4041	2.86531	9.06091	8.61	74.1321	2.93428	9.27901
8.22	67.5684	2.86705	9.06642	8.62	74.3044	2.93598	9.28440
8.23	67.7329	2.86880	9.07193	8.63	74.4769	2.93769	9.28978
8.24	67.8976	2.87054	9.07744	8.64	74.6496	2.93939	9.29516
8.25	68.0625	2.87228	9.08295	8.65	74.8225	2.94109	9.30054
8.26	68.2276	2.87402	9.08845	8.66	74.9956	2.94279	9.30591
8.27	68.3929	2.87576	9.09395	8.67	75.1689	2.94449	9.31128
8.28	68.5584	2.87750	9.09945	8.68	75.3424	2.94618	9.31665
8.29	68.7241	2.87924	9.10494	8.69	75.5161	2.94788	9.32202
8.30	68.8900	2.88097	9.11043	**8.70**	75.6900	2.94958	9.32738
8.31	69.0561	2.88271	9.11592	8.71	75.8641	2.95127	9.33274
8.32	69.2224	2.88444	9.12140	8.72	76.0384	2.95296	9.33809
8.33	69.3889	2.88617	9.12688	8.73	76.2129	2.95466	9.34345
8.34	69.5556	2.88791	9.13236	8.74	76.3876	2.95635	9.34880
8.35	69.7225	2.88964	9.13783	8.75	76.5625	2.95804	9.35414
8.36	69.8896	2.89137	9.14330	8.76	76.7376	2.95973	9.35949
8.37	70.0569	2.89310	9.14877	8.77	76.9129	2.96142	9.36483
8.38	70.2244	2.89482	9.15423	8.78	77.0884	2.96311	9.37017
8.39	70.3921	2.89655	9.15969	8.79	77.2641	2.96479	9.37550
8.40	70.5600	2.89828	9.16515	**8.80**	77.4400	2.96648	9.38083
8.41	70.7281	2.90000	9.17061	8.81	77.6161	2.96816	9.38616
8.42	70.8964	2.90172	9.17606	8.82	77.7924	2.96985	9.39149
8.43	71.0649	2.90345	9.18150	8.83	77.9689	2.97153	9.39681
8.44	71.2336	2.90517	9.18695	8.84	78.1456	2.97321	9.40213
8.45	71.4025	2.90689	9.19239	8.85	78.3225	2.97489	9.40744
8.46	71.5716	2.90861	9.19783	8.86	78.4996	2.97658	9.41276
8.47	71.7409	2.91033	9.20326	8.87	78.6769	2.97825	9.41807
8.48	71.9104	2.91204	9.20869	8.88	78.8544	2.97993	9.42338
8.49	72.0801	2.91376	9.21412	8.89	79.0321	2.98161	9.42868
8.50	72.2500	2.91548	9.21954	**8.90**	79.2100	2.98329	9.43398
8.51	72.4201	2.91719	9.22497	8.91	79.3881	2.98496	9.43928
8.52	72.5904	2.91890	9.23038	8.92	79.5664	2.98664	9.44458
8.53	72.7609	2.92062	9.23580	8.93	79.7449	2.98831	9.44987
8.54	72.9316	2.92233	9.24121	8.94	79.9236	2.98998	9.45516
8.55	73.1025	2.92404	9.24662	8.95	80.1025	2.99166	9.46044
8.56	73.2736	2.92575	9.25203	8.96	80.2816	2.99333	9.46573
8.57	73.4449	2.92746	9.25743	8.97	80.4609	2.99500	9.47101
8.58	73.6164	2.92916	9.26283	8.98	80.6404	2.99666	9.47629
8.59	73.7881	2.93087	9.26823	8.99	80.8201	2.99833	9.48156
8.60	73.9600	2.93258	9.27362	**9.00**	81.0000	3.00000	9.48683

TABLE A (Continued)

N	N²	√N	√10N	N	N²	√N	√10N
9.00	81.0000	3.00000	9.48683	**9.40**	88.3600	3.06594	9.69536
9.01	81.1801	3.00167	9.49210	9.41	88.5481	3.06757	9.70052
9.02	81.3604	3.00333	9.49737	9.42	88.7364	3.06920	9.70567
9.03	81.5409	3.00500	9.50263	9.43	88.9249	3.07083	9.71082
9.04	81.7216	3.00666	9.50789	9.44	89.1136	3.07246	9.71597
9.05	81.9025	3.00832	9.51315	9.45	89.3025	3.07409	9.72111
9.06	82.0836	3.00998	9.51840	9.46	89.4916	3.07571	9.72625
9.07	82.2649	3.01164	9.52365	9.47	89.6809	3.07734	9.73139
9.08	82.4464	3.01330	9.52890	9.48	89.8704	3.07896	9.73653
9.09	82.6281	3.01496	9.53415	9.49	90.0601	3.08058	9.74166
9.10	82.8100	3.01662	9.53939	**9.50**	90.2500	3.08221	9.74679
9.11	82.9921	3.01828	9.54463	9.51	90.4401	3.08383	9.75192
9.12	83.1744	3.01993	9.54987	9.52	90.6304	3.08545	9.75705
9.13	83.3569	3.02159	9.55510	9.53	90.8209	3.08707	9.76217
9.14	83.5396	3.02324	9.56033	9.54	91.0116	3.08869	9.76729
9.15	83.7225	3.02490	9.56556	9.55	91.2025	3.09031	9.77241
9.16	83.9056	3.02655	9.57079	9.56	91.3936	3.09192	9.77753
9.17	84.0889	3.02820	9.57601	9.57	91.5849	3.09354	9.78264
9.18	84.2724	3.02985	9.58123	9.58	91.7764	3.09516	9.78775
9.19	84.4561	3.03150	9.58645	9.59	91.9681	3.09677	9.79285
9.20	84.6400	3.03315	9.59166	**9.60**	92.1600	3.09839	9.79796
9.21	84.8241	3.03480	9.59687	9.61	92.3521	3.10000	9.80306
9.22	85.0084	3.03645	9.60208	9.62	92.5444	3.10161	9.80816
9.23	85.1929	3.03809	9.60729	9.63	92.7369	3.10322	9.81326
9.24	85.3776	3.03974	9.61249	9.64	92.9296	3.10483	9.81835
9.25	85.5625	3.04138	9.61769	9.65	93.1225	3.10644	9.82344
9.26	85.7476	3.04302	9.62289	9.66	93.3156	3.10805	9.82853
9.27	85.9329	3.04467	9.62808	9.67	93.5089	3.10966	9.83362
9.28	86.1184	3.04631	9.63328	9.68	93.7024	3.11127	9.83870
9.29	86.3041	3.04795	9.63846	9.69	93.8961	3.11288	9.84378
9.30	86.4900	3.04959	9.64365	**9.70**	94.0900	3.11448	9.84886
9.31	86.6761	3.05123	9.64883	9.71	94.2841	3.11609	9.85393
9.32	86.8624	3.05287	9.65401	9.72	94.4784	3.11769	9.85901
9.33	87.0489	3.05450	9.65919	9.73	94.6729	3.11929	9.86408
9.34	87.2356	3.05614	9.66437	9.74	94.8676	3.12090	9.86914
9.35	87.4225	3.05778	9.66954	9.75	95.0625	3.12250	9.87421
9.36	87.6096	3.05941	9.67471	9.76	95.2576	3.12410	9.87927
9.37	87.7969	3.06105	9.67988	9.77	95.4529	3.12570	9.88433
9.38	87.9844	3.06268	9.68504	9.78	95.6484	3.12730	9.88939
9.39	88.1721	3.06431	9.69020	9.79	95.8441	3.12890	9.89444
9.40	88.3600	3.06594	9.69536	**9.80**	96.0400	3.13050	9.89949

N	N²	√N	√10N	N	N²	√N	√10N
9.80	96.0400	3.13050	9.89949	**9.90**	98.0100	3.14643	9.94987
9.81	96.2361	3.13209	9.90454	9.91	98.2081	3.14802	9.95490
9.82	96.4324	3.13369	9.90959	9.92	98.4064	3.14960	9.95992
9.83	96.6289	3.13528	9.91464	9.93	98.6049	3.15119	9.96494
9.84	96.8256	3.13688	9.91968	9.94	98.8036	3.15278	9.96995
9.85	97.0225	3.13847	9.92472	9.95	99.0025	3.15436	9.97497
9.86	97.2196	3.14006	9.92975	9.96	99.2016	3.15595	9.97998
9.87	97.4169	3.14166	9.93479	9.97	99.4009	3.15753	9.98499
9.88	97.6144	3.14325	9.93982	9.98	99.6004	3.15911	9.98999
9.89	97.8121	3.14484	9.94485	9.99	99.8001	3.16070	9.99500
9.90	98.0100	3.14643	9.94987	**10.00**	100.000	3.16228	10.0000

TABLE B. ORDINATES OF THE NORMAL CURVE*

z or $\frac{x}{\sigma}$	y or Ordinate	z or $\frac{x}{\sigma}$	y or Ordinate
.00	.3989	1.75	.0863
.05	.3984	1.80	.0790
.10	.3970	1.85	.0721
.15	.3945	1.90	.0656
.20	.3910	1.95	.0596
.25	.3867	2.00	.0540
.30	.3814	2.05	.0488
.35	.3752	2.10	.0440
.40	.3683	2.15	.0396
.45	.3605	2.20	.0355
.50	.3521	2.25	.0317
.55	.3429	2.30	.0283
.60	.3332	2.35	.0252
.65	.3230	2.40	.0224
.70	.3123	2.45	.0198
.75	.3011	2.50	.0175
.80	.2897	2.55	.0154
.85	.2780	2.60	.0136
.90	.2661	2.65	.0119
.95	.2541	2.70	.0104
1.00	.2420	2.75	.0091
1.05	.2299	2.80	.0079
1.10	.2179	2.85	.0069
1.15	.2059	2.90	.0060
1.20	.1942	2.95	.0051
1.25	.1826	3.00	.0044
1.30	.1714	3.10	.0033
1.35	.1604	3.20	.0024
1.40	.1497	3.30	.0017
1.45	.1394	3.40	.0012
1.50	.1295	3.50	.00087
1.55	.1200	3.75	.00035
1.60	.1109	4.00	.00013
1.65	.1023	4.50	.000015
1.70	.0940	5.00	.0000015

* Table B is reprinted from H. E. Garrett, *Statistics in Psychology and Education* (5th ed.; New York: David McKay Co.), by permission of the author and publisher.

TABLE C.

Fractional Parts of the Total Area (Taken as 10,000) under the Normal Probability Curve, Corresponding to Distances on the Baseline between the Mean and Successive Points Laid Off from the Mean in Units of Standard Deviation.*

Example: between the mean and a point 1.38σ $\left(\dfrac{x}{\sigma} = 1.38\right)$ are found 41.62% of the entire area under the curve.

$\dfrac{x}{\sigma}$	.00	.01	.02	.03	.04	.05	.06	.07	.08	.09
0.0	0000	0040	0080	0120	0160	0199	0239	0279	0319	0359
0.1	0398	0438	0478	0517	0557	0596	0636	0675	0714	0753
0.2	0793	0832	0871	0910	0948	0987	1026	1064	1103	1141
0.3	1179	1217	1255	1293	1331	1368	1406	1443	1480	1517
0.4	1554	1591	1628	1664	1700	1736	1772	1808	1844	1879
0.5	1915	1950	1985	2019	2054	2088	2123	2157	2190	2224
0.6	2257	2291	2324	2357	2389	2422	2454	2486	2517	2549
0.7	2580	2611	2642	2673	2704	2734	2764	2794	2823	2852
0.8	2881	2910	2939	2967	2995	3023	3051	3078	3106	3133
0.9	3159	3186	3212	3238	3264	3289	3315	3340	3365	3389
1.0	3413	3438	3461	3485	3508	3531	3554	3577	3599	3621
1.1	3643	3665	3686	3708	3729	3749	3770	3790	3810	3830
1.2	3849	3869	3888	3907	3925	3944	3962	3980	3997	4015
1.3	4032	4049	4066	4082	4099	4115	4131	4147	4162	4177
1.4	4192	4207	4222	4236	4251	4265	4279	4292	4306	4319
1.5	4332	4345	4357	4370	4383	4394	4406	4418	4429	4441
1.6	4452	4463	4474	4484	4495	4505	4515	4525	4535	4545
1.7	4554	4564	4573	4582	4591	4599	4608	4616	4625	4633
1.8	4641	4649	4656	4664	4671	4678	4686	4693	4699	4706
1.9	4713	4719	4726	4732	4738	4744	4750	4756	4761	4767
2.0	4772	4778	4783	4788	4793	4798	4803	4808	4812	4817
2.1	4821	4826	4830	4834	4838	4842	4846	4850	4854	4857
2.2	4861	4864	4868	4871	4875	4878	4881	4884	4887	4890
2.3	4893	4896	4898	4901	4904	4906	4909	4911	4913	4916
2.4	4918	4920	4922	4925	4927	4929	4931	4932	4934	4936
2.5	4938	4940	4941	4943	4945	4946	4948	4949	4951	4952
2.6	4953	4955	4956	4957	4959	4960	4961	4962	4963	4964
2.7	4965	4966	4967	4968	4969	4970	4971	4972	4973	4974
2.8	4974	4975	4976	4977	4977	4978	4979	4979	4980	4981
2.9	4981	4982	4982	4983	4984	4984	4985	4985	4986	4986
3.0	4986.5	4986.9	4987.4	4987.8	4988.2	4988.6	4988.9	4989.3	4989.7	4990.0
3.1	4990.3	4990.6	4991.0	4991.3	4991.6	4991.8	4992.1	4992.4	4992.6	4992.9
3.2	4993.129									
3.3	4995.166									
3.4	4996.631									
3.5	4997.674									
3.6	4998.409									
3.7	4998.922									
3.8	4999.277									
3.9	4999.519									
4.0	4999.683									
4.5	4999.966									
5.0	4999.997133									

* Table C is reprinted from Table A of H. E. Garrett, *Statistics in Psychology and Education* (5th ed.; New York: David McKay Co.), by permission of the author and publishers.

TABLE D. DEVIATES AND ORDINATES OF THE NORMAL CURVE CORRESPONDING TO AREAS FROM μ TO z

Area	z or $\frac{x}{\sigma}$	y Ordinate	Area	z or $\frac{x}{\sigma}$	y Ordinate
.000	.0000	.3989	.260	.7063	.3109
.005	.0125	.3989	.265	.7225	.3078
.010	.0251	.3988	.270	.7388	.3036
.015	.0376	.3987	.275	.7754	.2999
.020	.0502	.3984	.280	.7722	.2961
.025	.0627	.3982	.285	.7892	.2922
.030	.0753	.3978	.290	.8064	.2882
.035	.0878	.3974	.295	.8239	.2841
.040	.1004	.3969	.300	.8416	.2800
.045	.1130	.3964	.305	.8596	.2757
.050	.1257	.3958	.310	.8779	.2714
.055	.1383	.3951	.315	.8965	.2669
.060	.1510	.3944	.320	.9154	.2624
.065	.1637	.3936	.325	.9346	.2578
.070	.1764	.3928	.330	.9542	.2531
.075	.1891	.3919	.335	.9741	.2482
.080	.2019	.3909	.340	.9945	.2433
.085	.2147	.3899	.345	1.0152	.2383
.090	.2275	.3887	.350	1.0364	.2332
.095	.2404	.3876	.355	1.0581	.2279
.100	.2533	.3863	.360	1.0803	.2226
.105	.2663	.3850	.365	1.1031	.2171
.110	.2793	.3837	.370	1.1264	.2115
.115	.2924	.3822	.375	1.1503	.2059
.120	.3055	.3808	.380	1.1750	.2000
.125	.3186	.3792	.385	1.2004	.1941
.130	.3319	.3776	.390	1.2265	.1880
.135	.3451	.3759	.395	1.2536	.1818
.140	.3585	.3741	.400	1.2816	.1755
.145	.3719	.3723	.405	1.3016	.1690
.150	.3853	.3704	.410	1.3408	.1624
.155	.3989	.3684	.415	1.3722	.1556
.160	.4125	.3664	.420	1.4051	.1487
.165	.4261	.3643	.425	1.4395	.1416
.170	.4399	.3261	.430	1.4757	.1343
.175	.4538	.3599	.435	1.5141	.1268
.180	.4677	.3576	.440	1.5548	.1191
.185	.4817	.3552	.445	1.5982	.1112
.190	.4959	.3528	.450	1.6449	.1031
.195	.5101	.3503	.455	1.6954	.0948
.200	.5244	.3477	.460	1.7507	.0862
.205	.5388	.3450	.465	1.8119	.0773
.210	.5534	.3423	.470	1.8808	.0680
.215	.5681	.3395	.475	1.9600	.0584
.220	.5828	.3366	.480	2.0537	.0484
.225	.5978	.3337	.485	2.1701	.0379
.230	.6128	.3306	.490	2.3263	.0267
.235	.6280	.3275	.495	2.5758	.0145
.240	.6433	.3244	.496	2.6521	.0118
.245	.6588	.3211	.497	2.7478	.0091
.250	.6745	.3178	.498	2.8782	.0063
.255	.6903	.3144	.499	3.0902	.0034

TABLE E. DISTRIBUTION OF t*

df	p = .1	.05	.02	.01	.001
1	6.314	12.706	31.821	63.657	636.619
2	2.920	4.303	6.965	9.925	31.598
3	2.353	3.182	4.541	5.841	12.941
4	2.132	2.776	3.747	4.604	8.610
5	2.015	2.571	3.365	4.032	6.859
6	1.943	2.447	3.143	3.707	5.959
7	1.895	2.365	2.998	3.499	5.405
8	1.860	2.306	2.896	3.355	5.041
9	1.833	2.262	2.821	3.250	4.781
10	1.812	2.228	2.764	3.169	4.587
11	1.796	2.201	2.718	3.106	4.437
12	1.782	2.179	2.681	3.055	4.318
13	1.771	2.160	2.650	3.012	4.221
14	1.761	2.145	2.624	2.977	4.140
15	1.753	2.131	2.602	2.947	4.073
16	1.746	2.120	2.583	2.921	4.015
17	1.740	2.110	2.567	2.898	3.965
18	1.734	2.101	2.552	2.878	3.922
19	1.729	2.093	2.539	2.861	3.883
20	1.725	2.086	2.528	2.845	3.850
21	1.721	2.080	2.518	2.831	3.819
22	1.717	2.074	2.508	2.819	3.792
23	1.714	2.069	2.500	2.807	3.767
24	1.711	2.064	2.492	2.797	3.745
25	1.708	2.060	2.485	2.787	3.725
26	1.706	2.056	2.479	2.779	3.707
27	1.703	2.052	2.473	2.771	3.690
28	1.701	2.048	2.467	2.763	3.674
29	1.699	2.045	2.462	2.756	3.659
30	1.697	2.042	2.457	2.750	3.646
40	1.684	2.021	2.423	2.704	3.551
60	1.671	2.000	2.390	2.660	3.460
120	1.658	1.980	2.358	2.617	3.373
∞	1.645	1.960	2.326	2.576	3.291

* Table E is taken from Table III of Fisher & Yates: *Statistical Tables for Biological, Agricultural and Medical Research*, published by Oliver & Boyd Ltd., Edinburgh, and reprinted in McNemar, *Psychological Statistics* (3rd ed.; New York: John Wiley & Sons, Inc.) by permission of the author and publishers.
The values of p are given for a two-tailed test.

TABLE F. TRANSFORMATION OF *r* TO z_r*

r	z_r	*r*	z_r	*r*	z_r
.01	.010	.34	.354	.67	.811
.02	.020	.35	.366	.68	.829
.03	.030	.36	.377	.69	.848
.04	.040	.37	.389	.70	.867
.05	.050	.38	.400	.71	.887
.06	.060	.39	.412	.72	.908
.07	.070	.40	.424	.73	.929
.08	.080	.41	.436	.74	.950
.09	.090	.42	.448	.75	.973
.10	.100	.43	.460	.76	.996
.11	.110	.44	.472	.77	1.020
.12	.121	.45	.485	.78	1.045
.13	.131	.46	.497	.79	1.071
.14	.141	.47	.510	.80	1.099
.15	.151	.48	.523	.81	1.127
.16	.161	.49	.536	.82	1.157
.17	.172	.50	.549	.83	1.188
.18	.181	.51	.563	.84	1.221
.19	.192	.52	.577	.85	1.256
.20	.203	.53	.590	.86	1.293
.21	.214	.54	.604	.87	1.333
.22	.224	.55	.618	.88	1.376
.23	.234	.56	.633	.89	1.422
.24	.245	.57	.648	.90	1.472
.25	.256	.58	.663	.91	1.528
.26	.266	.59	.678	.92	1.589
.27	.277	.60	.693	.93	1.658
.28	.288	.61	.709	.94	1.738
.29	.299	.62	.725	.95	1.832
.30	.309	.63	.741	.96	1.946
.31	.321	.64	.758	.97	2.092
.32	.332	.65	.775	.98	2.298
.33	.343	.66	.793	.99	2.647

* Table *F* is reprinted from Table *B* of McNemar, *Psychological Statistics* (3rd ed., New York: John Wiley & Sons, Inc.), by permission of the author and publishers.

TABLE G. TRANSFORMATION OF z TO r*

z	.00	.01	.02	.03	.04	.05	.06	.07	.08	.09
.0	.0000	.0100	.0200	.0300	.0400	.0500	.0599	.0699	.0798	.0898
.1	.0997	.1096	.1194	.1293	.1391	.1489	.1586	.1684	.1781	.1877
.2	.1974	.2070	.2165	.2260	.2355	.2449	.2543	.2636	.2729	.2821
.3	.2913	.3004	.3095	.3185	.3275	.3364	.3452	.3540	.3627	.3714
.4	.3800	.3885	.3969	.4053	.4136	.4219	.4301	.4382	.4462	.4542
.5	.4621	.4699	.4777	.4854	.4930	.5005	.5080	.5154	.5227	.5299
.6	.5370	.5441	.5511	.5580	.5649	.5717	.5784	.5850	.5915	.5980
.7	.6044	.6107	.6169	.6231	.6291	.6351	.6411	.6469	.6527	.6584
.8	.6640	.6696	.6751	.6805	.6858	.6911	.6963	.7014	.7064	.7114
.9	.7163	.7211	.7259	.7306	.7352	.7398	.7443	.7487	.7531	.7574
1.0	.7616	.7658	.7699	.7739	.7779	.7818	.7857	.7895	.7932	.7969
1.1	.8005	.8041	.8076	.8110	.8144	.8178	.8210	.8243	.8275	.8306
1.2	.8337	.8367	.8397	.8426	.8455	.8483	.8511	.8538	.8565	.8591
1.3	.8617	.8643	.8668	.8692	.8717	.8741	.8764	.8787	.8810	.8832
1.4	.8854	.8875	.8896	.8917	.8937	.8957	.8977	.8996	.9015	.9033
1.5	.9051	.9069	.9087	.9104	.9121	.9138	.9154	.9170	.9186	.9201
1.6	.9217	.9232	.9246	.9261	.9275	.9289	.9302	.9316	.9329	.9341
1.7	.9354	.9366	.9379	.9391	.9402	.9414	.9425	.9436	.9447	.9458
1.8	.9468	.9478	.9488	.9498	.9508	.9518	.9527	.9536	.9545	.9554
1.9	.9562	.9571	.9579	.9587	.9595	.9603	.9611	.9618	.9626	.9633
2.0	.9640	.9647	.9654	.9661	.9668	.9674	.9680	.9686	.9693	.9699
2.1	.9704	.9710	.9716	.9722	.9727	.9732	.9738	.9743	.9748	.9753
2.2	.9757	.9762	.9767	.9771	.9776	.9780	.9785	.9789	.9793	.9797
2.3	.9801	.9805	.9809	.9812	.9816	.9820	.9823	.9827	.9830	.9834
2.4	.9837	.9840	.9843	.9846	.9849	.9852	.9855	.9858	.9861	.9864
2.5	.9866	.9869	.9871	.9874	.9876	.9879	.9881	.9884	.9886	.9888
2.6	.9890	.9892	.9894	.9897	.9899	.9901	.9903	.9904	.9906	.9908
2.7	.9910	.9912	.9914	.9915	.9917	.9919	.9920	.9922	.9923	.9925
2.8	.9926	.9928	.9929	.9931	.9932	.9933	.9935	.9936	.9937	.9938
2.9	.9940	.9941	.9942	.9943	.9944	.9945	.9946	.9948	.9948	.9950

* Table G is taken from Table VII of Fisher & Yates: *Statistical Tables for Biological, Agricultural and Medical Research*, published by Oliver & Boyd Ltd., Edinburgh, and reprinted in McNemar, *Psychological Statistics* (3rd ed.; New York: John Wiley & Sons, Inc.) by permission of the author and publishers.

TABLE Ha. F DISTRIBUTION, UPPER 2.5 PERCENT POINTS*

Degrees of freedom for numerator

Denom.	1	2	3	4	5	6	7	8	9	10	12	15	20	24	30	40	60	120	∞
1	161	200	216	225	230	234	237	239	241	242	244	246	248	249	250	251	252	253	254
2	18.5	19.0	19.2	19.2	19.3	19.3	19.4	19.4	19.4	19.4	19.4	19.4	19.4	19.5	19.5	19.5	19.5	19.5	19.5
3	10.1	9.55	9.28	9.12	9.01	8.94	8.89	8.85	8.81	8.79	8.74	8.70	8.66	8.64	8.62	8.59	8.57	8.55	8.53
4	7.71	6.94	6.59	6.39	6.26	6.16	6.09	6.04	6.00	5.96	5.91	5.86	5.80	5.77	5.75	5.72	5.69	5.66	5.63
5	6.61	5.79	5.41	5.19	5.05	4.95	4.88	4.82	4.77	4.74	4.68	4.62	4.56	4.53	4.50	4.46	4.43	4.40	4.37
6	5.99	5.14	4.76	4.53	4.39	4.28	4.21	4.15	4.10	4.06	4.00	3.94	3.87	3.84	3.81	3.77	3.74	3.70	3.67
7	5.59	4.74	4.35	4.12	3.97	3.87	3.79	3.73	3.68	3.64	3.57	3.51	3.44	3.41	3.38	3.34	3.30	3.27	3.23
8	5.32	4.46	4.07	3.84	3.69	3.58	3.50	3.44	3.39	3.35	3.28	3.22	3.15	3.12	3.08	3.04	3.01	2.97	2.93
9	5.12	4.26	3.86	3.63	3.48	3.37	3.29	3.23	3.18	3.14	3.07	3.01	2.94	2.90	2.86	2.83	2.79	2.75	2.71
10	4.96	4.10	3.71	3.48	3.33	3.22	3.14	3.07	3.02	2.98	2.91	2.85	2.77	2.74	2.70	2.66	2.62	2.58	2.54
11	4.84	3.98	3.59	3.36	3.20	3.09	3.01	2.95	2.90	2.85	2.79	2.72	2.65	2.61	2.57	2.53	2.49	2.45	2.40
12	4.75	3.89	3.49	3.26	3.11	3.00	2.91	2.85	2.80	2.75	2.69	2.62	2.54	2.51	2.47	2.43	2.38	2.34	2.30
13	4.67	3.81	3.41	3.18	3.03	2.92	2.83	2.77	2.71	2.67	2.60	2.53	2.46	2.42	2.38	2.34	2.30	2.25	2.21
14	4.60	3.74	3.34	3.11	2.96	2.85	2.76	2.70	2.65	2.60	2.53	2.46	2.39	2.35	2.31	2.27	2.22	2.18	2.13
15	4.54	3.68	3.29	3.06	2.90	2.79	2.71	2.64	2.59	2.54	2.48	2.40	2.33	2.29	2.25	2.20	2.16	2.11	2.07
16	4.49	3.63	3.24	3.01	2.85	2.74	2.66	2.59	2.54	2.49	2.42	2.35	2.28	2.24	2.19	2.15	2.11	2.06	2.01
17	4.45	3.59	3.20	2.96	2.81	2.70	2.61	2.55	2.49	2.45	2.38	2.31	2.23	2.19	2.15	2.10	2.06	2.01	1.96
18	4.41	3.55	3.16	2.93	2.77	2.66	2.58	2.51	2.46	2.41	2.34	2.27	2.19	2.15	2.11	2.06	2.02	1.97	1.92
19	4.38	3.52	3.13	2.90	2.74	2.63	2.54	2.48	2.42	2.38	2.31	2.23	2.16	2.11	2.07	2.03	1.98	1.93	1.88
20	4.35	3.49	3.10	2.87	2.71	2.60	2.51	2.45	2.39	2.35	2.28	2.20	2.12	2.08	2.04	1.99	1.95	1.90	1.84
21	4.32	3.47	3.07	2.84	2.68	2.57	2.49	2.42	2.37	2.32	2.25	2.18	2.10	2.05	2.01	1.96	1.92	1.87	1.81
22	4.30	3.44	3.05	2.82	2.66	2.55	2.46	2.40	2.34	2.30	2.23	2.15	2.07	2.03	1.98	1.94	1.89	1.84	1.78
23	4.28	3.42	3.03	2.80	2.64	2.53	2.44	2.37	2.32	2.27	2.20	2.13	2.05	2.01	1.96	1.91	1.86	1.81	1.76
24	4.26	3.40	3.01	2.78	2.62	2.51	2.42	2.36	2.30	2.25	2.18	2.11	2.03	1.98	1.94	1.89	1.84	1.79	1.73
25	4.24	3.39	2.99	2.76	2.60	2.49	2.40	2.34	2.28	2.24	2.16	2.09	2.01	1.96	1.92	1.87	1.82	1.77	1.71
30	4.17	3.32	2.92	2.69	2.53	2.42	2.33	2.27	2.21	2.16	2.09	2.01	1.93	1.89	1.84	1.79	1.74	1.68	1.62
40	4.08	3.23	2.84	2.61	2.45	2.34	2.25	2.18	2.12	2.08	2.00	1.92	1.84	1.79	1.74	1.69	1.64	1.58	1.51
60	4.00	3.15	2.76	2.53	2.37	2.25	2.17	2.10	2.04	1.99	1.92	1.84	1.75	1.70	1.65	1.59	1.53	1.47	1.39
120	3.92	3.07	2.68	2.45	2.29	2.18	2.09	2.02	1.96	1.91	1.83	1.75	1.66	1.61	1.55	1.50	1.43	1.35	1.25
∞	3.84	3.00	2.60	2.37	2.21	2.10	2.01	1.94	1.88	1.83	1.75	1.67	1.57	1.52	1.46	1.39	1.32	1.22	1.00

Degrees of freedom for denominator

Interpolation should be performed using reciprocals of the degrees of freedom.

* This table is reproduced with the permission of Professor E. S. Pearson from M. Merrington and C. M. Thompson, "Tables of percentage points of the inverted beta (F) distribution." *Biometrika*, Vol. 33 (1943), p. 73.

TABLE Hb. F DISTRIBUTION, UPPER 5 PERCENT POINTS*

Degrees of freedom for numerator

Denominator	1	2	3	4	5	6	7	8	9	10	12	15	20	24	30	40	60	120	∞
1	648	800	864	900	922	937	948	957	963	969	977	985	993	997	1,001	1,006	1,010	1,014	1,018
2	38.5	39.0	39.2	39.2	39.3	39.3	39.4	39.4	39.4	39.4	39.4	39.4	39.4	39.5	39.5	39.5	39.5	39.5	39.5
3	17.4	16.0	15.4	15.1	14.9	14.7	14.6	14.5	14.5	14.4	14.3	14.3	14.2	14.1	14.1	14.0	14.0	13.9	13.9
4	12.2	10.6	9.98	9.60	9.36	9.20	9.07	8.98	8.90	8.84	8.75	8.66	8.56	8.51	8.46	8.41	8.36	8.31	8.26
5	10.0	8.43	7.76	7.39	7.15	6.98	6.85	6.76	6.68	6.62	6.52	6.43	6.33	6.28	6.23	6.18	6.12	6.07	6.02
6	8.81	7.26	6.60	6.23	5.99	5.82	5.70	5.60	5.52	5.46	5.37	5.27	5.17	5.12	5.07	5.01	4.96	4.90	4.85
7	8.07	6.54	5.89	5.52	5.29	5.12	4.99	4.90	4.82	4.76	4.67	4.57	4.47	4.42	4.36	4.31	4.25	4.20	4.14
8	7.57	6.06	5.42	5.05	4.82	4.65	4.53	4.43	4.36	4.30	4.20	4.10	4.00	3.95	3.89	3.84	3.78	3.73	3.67
9	7.21	5.71	5.08	4.72	4.48	4.32	4.20	4.10	4.03	3.96	3.87	3.77	3.67	3.61	3.56	3.51	3.45	3.39	3.33
10	6.94	5.46	4.83	4.47	4.24	4.07	3.95	3.85	3.78	3.72	3.62	3.52	3.42	3.37	3.31	3.26	3.20	3.14	3.08
11	6.72	5.26	4.63	4.28	4.04	3.88	3.76	3.66	3.59	3.53	3.43	3.33	3.23	3.17	3.12	3.06	3.00	2.94	2.88
12	6.55	5.10	4.47	4.12	3.89	3.73	3.61	3.51	3.44	3.37	3.28	3.18	3.07	3.02	2.96	2.91	2.85	2.79	2.72
13	6.41	4.97	4.35	4.00	3.77	3.60	3.48	3.39	3.31	3.25	3.15	3.05	2.95	2.89	2.84	2.78	2.72	2.66	2.60
14	6.30	4.86	4.24	3.89	3.66	3.50	3.38	3.28	3.21	3.15	3.05	2.95	2.84	2.79	2.73	2.67	2.61	2.55	2.49
15	6.20	4.77	4.15	3.80	3.58	3.41	3.29	3.20	3.12	3.06	2.96	2.86	2.76	2.70	2.64	2.59	2.52	2.46	2.40
16	6.12	4.69	4.08	3.73	3.50	3.34	3.22	3.12	3.05	2.99	2.89	2.79	2.68	2.63	2.57	2.51	2.45	2.38	2.32
17	6.04	4.62	4.01	3.66	3.44	3.28	3.16	3.06	2.98	2.92	2.82	2.72	2.62	2.56	2.50	2.44	2.38	2.32	2.25
18	5.98	4.56	3.95	3.61	3.38	3.22	3.10	3.01	2.93	2.87	2.77	2.67	2.56	2.50	2.44	2.38	2.32	2.26	2.19
19	5.92	4.51	3.90	3.56	3.33	3.17	3.05	2.96	2.88	2.82	2.72	2.62	2.51	2.45	2.39	2.33	2.27	2.20	2.13
20	5.87	4.46	3.86	3.51	3.29	3.13	3.01	2.91	2.84	2.77	2.68	2.57	2.46	2.41	2.35	2.29	2.22	2.16	2.09
21	5.83	4.42	3.82	3.48	3.25	3.09	2.97	2.87	2.80	2.73	2.64	2.53	2.42	2.37	2.31	2.25	2.18	2.11	2.04
22	5.79	4.38	3.78	3.44	3.22	3.05	2.93	2.84	2.76	2.70	2.60	2.50	2.39	2.33	2.27	2.21	2.14	2.08	2.00
23	5.75	4.35	3.75	3.41	3.18	3.02	2.90	2.81	2.73	2.67	2.57	2.47	2.36	2.30	2.24	2.18	2.11	2.04	1.97
24	5.72	4.32	3.72	3.38	3.15	2.99	2.87	2.78	2.70	2.64	2.54	2.44	2.33	2.27	2.21	2.15	2.08	2.01	1.94
25	5.69	4.29	3.69	3.35	3.13	2.97	2.85	2.75	2.68	2.61	2.51	2.41	2.30	2.24	2.18	2.12	2.05	1.98	1.91
30	5.57	4.18	3.59	3.25	3.03	2.87	2.75	2.65	2.57	2.51	2.41	2.31	2.20	2.14	2.07	2.01	1.94	1.87	1.79
40	5.42	4.05	3.46	3.13	2.90	2.74	2.62	2.53	2.45	2.39	2.29	2.18	2.07	2.01	1.94	1.88	1.80	1.72	1.64
60	5.29	3.93	3.34	3.01	2.79	2.63	2.51	2.41	2.33	2.27	2.17	2.06	1.94	1.88	1.82	1.74	1.67	1.58	1.48
120	5.15	3.80	3.23	2.89	2.67	2.52	2.39	2.30	2.22	2.16	2.05	1.95	1.82	1.76	1.69	1.61	1.53	1.43	1.31
∞	5.02	3.69	3.12	2.79	2.57	2.41	2.29	2.19	2.11	2.05	1.94	1.83	1.71	1.64	1.57	1.48	1.39	1.27	1.00

Degrees of freedom for denominator

Interpolation should be performed using reciprocals of the degrees of freedom.

* This table is reproduced with the permission of Professor E. S. Pearson from Merrington and Thompson, "Tables of percentage points of the inverted beta (F) distribution."

TABLE Hc. F DISTRIBUTION, UPPER 1 PERCENT POINTS*

Degrees of freedom for numerator

Degrees of freedom for denominator	1	2	3	4	5	6	7	8	9	10	12	15	20	24	30	40	60	120	∞
1	4,052	5,000	5,403	5,625	5,764	5,859	5,928	5,982	6,023	6,056	6,106	6,157	6,209	6,235	6,261	6,287	6,313	6,339	6,366
2	98.5	99.0	99.2	99.2	99.3	99.3	99.4	99.4	99.4	99.4	99.4	99.4	99.4	99.5	99.5	99.5	99.5	99.5	99.5
3	34.1	30.8	29.5	28.7	28.2	27.9	27.7	27.5	27.3	27.2	27.1	26.9	26.7	26.6	26.5	26.4	26.3	26.2	26.1
4	21.2	18.0	16.7	16.0	15.5	15.2	15.0	14.8	14.7	14.5	14.4	14.2	14.0	13.9	13.8	13.7	13.7	13.6	13.5
5	16.3	13.3	12.1	11.4	11.0	10.7	10.5	10.3	10.2	10.1	9.89	9.72	9.55	9.47	9.38	9.29	9.20	9.11	9.02
6	13.7	10.9	9.78	9.15	8.75	8.47	8.26	8.10	7.98	7.87	7.72	7.56	7.40	7.31	7.23	7.14	7.06	6.97	6.88
7	12.2	9.55	8.45	7.85	7.46	7.19	6.99	6.84	6.72	6.62	6.47	6.31	6.16	6.07	5.99	5.91	5.82	5.74	5.65
8	11.3	8.65	7.59	7.01	6.63	6.37	6.18	6.03	5.91	5.81	5.67	5.52	5.36	5.28	5.20	5.12	5.03	4.95	4.86
9	10.6	8.02	6.99	6.42	6.06	5.80	5.61	5.47	5.35	5.26	5.11	4.96	4.81	4.73	4.65	4.57	4.48	4.40	4.31
10	10.0	7.56	6.55	5.99	5.64	5.39	5.20	5.06	4.94	4.85	4.71	4.56	4.41	4.33	4.25	4.17	4.08	4.00	3.91
11	9.65	7.21	6.22	5.67	5.32	5.07	4.89	4.74	4.63	4.54	4.40	4.25	4.10	4.02	3.94	3.86	3.78	3.69	3.60
12	9.33	6.93	5.95	5.41	5.06	4.82	4.64	4.50	4.39	4.30	4.16	4.01	3.86	3.78	3.70	3.62	3.54	3.45	3.36
13	9.07	6.70	5.74	5.21	4.86	4.62	4.44	4.30	4.19	4.10	3.96	3.82	3.66	3.59	3.51	3.43	3.34	3.25	3.17
14	8.86	6.51	5.56	5.04	4.70	4.46	4.28	4.14	4.03	3.94	3.80	3.66	3.51	3.43	3.35	3.27	3.18	3.09	3.00
15	8.68	6.36	5.42	4.89	4.56	4.32	4.14	4.00	3.89	3.80	3.67	3.52	3.37	3.29	3.21	3.13	3.05	2.96	2.87
16	8.53	6.23	5.29	4.77	4.44	4.20	4.03	3.89	3.78	3.69	3.55	3.41	3.26	3.18	3.10	3.02	2.93	2.84	2.75
17	8.40	6.11	5.19	4.67	4.34	4.10	3.93	3.79	3.68	3.59	3.46	3.31	3.16	3.08	3.00	2.92	2.83	2.75	2.65
18	8.29	6.01	5.09	4.58	4.25	4.01	3.84	3.71	3.60	3.51	3.37	3.23	3.08	3.00	2.92	2.84	2.75	2.66	2.57
19	8.19	5.93	5.01	4.50	4.17	3.94	3.77	3.63	3.52	3.43	3.30	3.15	3.00	2.92	2.84	2.76	2.67	2.58	2.49
20	8.10	5.85	4.94	4.43	4.10	3.87	3.70	3.56	3.46	3.37	3.23	3.09	2.94	2.86	2.78	2.69	2.61	2.52	2.42
21	8.02	5.78	4.87	4.37	4.04	3.81	3.64	3.51	3.40	3.31	3.17	3.03	2.88	2.80	2.72	2.64	2.55	2.46	2.36
22	7.95	5.72	4.82	4.31	3.99	3.76	3.59	3.45	3.35	3.26	3.12	2.98	2.83	2.75	2.67	2.58	2.50	2.40	2.31
23	7.88	5.66	4.76	4.26	3.94	3.71	3.54	3.41	3.30	3.21	3.07	2.93	2.78	2.70	2.62	2.54	2.45	2.35	2.26
24	7.82	5.61	4.72	4.22	3.90	3.67	3.50	3.36	3.26	3.17	3.03	2.89	2.74	2.66	2.58	2.49	2.40	2.31	2.21
25	7.77	5.57	4.68	4.18	3.86	3.63	3.46	3.32	3.22	3.13	2.99	2.85	2.70	2.62	2.53	2.45	2.36	2.27	2.17
30	7.56	5.39	4.51	4.02	3.70	3.47	3.30	3.17	3.07	2.98	2.84	2.70	2.55	2.47	2.39	2.30	2.21	2.11	2.01
40	7.31	5.18	4.31	3.83	3.51	3.29	3.12	2.99	2.89	2.80	2.66	2.52	2.37	2.29	2.20	2.11	2.02	1.92	1.80
60	7.08	4.98	4.13	3.65	3.34	3.12	2.95	2.82	2.72	2.63	2.50	2.35	2.20	2.12	2.03	1.94	1.84	1.73	1.60
120	6.85	4.79	3.95	3.48	3.17	2.96	2.79	2.66	2.56	2.47	2.34	2.19	2.03	1.95	1.86	1.76	1.66	1.53	1.38
∞	6.63	4.61	3.78	3.32	3.02	2.80	2.64	2.51	2.41	2.32	2.18	2.04	1.88	1.79	1.70	1.59	1.47	1.32	1.00

Interpolation should be performed using reciprocals of the degrees of freedom.

* This table is reproduced with the permission of Professor E. S. Pearson from Merrington and Thompson, "Tables of percentage points of the inverted beta (F) distribution."

TABLE Hd. F DISTRIBUTION, UPPER 0.5 PERCENT POINTS*

Degrees of freedom for numerator

Denom.	1	2	3	4	5	6	7	8	9	10	12	15	20	24	30	40	60	∞
1	16,211	20,000	21,615	22,500	23,056	23,437	23,715	23,925	24,091	24,224	24,426	24,630	24,836	24,940	25,044	25,148	25,253	25,465
2	198	199	199	199	199	199	199	199	199	199	199	199	199	199	199	199	199	200
3	55.6	49.8	47.5	46.2	45.4	44.8	44.4	44.1	43.9	43.7	43.4	43.1	42.8	42.6	42.5	42.3	42.1	41.8
4	31.3	26.3	24.3	23.2	22.5	22.0	21.6	21.4	21.1	21.0	20.7	20.4	20.2	20.0	19.9	19.8	19.6	19.3
5	22.8	18.3	16.5	15.6	14.9	14.5	14.2	14.0	13.8	13.6	13.4	13.1	12.9	12.8	12.7	12.5	12.4	12.1
6	18.6	14.5	12.9	12.0	11.5	11.1	10.8	10.6	10.4	10.3	10.0	9.81	9.59	9.47	9.36	9.24	9.12	8.88
7	16.2	12.4	10.9	10.1	9.52	9.16	8.89	8.68	8.51	8.38	8.18	7.97	7.75	7.65	7.53	7.42	7.31	7.08
8	14.7	11.0	9.60	8.81	8.30	7.95	7.69	7.50	7.34	7.21	7.01	6.81	6.61	6.50	6.40	6.29	6.18	5.95
9	13.6	10.1	8.72	7.96	7.47	7.13	6.88	6.69	6.54	6.42	6.23	6.03	5.83	5.73	5.62	5.52	5.41	5.19
10	12.8	9.43	8.08	7.34	6.87	6.54	6.30	6.12	5.97	5.85	5.66	5.47	5.27	5.17	5.07	4.97	4.86	4.64
11	12.2	8.91	7.60	6.88	6.42	6.10	5.86	5.68	5.54	5.42	5.24	5.05	4.86	4.76	4.65	4.55	4.45	4.23
12	11.8	8.51	7.23	6.52	6.07	5.76	5.52	5.35	5.20	5.09	4.91	4.72	4.53	4.43	4.33	4.23	4.12	3.90
13	11.4	8.19	6.93	6.23	5.79	5.48	5.25	5.08	4.94	4.82	4.64	4.46	4.27	4.17	4.07	3.97	3.87	3.65
14	11.1	7.92	6.68	6.00	5.56	5.26	5.03	4.86	4.72	4.60	4.43	4.25	4.06	3.96	3.86	3.76	3.66	3.44
15	10.8	7.70	6.48	5.80	5.37	5.07	4.85	4.67	4.54	4.42	4.25	4.07	3.88	3.79	3.69	3.58	3.48	3.26
16	10.6	7.51	6.30	5.64	5.21	4.91	4.69	4.52	4.38	4.27	4.10	3.92	3.73	3.64	3.54	3.44	3.33	3.11
17	10.4	7.35	6.16	5.50	5.07	4.78	4.56	4.39	4.25	4.14	3.97	3.79	3.61	3.51	3.41	3.31	3.21	2.98
18	10.2	7.21	6.03	5.37	4.96	4.66	4.44	4.28	4.14	4.03	3.86	3.68	3.50	3.40	3.30	3.20	3.10	2.87
19	10.1	7.09	5.92	5.27	4.85	4.56	4.34	4.18	4.04	3.93	3.76	3.59	3.40	3.31	3.21	3.11	3.00	2.78
20	9.94	6.99	5.82	5.17	4.76	4.47	4.26	4.09	3.96	3.85	3.68	3.50	3.32	3.22	3.12	3.02	2.92	2.69
21	9.83	6.89	5.73	5.09	4.68	4.39	4.18	4.01	3.88	3.77	3.60	3.43	3.24	3.15	3.05	2.95	2.84	2.61
22	9.73	6.81	5.65	5.02	4.61	4.32	4.11	3.94	3.81	3.70	3.54	3.36	3.18	3.08	2.98	2.88	2.77	2.55
23	9.63	6.73	5.58	4.95	4.54	4.26	4.05	3.88	3.75	3.64	3.47	3.30	3.12	3.02	2.92	2.82	2.71	2.48
24	9.55	6.66	5.52	4.89	4.49	4.20	3.99	3.83	3.69	3.59	3.42	3.25	3.06	2.97	2.87	2.77	2.66	2.43
25	9.48	6.60	5.46	4.84	4.43	4.15	3.94	3.78	3.64	3.54	3.37	3.20	3.01	2.92	2.82	2.72	2.61	2.38
30	9.18	6.35	5.24	4.62	4.23	3.95	3.74	3.58	3.45	3.34	3.18	3.01	2.82	2.73	2.63	2.52	2.42	2.18
40	8.83	6.07	4.98	4.37	3.99	3.71	3.51	3.35	3.22	3.12	2.95	2.78	2.60	2.50	2.40	2.30	2.18	1.93
60	8.49	5.80	4.73	4.14	3.76	3.49	3.29	3.13	3.01	2.90	2.74	2.57	2.39	2.29	2.19	2.08	1.96	1.69
120	8.18	5.54	4.50	3.92	3.55	3.28	3.09	2.93	2.81	2.71	2.54	2.37	2.19	2.09	1.98	1.87	1.75	1.43
∞	7.88	5.30	4.28	3.72	3.35	3.09	2.90	2.74	2.62	2.52	2.36	2.19	2.00	1.90	1.79	1.67	1.53	1.00

Degrees of freedom for denominator

Interpolation should be performed using reciprocals of the degrees of freedom.

* This table is reproduced with the permission of Professor E. S. Pearson from Merrington and Thompson, "Tables of percentage points of the inverted beta (F) distribution."

TABLE I. CRITICAL VALUES OF CHI SQUARE*

p / df	.99	.98	.95	.90	.80	.70	.50	.30	.20	.10	.05	.02	.01	.001
1	.00016	.00063	.0039	.016	.064	.15	.46	1.07	1.64	2.71	3.84	5.41	6.64	10.83
2	.02	.04	.10	.21	.45	.71	1.39	2.41	3.22	4.60	5.99	7.82	9.21	13.82
3	.12	.18	.35	.58	1.00	1.42	2.37	3.66	4.64	6.25	7.82	9.84	11.34	16.27
4	.30	.43	.71	1.06	1.65	2.20	3.36	4.88	5.99	7.78	9.49	11.67	13.28	18.46
5	.55	.75	1.14	1.61	2.34	3.00	4.35	6.06	7.29	9.24	11.07	13.39	15.09	20.52
6	.87	1.13	1.64	2.20	3.07	3.83	5.35	7.23	8.56	10.64	12.59	15.03	16.81	22.46
7	1.24	1.56	2.17	2.83	3.82	4.67	6.35	8.38	9.80	12.02	14.07	16.62	18.48	24.32
8	1.65	2.03	2.73	3.49	4.59	5.53	7.34	9.52	11.03	13.36	15.51	18.17	20.09	26.12
9	2.09	2.53	3.32	4.17	5.38	6.39	8.34	10.66	12.24	14.68	16.92	19.68	21.67	27.88
10	2.56	3.06	3.94	4.86	6.18	7.27	9.34	11.78	13.44	15.99	18.31	21.16	23.21	29.59
11	3.05	3.61	4.58	5.58	6.99	8.15	10.34	12.90	14.63	17.28	19.68	22.62	24.72	31.26
12	3.57	4.18	5.23	6.30	7.81	9.03	11.34	14.01	15.81	18.55	21.03	24.05	26.22	32.91
13	4.11	4.76	5.89	7.04	8.63	9.93	12.34	15.12	16.98	19.81	22.36	25.47	27.69	34.53
14	4.66	5.37	6.57	7.79	9.47	10.82	13.34	16.22	18.15	21.06	23.68	26.87	29.14	36.12
15	5.23	5.98	7.26	8.55	10.31	11.72	14.34	17.32	19.31	22.31	25.00	28.26	30.58	37.70
16	5.81	6.61	7.96	9.31	11.15	12.62	15.34	18.42	20.46	23.54	26.30	29.63	32.00	39.29
17	6.41	7.26	8.67	10.08	12.00	13.53	16.34	19.51	21.62	24.77	27.59	31.00	33.41	40.75
18	7.02	7.91	9.39	10.86	12.86	14.44	17.34	20.60	22.76	25.99	28.87	32.35	34.80	42.31
19	7.63	8.57	10.12	11.65	13.72	15.35	18.34	21.69	23.90	27.20	30.14	33.69	36.19	43.82
20	8.26	9.24	10.85	12.44	14.58	16.27	19.34	22.78	25.04	28.41	31.41	35.02	37.57	45.32
21	8.90	9.92	11.59	13.24	15.44	17.18	20.34	23.86	26.17	29.62	32.67	36.34	38.93	46.80
22	9.54	10.60	12.34	14.04	16.31	18.10	21.24	24.94	27.30	30.81	33.92	37.66	40.29	48.27
23	10.20	11.29	13.09	14.85	17.19	19.02	22.34	26.02	28.43	32.01	35.17	38.97	41.64	49.73
24	10.86	11.99	13.85	15.66	18.06	19.94	23.34	27.10	29.55	33.20	36.42	40.27	42.98	51.18
25	11.52	12.70	14.61	16.47	18.94	20.87	24.34	28.17	30.68	34.38	37.65	41.57	44.31	52.62
26	12.20	13.41	15.38	17.29	19.82	21.79	25.34	29.25	31.80	35.56	38.88	42.86	45.64	54.05
27	12.88	14.12	16.15	18.11	20.70	22.72	26.34	30.32	32.91	36.74	40.11	44.14	46.96	55.48
28	13.56	14.85	16.93	18.94	21.59	23.65	27.34	31.39	34.03	37.92	41.34	45.42	48.28	56.89
29	14.26	15.57	17.71	19.77	22.48	24.58	28.34	32.46	35.14	39.09	42.56	46.69	49.59	58.30
30	14.95	16.31	18.49	20.60	23.36	25.51	29.34	33.53	36.25	40.26	43.77	47.96	50.89	59.70

* Table I is abridged Table IV of Fisher and Yates' "Statistical Tables For Biological, Agricultural and Medical Research." Published by Oliver and Boyd, Ltd., abridged in Siegel's Nonparametric Statistics (1956: McGraw-Hill Book Co.). Used by permission.

THE GREEK ALPHABET

A	α	alpha	N	ν	nu
B	β	beta	Ξ	ξ	xi
Γ	γ	gamma	O	o	omicron
Δ	δ	delta	Π	π	pi
E	ϵ	epsilon	P	ρ	rho
Z	ζ	zeta	Σ	σ	sigma
H	η	eta	T	τ	tau
Θ	θ	theta	Υ	υ	upsilon
I	ι	iota	Φ	ϕ	phi
K	κ	kappa	X	χ	chi
Λ	λ	lambda	Ψ	ψ	psi
M	μ	mu	Ω	ω	omega

Index

This book has been set in 11 point and 10 point Modern #21, leaded 2 points. Chapter numbers are in 14 point Venus Medium Extended, and chapter titles are in 18 point Venus Medium Extended. The size of the type page is 27 x 45½ picas.